American Rhododendron Hybrids

1980

To Lura
from Martha

THE AMERICAN RHODODENDRON SOCIETY
14635 S.W. Bull Mountain Road
Tigard, Oregon 97223

Christmas 1981

9 8 7 6 5 4 3 2 1
ISBN: 0-9604524-1-9

Editor:
Meldon Kraxberger

Library of Congress Card Catalog
Number 80-67040

You are invited to join the American Rhododendron Society. Membership entitles you to four quarterly bulletins a year, affiliation with Chapter of your choice or non-chapter and participation in annual Seed Exchange program. As of 1980, membership is $12.00 per year. For details, write Executive Secretary, Fran Egan, 14635 S.W. Bull Mountain Road, Tigard, Oregon 97223.

CHAPTER PRESIDENTS

AZALEA
Dr. Joseph H. Coleman
BIRMINGHAM
Richard Cooper
CALIFORNIA
E. Parker Smith
CENTRAL GULF COAST
Eugene J. Aromi
CONNECTICUT
Mrs. Philip E. Taylor
DE ANZA
John Hixson
DENMARK
Vagn Jorgensen
EUGENE
Harold Greer
GRAYS HARBOR
James Shrauger
GREAT LAKES
Felix A. Robinson, Jr.
INDIANA
H. Roland Schroeder, Jr.
JUAN de FUCA
Frank Chamberlin
KOMO KULSHAN
Greg Haner
LEWIS COUNTY
Melvin Lueken
MASSACHUSETTS
A. Richard Brooks
MIDDLE ATLANTIC
Austin C. Kennell
MID WEST
William Rapshys
MONTEREY BAY
Melvin C. Allen
NEW JERSEY
David Wuebbens
NEW YORK
William Tietjen
NORTH KITSAP
T. A. Peterschmidt

OLYMPIA
Buzz Hettinger
OLYMPIC PENINSULA
Mrs. John Buhler, Jr.
PHILADELPHIA
Vernon Quarles
PIEDMONT
Marshall G. Stilwell
PORTLAND
Frank D. Mossman, MD
POTOMAC VALLEY
Norton Boothe
PRINCETON
Patricia Pfeiffer
SAN MATEO
Bill Lofthouse
SEATTLE
Ralph H. Nichols
SHELTON
Helen Agoa
SIUSLAW
Michael J. Bones
SOUTHERN CALIFORNIA
Carl Duel
SOUTHEASTERN
Dr. H. Furman Cantrell
SOUTHWESTERN OREGON
Willard E. Morgan
TACOMA
Frank A. Lough
TAPPAN ZEE
Hans E. Bussink
TUALATIN VALLEY
Harold T. Krug
VALLEY FORGE
Clarence Ziegler
VANCOUVER
Harold A. Johnson
WILLIAM BARTRAM
Dr. Curtis Sidden
WILLAMETTE
June Brennan

AMERICAN RHODODENDRON HYBRIDS

FOREWORD

After many years of collecting data and, in spite of many delays, The American Hybrids book has come to fruition. This is the ninth book to be published by the American Rhododendron Society and there are continuing plans for additional books in the future.

Thanks should be given to the first committee for its work on this book under the direction of George Clarke. Special thanks is given to Meldon Kraxberger and Ted Van Veen and their committee for gathering all of the information for this publication.

The first rhododendron hybrids were developed in the early 1800's in England. Hybridizing rhododendrons in America had a slow beginning with a few hybridizers introducing their new hybrids in the early 1930's. This slow development has mushroomed to a major hobby for our dedicated rhododendron enthusiasts, both the home gardener and the commercial grower. The word hybrid, according to Webster, means an offspring between two plants of different races, breeds, varieties, species, or genera. Such a mundane definition does not describe the results of a rhodie hybridizer as he starts work with the colorful palette offered by the genus Rhododendron.

In the early days, our hybrids were the results of nature along with man's random, uncontrolled dabbling of pollen in the "Burbank" fashion on numerous rhododendron plants. While this method is still done today, the dedicated hybridizer now plans his crosses backed with research and a study of the numerous species and hybrids available to work with. Planned crosses are often outlined and diagramed years in advance, concentrating on the desirable characteristics of the parent plants to produce new and exciting hybrids for the future. The new methods of handling and storing of pollen, increased ease of record keeping, seed propagation and cultural practices are just some of the many techniques in which the hybridizer must be knowledgeable and skilled in order to produce new plants.

Today we find new hybrids suitable for all types of landscape gardening. The plants vary in size from the miniature rock garden plants to dwarf to medium to large sized plants for the modern garden. Hardiness or adaptability of plants for warm climates and for extreme cold, along with the year-round qualities of the plant, are being evaluated. Last but not least is the improvement in the substance, quality and color of the flowers. Small to large flowers, lovely forms, new bi-colors and soft pastels are now available. Thus the colorful artist's palette comes forth in the hands of the rhododendron breeder.

Many of the old 'tried and true' rhododendron hybrids will still be grown. However, the new hybrids are welcome for the Eighties, and for the new century just ahead. With the advanced technology of tissue culture, we should hopefully eliminate the long time required by a commercial grower to have sufficient stock of a new plant for the market.

The old saying, "Look close at an individual flower' is standard procedure for the hybridizer along with careful observation of the qualities of the entire plant.

Through this book, we gain an appreciation for the pioneer rhododendron breeder, who developed the foundation and provided challenges for the breeders of today and for the future. The American Rhododendron Society will be ever grateful to the hybridizers of rhododendrons and for the dedicated time of this Committee to produce this book.

— Fred C. Galle, President, ARS — 1980

ACKNOWLEDGEMENTS

The initial framework for the lists was laid many years ago. George Clarke, Chairman, Dr. Robert Ticknor, Secretary, were assisted by Dr. Harold Clarke, David Goheen, Louis Grothaus, John Henny, Howard Slonecker, Theodore Van Veen, and Cyrus Ward. It is impossible to know now, after such a lapse of time, just how many growers out of this region responded to the ratings survey.

The six regional hybridizing articles have been contributed by H. Furman Cantrell, Margery Farwell, Richard Murcott, Dr. Frank Mossman, George W. Ring, and Dr. Thomas L. Ring.

The technique of making difficult crosses has been shared with you by Weldon Delp.

The basic landscape principles have been presented by S.E. and C.H. Sanders.

The "Good Doer" project has been the work of many months by George R. Ring. The collation was done by Bruno Kaelin.

The table of rhododendrons by bloom sequence, stature and size has been prepared by Kendall Gambrill.

The 1979-80 committee is Theodore Van Veen, George Clarke, Robert Ticknor, Cyrus Ward, Ed Egan and Edwin Parker. Most especially there would have been no "American Rhododendron Hybrids" book without the help of Theodore Van Veen, Ed Egan and Edwin Parker.

Meldon Kraxberger

CONTENTS

Foreword. 5
Acknowledgements 7
Rhododendron Hybridizing in New England, Richard Murcott. . 11
Hybridizing in the Central Eastern United States,
   George L. Ring, III 14
Hybridizing in the Southeastern United States,
   H. Furman Cantrell. 19
Hybridizing in the Great Lakes Region, Thomas L. Ring, M.D. . 21
Rhododendron Hybridizing in the Northwest,
   Frank D. Mossman, M.D.. 26
California Hybridizing, Margery C. Farwell 29
Registered American Hybrids. 32
Unregistered American Hybrids. 174
American Hybridizers 190
How to Succeed in Producing Rhododendron Seed,
   Weldon E. Delp. 195
Rhododendrons in Landscape Design, S.E. and C.H. Sanders . . .198
Rhododendron Hybrids — Color, Sequence and Height,
   Kendall W. Gambrill 200
Award Plants 212
The "Good-Doers". 216
   Introduction, George L. Ring, III .216
   Collation, Bruno Kaelin. 217
Azalea Chapter. 228
California Chapter. 237
Connecticut Chapter. 217
De Anza Chapter 241
Grays Harbor Chapter. 234
Great Lakes Chapter. 229
Indiana Chapter 231
Middle Atlantic Chapter 222
Monterey Bay Chapter 242
New York Chapter 218
Piedmont Chapter. 223
Potomac Chapter 221
Princeton Chapter. 219
San Mateo Chapter. 239
Seattle Chapter. 232
Shelton Chapter 233
Southeastern Chapter 224
Southern California Chapter 243
Tualatin Valley Chapter 236
William Bartram Chapter 226

List of Illustrations

'Isabel Pierce' 36
'Scintillation'. 40
'Anna Baldsiefen' 48
'Epoch' 56
'Sugar Pink' 73
'Dora Amateis' 73
'Queen Anne's' 80
'Noyo Brave' 88
'Riplet' 92
'Windbeam' 101
'Blue Pacific' 109
'Mary Fleming' 113
'Springfield' 116
'Odee Wright' 117
'Hotei' 120
'Shamrock' 128
'Taurus' 133
'Henry Yates' 136
'Swansdown' 144
'Lem's Cameo' 148
'Dexter's Springtime' 152
'Trude Webster' 156
'C.I.S.' 160
Front Cover — 'Goldstrike' *photo by Cecil Smith*

Back Cover — Crystal Springs Rhododendron Garden in Portland, OR. *photo by A.W. Kraxberger*

RHODODENDRON HYBRIDIZING IN NEW ENGLAND

Richard Murcott
East Norwich, New York

Beautiful, hardy and different. These are the general goals for Northeastern rhododendron hybridizers. The major limiting factor in growing rhododendrons in the Northeast is the climate. There are really two climates in this area. On Long Island, Cape Cod and immediately along the coast, the ocean moderates the winter minimum and the summer maximum temperature. But inland, away from the water, it is a whole other climate, 20 degrees colder in winter and 10 degrees warmer in summer.

Rhododendron *fortunei* has been the premier species in the background of successful Northeast hybrids. And for good reason. It is beautiful and hardy. Nearing, Gable, Dexter and Hardgrove all used it. It forms the foundation of the Dexter hybrids which today are still considered among the most desirable hybrids that we can grow. The Dexter hybrids were the starting point for Howard Phipps and his hybrids which are certainly going to be the most sought after hybrids of the 1980's and 90's.

But "the times, they are a changin'". Charles Dexter recognized the need for more compact growing plants so, in his last hybrids, he started to cross *haematodes* into his hybrids. Even Howard Phipps started to grow open pollinated *yakushimanum* seed in his search for compact plants.

And this is the general direction in which most hybridizers are heading now. Plants that have a maximum height of four feet, completely clothed with foliage to the ground and covered, in season, with large flowers seem to be the contemporary goal. R. *yakushimanum* has replaced *fortunei* as the base for hybrids. The compactness and extreme hardiness of *yakushimanum* is the trait hybridizers are trying to capture together with large showy flowers. But hardy, hardy, hardy. Everyone realizes the futility of marginally hardy hybrids. In the last conversation I had with Don Hardgrove, he repeatedly spoke of the absolute need to have hardiness on BOTH sides of the cross. This was especially interesting because most of his crosses did not have this quality. Hybridizers in the moderate climate areas seem to obtain reliable hybrids with hardiness only on one side of the cross.

The influence of *yakushimanum* on the rhododendron hybrids developed in the 1980's and 90's will be absolutely enormous. Second in influence will be *smirnowii*. Both species are very hardy, dense growing (if you get the correct *smirnowii* — some are trees) and indumented. Hybridizers in this area have been crossing *yakushimanum* with tender red species, in a so-far-unsuccessful quest for an indumented, low growing red hybrid — really a red *yakushimanum*. This has led accidentally to a large array of pink hybrids, growing in a manner similar to 'Boule de Neige'. Some are attractive but none have the pizzaz of a Dexter or Phipps pink. It has been my contention for a long time that we already have superb pinks and to try to compete with Messers Dexter and Phipps is futile and wasteful. What we need are reds, yellows and oranges.

Hardgrove's best two hybrids — 'Donna Hardgrove' and 'Golden Star' — are quite outstanding yellows in the coastal Northeast; both have the hardy form of *fortunei* as the seed parent. Hardgrove showed that *fortunei* should be the starting point for yellow since it seems to transmit that color to the progeny together with large flowers and hardiness.

We are really half-way there in the development of good, very hardy yellows. The Hardgroves are certainly hardy on Long Island and are certainly yellow and orange. 'Golden Star' and 'Donna Hardgrove' need improvement in their truss form (no top flower), should be made hardier and, in the case of 'Golden Star', should be made more compact. 'Donna Hardgrove' should really be tried out as a commercial, field grown rhododendron. It is bud hardy in Rockland County (an area in the colder part of the region), quite compact growing and definitely in the desired orange-yellow color range.

Hybridizers growing in the colder areas are very restricted in their choice of parents. R. *brachycarpum,* any of the white *catawbiense, smirnowii, yakushimanum, metternichii* and 'Mars' are all being used for the elepidote hybrids; *carolinianum, mucronulatum* and *dauricum* being the principal starting point for the lepidote hybrids. The deciduous azaleas are all basically very hardy and are being worked with extensively.

Of course, the greater challenge faces the hybridizer is this frigid area. Parent species all have detractions that we, in the warmer areas, consider deadly: small flowers, small trusses, lack-luster color and, if red, blued. But we are comparing these plants with what we can grow already, which isn't fair. Compared to the blooming plants that are now grown in the coldest areas, these 'starting point' rhododendrons are super.

There is in the Northeast a widespread interest in dwarf rhododendrons and I suspect that we will be seeing many of these in the future. The problem here is that the slow rate of growth of these diminutive plants virtually precludes their propagation by commercial nurserymen. Hybrids of *yakushimanum* and a slew of lepidotes all produce beautiful plants if you have the patience to wait for their development. Their small size helps them in the winter as they are inevitably covered with snow and thus insulated from extremely low temperatures.

I am extremely enthusiastic about future rhododendron hybrids in the Northeast. There are a great many interested hybridizers growing large quantities of seed from good crosses. I am sure that, by the turn of the century, we will have made available to gardeners in all sections of the region rhododendrons in all colors, growth habits and leaf characteristics.

Many rhododendron terms are carelessly and incorrectly used in casual conversation.

The word "specie" should not be used when you mean species. Species is the correct term for the class of plants below the rank of genus; the word is both singular and plural. Specie only means hard money.

A selected seedling is just that — a seedling selected from a batch of seedlings because of some certain characteristic.

A sibling is one of the many seedlings raised from one seed pod.

A cultivar is a cultural variety, the result of selection or cross-breeding.

A variety is a group of individuals within a species which often reproduce distinguishing characteristics in their progeny in the wild. The word is now widely used to give specific rank to one clone of a grex.

A clone applies to one selected seedling in a grex and plants raised from it only by vegetative methods.

Grex is a Latin word meaning simply a group of seedlings from the same cross, but not necessarily from the same crossing. Plural of this word is greges. Within a grex may occur many variations of color, quality and form. If a cross was repeated by another than the original hybridizer using the same parentage but not the identical parents the grex name was the same. Now only clonal names are given.

A single rhododendron corolla is a flower, not a floret. All the flowers emerging from one bud, be it one or thirty, constitute a truss. One truss has only one rachis. Many rhododendrons, especially dwarfs, produce multiple buds at their terminals and so multiple trusses, each with its own rachis.

RHODODENDRON HYBRIDIZING IN CENTRAL EASTERN
UNITED STATES

George W. Ring, III
Fairfax, Virginia

This area of the United States has warm to hot, humid summers,
cold dry winters, and winds less than the mid-west but greater than
the Pacific Northwest. Soils are sandy near the coast, with silty clays
further inland. Rhododendrons native to the region are *R. maximum,*
usually found in shaded, moist ravines, *R. catawbiense,* found at exposed higher elevations in the southern part of the region, and the
native azaleas *R. nudiflorum, viscosum, atlanticum, arborescens, roseum* and *calendulaceum.*

Most hybrid deciduous azaleas grow here with ease, although pow-
dery mildew is a problem with some varieties. Lepidote rhododendrons
generally require special culture, and most alpine species rarely succeed. Elepidote rhododendrons in the Ponticum and Fortunei Series
and their hybrids generally do well, especially those species indige-
neous to Japan with its hot-humid summers; they seem to have adapt-
ed to cultural conditions in the eastern United States similar to those
in their homeland. Evergreen azaleas hardier than the southern Bel-
gian *indicas* mostly thrive and are widely planted. In the 1920's, only
a few Waterer and Ghent hybrids, plus a few evergreen azaleas, were
available to gardeners in this region. Those pioneer hybridizers, Joseph
Gable, Guy Nearing and B. Y. Morrison, changed all that by their
work and laid a solid foundation for legions of their followers to further develop improved varieties of rhododendrons, including azaleas,
for the region.

The late Joseph Gable, a gentle, general farmer in Pennsylvania,
who, in the 1920's, started to develop new rhododendrons for the rigor-
ous climate of eastern Pennsylvania, also founded a new race of per-
sistent-leaved azaleas based on the two hardy species, *R. poukhanense*
and *kaempferi,* combined with a few available hybrids such as 'Hexe'
for the hose-in-hose character. His selections from thousands of
seedlings are now the backbone of the azalea market in the East and
some varieties, such as 'Louise Gable' and 'Rosebud,' are also grown
widely in the West. They have also won awards in England. Gable's
work with rhododendrons, although started at about the same time as
the work with azaleas, is just now coming to maturity because of the
longer time required for bloom and evaluation. 'David Gable',
'Atroflo', 'Caroline', 'Mary Belle', 'Pink Twins', 'Pioneer' and many
others now becoming well known are described more fully in "Hybrids
and Hybridizers". A recent "find" of Gable correspondence has
revealed his early appreciation for the beauty of the genus and also
that his knowledge of rhododendrons went far beyond even the most

credits accorded him in the past.

Guy Nearing worked closely with Joseph Gable, the two sharing seeds, pollen, plants and ideas. In spite of setbacks which would have discouraged most others, Nearing persevered and, through keen observation, selected superior rhododendron hybrids such as 'Windbeam', 'Lenape', 'Rochelle', 'Macopen', 'Red Lion' and a conservative but highly valuable list of others. Even now, a study group in New Jersey and New York is working to evaluate later developed varieties in order to make the best of these available to rhododendron lovers everywhere.

Also described in "Hybrids and Hybridizers", B. Y. Morrison, as first director of the National Arboretum in Washington, D.C., developed an entirely new race of evergreen azaleas in a breeding program which produced 75,000 seedlings grown to blooming size. Although most are not as hardy as the Gables, the Glenn Dale azaleas greatly extend the range of colors, blooming times and plant habits available for gardeners and landscapers for Washington, D.C., and similar areas of the East. Many of the 454 selections are widely grown today, such as 'Gaiety', 'Geisha', 'Dayspring', 'Martha Hitchcock' and 'Helen Close'.

More recent evergreen azalea hybridizers include Robert Gartrell who has patiently developed hardier compact plants, mostly of the Satsuki type, and G. Albert Reid who has produced hardy evergreen azaleas with flowers approaching, and sometimes exceeding, florist forcing varieties. Gartrell's 'Lady Louise', 'Redmond', 'Nancy of Robin Hill', and Al Reid's 'Opal', 'Linwood Lustre' and 'Linwood Pink Giant' are outstanding examples of their work.

Joseph Gable said in one of his talks to horticulturists "we are sure to realize sooner or later that creation is not complete", and there are many rhododendron growers who evidently agree with his conclusion. For now there are many hybridizers and growers following in the same steps of the pioneers of the central eastern region. Many of this new generation have specific objectives for improvements of rhododendrons for their area. But whatever their objectives, all agree that the pure enjoyment and pleasant anticipation of seeing new plants come into bloom are strong incentives to continue their quest.

Of the objectives for improvement, here are some being pursued today in the central eastern region:

1. Mildew resistance in the foliage of deciduous azaleas (Hardy, Stepka).

2. Smaller evergreen azaleas, some perhaps suitable for bonsai treatment (Hardy, Ring, McDonald, Hill).

3. Heavier texture, long-lasting flowers, especially through polyploidy (Byrkit, Wagner).

4. Disease and pest resistance (most all).

5. Easier to grow cultivars, especially elepidotes with yellow, orange

and red flowers (almost everyone).

6. Better strains of forcing, evergreen azaleas (McDonald, W.D. Smith).

7. Heat tolerance in practically all types (McDonald, Goodrich, and others).

8. Cultivars which mature in smaller sizes suitable for today's townhouse developments (most all).

9. Indumented cultivars to increase foliage interest in a full range of flower colors (most all).

10. Fragrance (Ring).

11. Strong, vigorous root systems for the heavier soils native to the area (almost all).

12. Improved lepidotes (G. D. Lewis). More work is needed on these to produce later blooming varieties.

13. Later blooming on elepidotes (Goodrich, Wister).

14. Yellow flowered evergreen azaleas (dream of many).

An informal survey of the Middle Atlantic, Potomac Valley, New Jersey, Princeton, Valley Forge and Philadelphia Chapters revealed more than 80 members of the American Rhododendron Society who are busy developing improved rhododendrons and azaleas, whether for a specific purpose or just for the fun of it. Individual levels of activity range from a few flats of seedlings to more than 5,000 each year. Further improvements in rhododendrons and azaleas will soon be coming to notice as a result of the work by these dedicated and busy plantsmen.

Hybridizers and/or growers of seedlings in the central eastern United States

Allen, John; Halethorpe, MD
Anderson, Alan; Franklin Lakes, NJ
Ayers, Jack; Oakton, VA
Bagoly, Lewis; Strafford, PA
Beaudry, Norman; Reston, VA
Becales, Joseph; Glen Mills, PA
Beutler, Eugenie; Basking Ridge, NJ
Blyskal, Walter; Spring Valley, NY
Bohnel, Emil; Pearl River, NY
Boeggeman, John; West Nyack, NY
Booth, Norton; Bethesda, MD
Brown, Lewis; Wrightsville, PA
Byrkit, Max; Williamsport, MD
Clark, Paul; Frostburg, MD
Courson, William; Silver Spring, MD
Davis, Preston; Alexandria, VA
Derieg, M. E.; Caldwell, NJ

Doppel, John; Oakland, MD
Edwards, Newton; Alexandria, VA
Fitzburgh, A. R.; Caldwell, NJ
Furman, Frank; Bridgewater, NJ
Gable, Caroline; Stewartstown, PA
Gartrell, Robert; Wyckoff, NJ
Goodman, Jerry; Caldwell, NJ
Goodrich, Col. & Mrs. R.; Vienna, VA
Hardy, Judson; Silver Spring, MD
Harper, Lewis; Lutherville, MD
Harrington, Ruth; Falls Church, VA
Heuser, Leon; Robbinsville, NJ
Heyderhoff, Henry; Bloomingdale, NJ
Hill, Louisa; Wilmington, DE
Hindla, Louis; Bohemia, NY
Hyatt, Donald; McLean, VA
Kaelin, Bruno; Centreville, VA
Keagy, M. M.; York, PA
Kennell, Austin; Waynesboro, VA
Kessler, Clair; Spring Grove, PA
Knippenberg, Mrs. John; Wayne, NJ
Lay, David; Kilmarnock, VA
Lewis, G. D.; Colts Neck, NJ
Luettgen, A. J.; Spring Grove, PA
Martin, Alfred; Philadelphia, PA
McDonald, Sandra; Hampton, VA
Miller, George; Hanover, PA
Miller, Ross; Franklin Lakes, NJ
Mitchell, Col. John; Vienna, VA
Morris, Elmer; Manasquan, NJ
Mraw, Louis; Trenton, NJ
Muntz, Henry; Newfoundland, NJ
Nosal, Matthew; Calverton, NY
Oleri, Mary; Closter, NJ
Patterson, Robert; McLean, VA
Pecherer, B.; Montclair, NJ
Phipps, Harold; Takoma Park, MD
Pryor, Robert; Washington, D.C.
Reeder, D. A.; Clarksville, MD
Reid, G. Albert; Linwood, NJ
Reiley, Harold; Woodsboro, MD
Rhein, William; Mechanicsburg, PA
Ring, George; Fairfax, VA
Schaefer, Paul; Rockville, MD
Schannen, Henry; Trenton, NJ
Schulman, Cyril; Washington, D.C.

Scott, Hugh; Washington, D.C.
Seidler, Carl; Anderson, SC
Shapiro, Ben & Marion; East Brunswick, NJ
Shirven, Maynard; Alexandria, VA
Smith, W. David; Spring Grove, PA
Spencer, Thais; Fulton, MD
Stelloh, Robert; Potomac, MD
Stepka, William; Richmond, VA
Sullivan, William; Roseland, NJ
Thomson, Charles; Kensington, MD
Vernimb, Bryan; Howell, NJ
Wagner, David; Burtonsville, MD
Walton, Pat; Upper Saddle River, NJ
Weiskittel, Harry; Baltimore, MD
Welsh, Jerome; Oxon Hill, MD
West, Franklin; Gladwyne, PA
Winter, Fred; Pottstown, VA
Winter, Joan; Norfolk, VA
Wister, Mrs. John; Swarthmore, PA
Wuebbens, David; Little Falls, NJ
Yavorsky, Leon; Freehold, NJ

Azalea is but one of the many series in the genus Rhododendron. Properly written the name is always preceded by an R., as *R. schlippenbachii* or R. 'Rosebud'.

Doubling is accomplished in a rhododendron by the stamens and pistil becoming petaloid, seriously inhibiting the plant's ability to form seed. Such flowers remain in fresh condition much longer than normal flowers. Another type of doubling is the hose-in-hose form in which the calyx becomes one cup set within another.

Among rhododendron species in the wild — in common with many another of Nature's most scented flowers — fragrance apparently coincides with white or very pastel shades in the flower. Also a great many with this very desirable trait are definitely tender, a big problem for the hybridizer.

HYBRIDIZING IN THE SOUTHEASTERN UNITED STATES

H. Furman Cantrell, Ph.D.
Piedmont, South Carolina

The efforts of hybridizers in the Southeast have been varied and have included evergreen and deciduous azaleas as well as rhododendrons. Perhaps this is due to the interests of the hybridizers because of the popularity of both kinds of azaleas in this part of the country. Most of the hybridizers indicate their primary motivation as a desire to improve upon existing hybrids or species. Some of this motivation has come from seeing many of the beautiful natural hybrids among the native azaleas as well as the flowering of their own seedlings. Nevertheless, there is always that hope that a cross will yield that special, sought-after prize.

Much of the rhododendron hybridizing has taken place in Western North Carolina. Russ and Velma Haag from Brevard have been very active hybridizers in the area. Their goals have been varied, but have included a good yellow hybrid and a good blue hybrid. Presently, they have one of each under evaluation. Both hybrids are outstanding in flower color and appear to have good plant form also. Cold hardiness is an important trait in their area, and these plants appear to qualify. Their activities include a variety of other crosses involving both large and small leaf plants. A visit to their garden reveals a large number of promising seedlings.

Not far away in the foothills, Dr. Ernest Yelton and Jim Todd have an assortment of their hybrids. Dr. Yelton has spent years in hybridizing large-leaf and small-leaf rhododendrons as well as deciduous azaleas. From this effort have come numerous, very nice hybrids. Jim Todd's efforts include a variety of crosses, but recently he has focused on hybrids with indumentum and improvement of the R. *yakushimanum-metternichii* type flowers. Some of his hybrids were exhibited at a recent chapter meeting on hybridizing.

In the Charlotte (Piedmont Chapter) area, the hybridizers include Dr. Donald Kellam, Marshall Stillwell, Dr. Robert Means and Dr. Reid Bahnson. All of them are working on rhododendron hybrids which are adaptable to that area where the summer temperature is warmer than in the mountains. Some of the crosses involve pollen collected in the Himalayas by Dr. Kellam. Results of these crosses are not yet available. This group also has the goal of improving on the existing forms and producing that really special seedling.

In the Atlanta area, Olin Holsomback has a number of crosses under evaluation. Heat tolerance is important in that area also.

Our area is fortunate to have Dr. August Kehr as a relatively new resident. Dr. Kehr has many of his hybrids in his garden in Flat Rock, North Carolina. A number of these will no doubt prove to be outstanding.

There are other members in this area who are hybridizing, and who will join the ranks of the veterans. Several chapter programs have been devoted to hybridizing, and more and more of our members are working on specific goals — the most common being good yellows and indumented hybrids. Others are working toward development of an outstanding red hybrid.

The azalea hybridizing in this area has been directed toward evergreens as well as the deciduous azaleas. Some very interesting evergreen crosses have come from the work of James Harris in the Atlanta area. He uses the Satsukis in many of his crosses, and has some very exciting crosses which are improvements over the parent Satsukis. He also is evaluating a hanging-basket azalea which is exceptional. Also in the Atlanta area, A. J. Boike is working with evergreen azaleas. He has several promising crosses under evaluation. Evergreen azaleas in the Southeast flower from late March until mid-June, and provide an almost endless array of colors and plant habits with which hybridizers can work. Most of them approach hybridizing with the specific goal of improving flower quality on a desirable plant or altering an inferior plant to enhance an attractive flower. The opportunities appear to be endless with the evergreen azaleas.

The native deciduous azaleas have captured the interest of many of our members with their spectacualr display of color and form. There are many natural hybrids, and in fact, it is often difficult to locate a specimen of a true species. Hybridizing has focused upon efforts to produce new and interesting color combinations as well as the introduction of fragrance to an already beautiful flower form. Walter Beasley from Lavonia, Georgia, has several crosses available in his nursery which have proven worthy introductions. Included are: *bakeri* x *arborescens, prunifolium* x *arborescens,* the Choptank River Hybrids (*atlanticum* x *nudiflorum*) and others. Al O'Rear in the Atlanta area is also working with deciduous azaleas with some of the same goals — improved flowering traits and adaptability to different climates.

At Callaway Gardens, Fred Galle has made numerous crosses of many azaleas and has a very interesting array of hybrids, including crosses of evergreen with deciduous azaleas. Many of his hybrids are growing in this famous garden.

This account is not a complete report of all hybridizing activity in the Southeastern area, but is representative of the general goals and objectives: improved flower traits, introduction of indumentum and more adaptability of plants to a specific climatic condition. Interest in this aspect of the genus Rhododendron is growing. The potential is great because of the large number of hybrids and species which grow here.

HYBRIDIZING IN THE GREAT LAKES REGION

Dr. Thomas L. Ring,
Bellaire, Ohio

Probably the first person to do significant hybridizing in the Great Lakes region was Warren Stokes, a nurseryman of Butler, PA, whose career spanned some fifty years, beginning about 1920.

Stokes is spoken of in terms of almost reverence by those who knew him, both for his qualities as a person and his skill with plants. It is said that he could pick from seedling flats those which would have red flowers and to grow such root systems on his flatted rhododendrons that individual plants would have to be separated by cutting their roots with a knife.

At one time Stokes had thousands of plants lined out and many beautiful flowered things appeared among them. Unfortunately most were lost because Stokes made no provisions to have his plants evaluated by knowledgeable people and preserved following his death.

A few clones exist in small numbers, preserved by people such as Weldon Delp and Orlando Pride. Among these are 'Indian Chief', 'Newport', 'Opal' and 'Bronze Wings'.

Other hybridizers no longer with us are Sam Baldanza of Benton Harbor, MI, who registered two clones of (*catawbiense compactum* x 'Mars'), and Julian Pot, a Chesterland, OH, nurseryman who produced a very superior foliage plant with good flowers which was selected and named 'Chesterland' by David Leach.

Henry Yates, Frostburg, MD, who died in 1970, produced many hybrids primarily from advanced generation crosses of Gable hybrids. Most are not yet available but the hardiest of those named are: 'Pink Punch', 'Brenda Lee', 'Guy Bradour', 'Yates' Hazel', 'Yates' Best', 'Earlene' and 'Apple Dumpling'.

Dean of active Great Lakes hybridizers is Orlando Pride, Butler, PA. As yet, there has not been a thorough study of "Lanny's" work, although attempts are under way. His own account of his fifty year love affair with rhododendrons will soon be published in the Quarterly Bulletin of the American Rhododendron Society.

'Edith', a shapely and extremely hardy late-blooming plant is the only Pride rhododendron which is widely available, although several of his very hardy evergreen azaleas are being offered.

The work of co-dean Anthony Shammarello of South Euclid, OH, has been well covered in "Hybrids and Hybridizers". Although Tony professes to be "too damned old" to raise seedlings, he can not resist annually making a few crosses, and new selections, involving a new red elepidote, continue to be made.

Another northern Ohioan, Peter Girard is best known for his evergreen azaleas but is also producing deciduous azaleas and rhododendrons with special interest in developing a blue elepidote. Pete has a clone he calls 'Peter A.' which is bluer than any this writer has seen, including West Coast varieties. It is under propagation but release will be delayed due to the loss of a block of rooted cuttings.

William Fetterhoff of Gibsonia, PA, is the hard luck hybridizer of the group. From the cross ((America x Blaze) x (America x Mars)) Bill got seven beautiful reds all of which subsequently succumbed to over-fertilization. The cross was repeated and even more seedlings were pricked off. These were all lost. However, through shared seeds with Weldon Delp and the author, several good reds from this cross have flowered and survive.

Bill is working for the hardy yellow elepidote, using his recently registered 'Adele's Yellow' (*maximum* x *wardii*), and (Boule de Neige x Yellow Creek) as basic parents.

H. Roland Schroeder, M.D., proprietor of Holly Hills Nursery, Evansville, IN, although becoming involved with rhododendron breeding as late as 1970, is growing 10,000 seedlings a year with the goal of developing plants suited to his area with improved cold, heat and phytophthora resistance as well as larger trusses. His program has already produced one large dividend in the form of a clone of *fortunei* which has bloomed in an exposed location after −26°F. This plant was one of the few survivors of several thousands lined out.

Dr. Tolstead, retired botanist, is doing much the same thing with many species in Elkins, WV, and, in turn, producing many hybrids with the hardy survivors.

The best known Great Lakes hybridizer and probably the best known rhododendron expert in the world today is David Leach, North Madison, OH. A discussion of Dr. Leach's work exceeds the limits of this paper. Suffice it to quote the late Warren Baldsiefen "His hybridizing program ... and the list of dazzling new hybrids one day to be released place his contributions on a par with those of Lionel de Rothschild and Anthony Waterer of England".

Surrounding the Hamlet of Harrisville, Pennsylvania, about 20 miles north of Butler, Pennsylvania, the topography is arranged in a natural bowl into which settle each winter masses of air several degrees colder than that of surrounding areas. In this less than congenial climate (selected for that purpose) thrives one of the most significant rhododendron breeding programs in the eastern United States, under the exacting eye of its executor, Weldon E. Delp.

Plants are container grown (used one gallon tin cans for one year plants and conveniently rectangular five gallon cans for older plants, all discards from a local industry) in a special mix under controlled temperature and day length. Using this system plants set flower buds in as little as 14 months from seed. Most yearling plants then go into a large shade house to face their first Harrisville winter. Survivors are placed in full exposure the next winter, with temperatures to −25°F or colder, and occasional 50 mph winds. A relatively few crosses

of special interest are brought into a cold house after having been
exposed to temperatures near zero and form an early spring flower
show, with each year's addition more spectacular than the last. Most
of Mr. Delp's crosses are made at this time.

Delp is also a master propagator so that there is little difficulty
in having a few rooted cuttings of promising things to be distributed
for testing in a variety of climates and soils.

Among Delp's named slections are 'Harrisville' and 'Slippery Rock'.
These two clones do not possess the flower quality of later creations
but rival *catawbiense* itself for hardiness. 'Christina', illustrated in
"Hybrids and Hybridizers", is named for his "right hand" and chief
transplanter (who happens also to be his mother). Other possible stars
of the future grown and flowered by Delp though not all his own
crosses are: yellow — (*brachycarpum* var. *tigerstedtii* x Crest) and
(*yakusimanum* x Gold Mohur); pink — ((*yakushimanum* x 'Mars') x
Dexter's Appleblossom); purple — (Sefton x Purple Splendour); red
— ((America x Blaze) x (America x Mars)) and (*smirnowii* x (*yakushimanum* x Princess Elizabeth)); flowers with blotches — (Sappho x
(Catalgla x Sappho)) and (Ice Cube x Blue Peter); lepidotes — many,
using his special form of *carolinianum* as one parent.

There are many more Great Lakes hybridizers. Clark Adams, Por-
terville, PA, a nurseryman, also interested in primulas; his wife is
a nationally known wild flower authority. Robert Blough, Johnstown,
PA, attorney, reports Fowle #19 seedlings good. Gordon Emerson,
advertising executive, Rock Creek, OH, has four clones of (America
x Consolini's best red), each later and redder than its predecessors.
Richard Fenicchia, former Rochester, NY, municipal garden superin-
tendent, has several clones performing well in the display garden at
Wooster, OH. D. L. Hinerman, M.D., pathologist at the University
of Michigan, makes at least 50 crosses each year; his (*smirnowii* x
yakushimanum FCC) is quite good. Mark Konrad, M.D., Sewickley,
PA, radiologist, has made (*maximum* x *yakushimanum*). George Krempasky, Latrobe, PA, a disabled steel worker, has produced (Catalgla
x Blue Peter) and other crosses. M. W. Michener, Franklin, PA, retired
greenhouse operator, has an outstanding hardy white with purple
blotch (Catalgla x Sappho) which is under propagation; Otto Prycl,
New Stanton, PA, has 'Anna Lise', a good red and a *smirnowii* hybrid
which is very hardy; T. L. Ring, Bellaire, OH, has two good reds from
((America x Blaze) x (America x Mars)); Gordon Walters, D.D.S.,
Butler, PA, has a seedling from 'President Lincoln'; and Maletta
Yates, Frostburg, MD, has resumed the work begun by her late hus-
band. (Mrs. H. R. Yates x *wardii*) is one of her good yellows.

In conclusion, the state of affairs in this district has been beautifully
elucidated by Dr. Hinerman. "This Chapter covers a very large region
of the country ranging from zone 7 to zone 4. A large percentage
of the area has an environment which is quite hostile to the average

rhododendron. Therefore we are well suited for the challenge of developing new rhododendrons having greater cold hardiness as well as more heat resistance. We can predict with certainty that there is in the process of development through hybridization a vastly superior race of rhododendrons surpassing our presently available rhododendrons in that they will possess super hardiness, excellent plant habit, and exotic, long-lasting flowers of ever greater breath-taking beauty".

Hybridizers and/or growers of seedlings in the Great Lakes district
Adams, Clark; Portersville, PA
Blough, Robert; Johnstown, PA
Bosley, Paul; Mentor, OH
Bradley, Bruce; Chelsea, MI
Brooks, Judson; Sewickley, PA
Browning, James; Pittsburg, PA
Davis, Fred; Kent, OH
Delp, Weldon; Harrisville, PA
Edinger, Robert; Mars, PA
Emerson, Gordon; Rock Creek, OH
Fenicchia, Richard; West Webster, NY
Fetterhoff, William; Gibsonia, PA
Ford, John; Wooster, OH
Girard, Peter, Sr.; Saybrook, OH
Heinze, John; Toledo, OH
Hinerman, D.L.; Ann Arbor, MI
Konrad, Mark; Sewickley, PA
Krempasky, George; Latrobe, PA
Leach, David; North Madison, OH
Lucas, R.J.; Newark, OH
Michener, M.W.; Franklin, PA
Moore, W.S.; East Liverpool, OH
Murdock, David; Pittsburg, PA
Neal, John; Kirkwood, MO
Pride, Orlando; Butler, PA
Prycl, Otto; New Stanton, PA
Ring, Thomas L.; Bellaire, OH
Robinson, Felix; Pittsburg, PA
Schmidt, Ernest; Cleveland, OH
Schroeder, H.R.; Evansville, IN
Scott, M.U.; Grosse Point Shores, MI
Shammarello, Anthony; South Euclid, OH
Snyder, Walter; Stoneboro, PA
Stanton, Ernest; Grosse Ile, MI
Tolstead, W.L.; Elkins, WV

Walters, Gordon; Butler, PA
White, Herbert; Shanks, WV
Wilson, Charles; Dover, OH
Yates, Maletta; Frostburg, MD

Color in rhododendron flowers is normally determined by plastid pigments, ranging from colorless through shades of cream and yellow, which are found in the tissues of the corolla. They are not solvent in sap. Other pigments soluable in the sap are the yellow and ivory-white flavones and flavonols, and the red and blue antho-cyanins. Together these in various combinations produce the flower color.

David Leach, Quar. Bul. ARS, 12 (1) 7

For registration clonal names should be markedly different from botanical names in Latin form. Names formed by combining parts of the Latin names of parent species, as 'Impsino', must not be used.

Names should consist of one, two, not more than three words. An arbitrary sequence of letters, an abbreviation, or a numeral is counted as a word but names containing such letters, abbreviations or numerals should be avoided.

An initial article should not be used as part of a name. Names beginning with an abbreviation, except for "Mrs.", should not be used. The only form of address that may be used is that required by national custom, generally that for a married woman.

Names should not exaggerate the merits of the clone; nor should they be used if they are likely to become inaccurate through future introductions. Names that refer to some attribute or attributes common or likely to become common in a group of related clones should not be used. Names likely to be confused with existing names should not be used. Names should not refer to a botanical or common name of a genus or common name of a species outside the genus Rhododendron, as 'Morning Glory', if they would easily lead to confusion.

Edwin Parker, Quar Bul, ARS, 28 (1) 21

RHODODENDRON HYBRIDIZING IN THE NORTHWEST

Dr. Frank D. Mossman
Vancouver, Washington

West of the Cascade Mountains and north of California is the area considered. Temperatures range from 10° to 100°F. but go occasionally lower and higher. The coastal areas are somewhat more mild. Humidity is high, except in summer. Taxes are ever higher thus growing space is progressively less available to the average home-owner. These factors are important in planning hybrids of any plants.

The three native rhododendrons of the area, *R. macrophyllum, occidentale,* and *albiflorum* have received little attention from local hybridizers. *R. occidentale* was a main genetic ingredient of the Knaphill and the later Exbury strain of azaleas, some of the showiest of all flowers grown in the Northwest.

The products of English hybridizing of the last century were the main rhododendrons here during the first third of this century and many large plants are still to be seen in older gardens, lavenders of various shades, magenta pinks and blue tinged reds, reflecting their *R. catawbiense, ponticum* and *caucasicum,* parentage.

As the ever greater number of new, exciting species came into domestic cultivation from the seemingly inexhaustible treasure-trove of the Himalayan Mountains, from 1850 to 1950, the quality of new hybrid rhododendrons reflected this vast gene pool. Pure colors were produced, white, pink, red, blue, purple, even yellow. Plant habit, ultimate size, leaf retention, leaf size, leaf shape and texture, winter appearance, cold hardiness, all have become more and more prominent in the thoughts of northwest hybridizers. In addition ease of propagation and age at appearance of first flower buds are important to commercial growers. Fragrance is often achieved. Blooming time has been a major consideration so that now rhododendron flowers are seen regularly from February through August and often before and after those months. Peak bloom is still April and May. Disease and insect resistance receive more and more attention.

Northwest rhododendron hybridizing began in the 1920's with James Barto, then Haldan Lem in 1930's through the 1960's and many, many others in the 1940's and later. The first efforts involved English and Dutch hybrids. Many of the English crosses were repeated. The progeny of such crosses were even better suited to this area because of natural selection. Most hybridizers maintained species rhododendron collections, too, for pleasure as well as for the gene source of primary or more complicated crosses.

Occasional very severe winters taught valuable lessons to hybridizers.

All the effort of producing new rhododendrons was for the pure pleasure of seeing new and better flowers whether by professional or amateur growers. Nobody ever realized any significant monetary profit from this magnificent effort to speed up nature's endeavors. The plants of early hybridizers have very often been forgotten as new and better clones developed. This has even been true of many plants given awards long ago. Many years are needed for the final judgement by the general growing public. The hybridizer's ultimate satisfaction is the new, glowing, pure-colored beauty on a compact plant, with pleasing leaves retained for three or more years, rooting readily from cuttings, budding in youth, suitable for the area soil and climate and disease and insect resistant. If the flowers are large, fragrant and sun-tolerant, the joy is even greater.

R. griffithianum, a large and fragrant-flowered white but relatively tender species from the lower Himalayan slopes was combined, in various ways, by the British hybridizers and later the Dutch with numerous other hardy species, such as *R. fortunei,* a large flowered fragrant pink, producing vigorous growing plants hardy in our Northwest but requiring much growing space. *R. griersonianum* produced combinations that bloomed young with salmon-colored flowers but were often willowy growers, too frequently intolerant of our occasional very cold winters, and notably intolerant of fertilizers.

Alpines are a delightful source of rock garden hybrids, and combined with Triflorums, produce glowing blues and purples, and even some whites and yellows, suitable for any portion of the garden, hedges, or small gardens.

R. repens and *williamsianum* with other dwarfs, such as *chrysanthum* produce some fascinating ground-creepers. Combined with large plants, many medium-sized plants have been produced. *R. yakushimanum* has been used for many years to produce low-growing, hardy plants with much disappointment but a few pleasing results.

Early flowering hybrids have come from *R. calophytum, sutchuenense, chrysanthum, mucronulatum,* and *dauricum,* and their hybrids. *R. auriculatum* and *discolor* are sources for late season bloom.

Many primary crosses, that is, species crossed species, have been made but too seldom has anyone pursued the F2 generation. This requires much space to grow many plants to produce the very few desired clones that we know can be expected from selfing a product of a primary cross or from crossing FI sister seedlings. Only F2 generation plants can produce the final goals of the hybridizer. For example: *R. williamsianum* crossed R. 'Loderi' gives plants half way between the two in plant habit and size of flower. A few F2 generation plants should have the stature of R. *williamsianum* and flower size of R. 'Loderi'!

A vast amount of effort and time has been spent to create a true butter yellow. The largest flowered, deepest yellow thus far is probably the English R. 'Crest', but older plants are leggy and retain only one year's leaves. The yellow is very good but the hybridizer feels a need for more yellow pigment. R. 'Hotei' is a startling deep greenish-yellow on a compact plant. The flowers and trusses are medium-size. *R. dichroanthum, wardii,* and *campylocarpum* are sources of yellow. Were the best forms used? Were the best forms brought to us domestic growers from their native wild state? Are better forms now available? A probable "yes" to all three questions.

The hardier Maddenii species and hybrids may be grown out-of-doors in the coastal areas. Much room for improvement of all our rhododendrons exists, beautiful though they are at present, and a great many devoted people are working thoughtfully with definite goals in mind.

Here are some hybridizers in the Northwest and some of their best rhododendron hybrids, commercially available at present. Robert Bovee — 'Miss Prim', 'Exotic', 'Mardi Gras' and 'Roma Sun'; Lester Brandt — 'Reve Rose' and 'Gold Mohur'; James Caperci — 'Kim' and 'Maricee'; Roy Clark — 'Olympic Lady', 'Puget Sound' and 'Hamma Hamma'; George Grace — 'Carolyn Grace'; Edgar and Harold Greer — 'Trude Webster', 'Sugar Pink', 'Coral Velvet' and 'Hallelujah'; Mary and Theodore Greig — 'Cutie'; John Henny — 'Cotton Candy', 'Full Moon' and 'Good News'; Rudolph Henny — 'C.I.S.', 'Ermine', 'Brickdust', 'Roseann', 'Goldbug', 'Fair Lady', 'Captain Jack', 'Fairytale' and 'Goldstrike'; Ray and Del James — 'Fawn', 'Tumalo', 'Springfield' and 'Sue'; Ben Lancaster — 'Snow Lady', 'Old Spice', 'Peach Lady', 'Bluette' and 'Rose Elf'; Hjalmer Larson — 'Etta Burrows', 'Blue Jay', and 'Elizabeth Titcomb'; Halfdan Lem — 'Anna', 'Lem's Cameo', 'Point Defiance', 'Smokey #9', 'Riplet', and 'Walloper'; John Lofthouse — 'Pink Petticoats'; Marshall Lyons — 'Blue River'; Frank Mossman — 'Taurus'; Endre Ostbo — 'King of Shrubs', 'Edna McCarty' and 'Edward Dunn'; Cecil Seabrook — 'Grace Seabrook'; Karl Sifferman — 'Hotei'; Cecil Smith — 'Nestucca' and 'Noyo Brave'; Robert Ticknor — 'Shamrock'; Theodore Van Veen, Sr. — 'Old Copper', 'Autumn Gold', 'Lucky Strike', 'Evening Glow' and 'Anna Rose Whitney'; William Whitney — 'Virginia Richards', 'Blue Pacific', 'Hurricane', 'Ruby Hart' and 'Double Date'; Arthur Wright, Sr. and Jr. — 'Doubloons', 'Odee Wright', 'Peeping Tom', 'Cary Ann' and 'Ocean Lake'.

CALIFORNIA HYBRIDIZING

Margery C. Farwell
Woodside, California

California's mild climate allows the growing of the Maddenii Series as garden plants; consequently a great deal of our hybridizing has been done using this series either as one or both parents.

MR. and MRS. MAURICE SUMNER have been hybridizing in the Maddenii Series since 1951. Four of their hybrids have been registered, one, 'Mi Amor' (*lindleyi* x *nuttallii*), has received the AM from the RHS in 1975. They are now working to add both red and yellow to these lepidotes that grow so well in the central area of California. Using 'King of Shrubs' they have produced some clear orange flowers in large round trusses, some with a very large calyx. These are being watched for registering. They are currently doing some work with *spinuliferum* x 'Seta' and *spinuliferum* x *cuffeanum* which they plan on using for some second generation crossing.

DR. JOHN EVANS enjoys working with the Maddeniis for their ease of cultivation, pleasant growth habit, well-built up trusses of excellent substance, good foliage, very pleasing fragrance, blooming period extending from February through mid-summer ('Forsterianum' to *rhabdotum*), variation in size from small compact shrubs to one that is tree-like. He has crossed *maddenii* with *cinnabarinum* to introduce color and tubular corollas. The progeny has proved more vigorous than the *cinnabarinum* parent with a well shaped plant. Jack is also working on the Vireyas but feels his work is too recent for comment.

The Vireya rhododendrons are much newer to us with a great deal of hybridizing still going on. These plants are more tender and somewhat borderline for many of us as a garden plant. Grown with some protection, they are becoming quite popular. The fact that they tend to bloom off and on the year round gives them an added appeal.

PETER SULLIVAN of San Francisco has had wide experience both in growing and hybridizing the Vireyas at the Strybing Arboretum in Golden Gate Park. His first consideration — to build into these difficult "prima donnas" a degree of hybrid vigor. There has been some success but he feels that some will never be terrestrialized. Second goal — to clone a few usable yellows and oranges. Third — to develop the tubular flower. Fourth — to capture tropical fragrance, a great challenge.

BILL MOYNIER of Southern California is also working with the Vireyas. In his climate, with a very few exemptions, the Vireyas thrive outdoors year round (minimum temperature 28° to 34°F). His goal is to produce high quality hybrids that are resistant to mildew, a very

important characteristic in Vireyas. Bill is also doing some work with
deciduous azaleas which are doing surprisingly well in view of their
reputation for needing considerable winter chilling. Many of these
crosses are also coming up resistant to mildew. His third interest is
the large-leafed hybrids that will not bud blast in the fall.

CARL DEUL, also of Southern California, is hybridizing with
Vireyas. His interest is a plant that can be offered to the florist trade
— compactness, good trusses of large flowers, blooming at a young
age. Another interest of Carl's is to create plants that will endure
the high mineral content and alkalinity in their tap water as well
as a climate with lack of winter dormancy. Some work on elepidotes
(*ponticum, yakushimanum* and *semiarum*) may prove to be valuable
parents. *Chapmanii* is the basis for his lepidote breeding along with
maddenii, boothii and diploid Triflorums. These are looking very
promising for difficult Southern California.

BOB SCOTT is currently working with the yellow lepidotes. He
has already had one yellow, 'Lemon Mist' (*xanthostephanum* x *leu-caspis*), receive the AE in 1969. His newer 'Meadowgold' has earned
the AM from the California Horticultural Society and a third along
this line has recently been registered 'Prairie Gold'. A change in the
direction for breeding yellows came about with the cross of 'Eldorado'
x *rhabdotum*. One of the offspring is upright with a good yellow flower
that favors the size and form of *rhabdotum*. This direction is being
explored further along with a parallel program which he hopes will
produce a few clear pinks and perhaps a red. 'Pink Snowflakes' (*race-mosum* x *moupinense*) is another of Bob's registered plants.

BILL MOYLES interests are, to quote, "a purely California orienta-
tion". His aims are early blooming (using the tender Arboreum, Irroratum and Grande Series), heat with low humidity tolerance, compactness and vigor. He has made some untraditional crosses: 'Rose
Elf' x *arboreum* — Cynthia-like color, pronounced nectaries, arboreal
habit; *aureum* x *grande,* and 'Hummingbird' x *hodgsonii.* He has also
made various lepidote crosses: 'Bric-a-Brac' x *scopulorum* and *burmanicum* x *chrysodoron* — this last produced deep yellows. Bill is also
growing and testing the Scott and Sullivan Vireya hybrids. His unregistered ((*arboreum* x 'Elizabeth') x *arboreum*) shows great promise;
it is a compact early red that buds heavily.

A Vireya gene pool is another of Bill's interests. Objective: to obtain
vigorous compact pot-plants for off season bloom by utilizing *wright-
ianum, jasminiflorum, lochae, macgregoriae, loranthiflorum* and to
obtain general heat tolerance by utilizing *chapmanii, iteophyllum, si-
miarum.* He is closely observing selections from John Patrick's
Taiwan/Hong Kong collections: *pachysanthum, championae, morii,*
and others, for adaptability to California.

DR. PAUL BOWMAN was one of the earliest growers in California
to turn to hybridizing, both in and out of the Maddenii Series. Al-

though his health does not permit him to get out into his garden now, his name is well known because of the many beautiful rhododendrons he has registered. Among his introductions are 'Else Frye' and 'Ruby F. Bowman'.

MENDEL'S LAW

Mendel's law is the law observed in the inheritance of many characteristics in plants and animals discovered by Gregor Mendel. Mendel's experiments were with garden peas. He proved that the height, color and other characteristics depend on the presence of genes which behave as units. The following example shows the operation of the law: Tallness being due to a factor T, and shortness to a factor t, a tall plant, arising by union in fertilization of two germ cells both bearing the factor T, is TT; a dwarf is tt. Crossing these, crossbreds Tt result, generation F_1. In their formation a process (Mendelian segregation) occurs such that germ cells, whether male or female, are composed of two kinds, T and t, in equal numbers. The offspring, generation F_2, which arise from the chance union of these germ cells in pairs, according to thg law of probability, are on an average in the following proportions: 1 TT, 2 Tt, 1 tt; and thus plants pure in tallness (TT) and dwarfness (tt), as well as crossbreds (Tt) are formed. Frequently, the individual Tt is itself indistinguishable from the pure form TT. The factor T is then called dominant and the t recessive. Generation F_1, containing only the Tt form, consists entirely of dominants and generation F_2 consists of three dominants (2 Tt, 1 TT) and one dwarf (tt) which is called recessive. Such qualitative and numerical regularity has been proved to exist in regard to very diverse qualities or characters which compose living things. The diversity of forms produced by crossbreeding by horticulturists generally results from a process of analytical variation or recombination of the factors composing the parental types.

The above principle is shown for one character only, height. Plant breeding would encompass many more such as form, color, hardiness and foliage, all combining at the same time in differing combinations.

REGISTERED

AMERICAN

HYBRIDS

The definitive word for the list is *registered*. On both the East and West Coasts there is an unknown quantity of fine rhododendron hybrids, named, but not yet officially registered. Some have become famous through public exposure; many have already found their way into cultivation on a commercial basis. Gable's 'Pioneer', 'Pink Twins' and the various and assorted 'Wallopers' are prime examples. These names are in the second list. The cut-off date for the list is January 1, 1980. It is extremely unlikely that some hybrid and its creator has not been missed — for which an apology in advance is offered.

Single quotes around clonal names in the parentage bracket have been eliminated in line with recent RHS listings. Presumably the first name in the parentage bracket is the seed parent (who can know for sure?). The date given is the date of publication of registration; the plant may have been around for a very long time. The name following is the hybridizer; naming and registration may be, and often is, by another grower. Ratings should ideally always be made in the area the plant is hybridized for and over a period of years; the only rating available should not be by the hybridizer. This method was so initiated for this list by the original committee years ago.

The quality rating is on a scale of 1 to 5: 1 is poor, 2 is below average, 3 is average, 4 is above average and 5 is superior. Left of / is flower; right of / is plant. If no rating is present, plant is too new or just too little known to be fairly rated; or it could be too old and not now grown. Hardiness is simply given as the accepted minimum temperature in 5° intervals that a well-matured plant may be expected to withstand. Some growers, especially in the trade, still use the original American system: H1 is −25°F, H2 is −15°F, H3 is −5°F, H4 is 5°F and H5 is 15°F. Dwarf is under 1½', semi-dwarf is under 3', low is under 4½', medium is under 6' and tall is over 6', at age of 10 years. All growers know climate, even micro-climate, type of soil, unusual weather conditions, exposure and just plain attention can alter the plant, and thus its rating.

Abe Arnott
Rating   (Marchioness of Lansdowne x Lee's Dark Purple).
Hardy to −5°F   1974, Weber. Lvs 6″ x 2″; fls 4″ wide, purple with
Tall   darker blotch, up to 16 per truss.
Late May

Abegail
Rating   (Loder's White x *calophytum*-pink form), 1979,
Hardy to 0°F   Phetteplace. Lvs 5½″ x 2″; fls 3″ wide, pink with
Tall   small dark dorsal blotch, up to 14 per ball truss.
Early April

Abraham Lincoln
                       (*catawbiense* hybrid), 1958, Parsons. Unknown
                       now.

Acadia   see Cornwallis

Adolph Heineman
                       (Jasper x Tally Ho), 1964, Seabrook.

Agate Pass Jewel
Rating   (*dichroanthum* x unknown), 1975, Nelson, rgstrd
Hardy to 5°F   Putney. Lvs 3½″ x 1½″; fls 1½″ wide, pale orange
Semi-dwarf   with faint green stripes inside and outside, up to
Mid-June   5 per lax truss.

Airy Fairy
Rating   (*lutescens* x *mucronulatum* Cornell Pink), 1977,
Hardy to 0°F   Maloney, intrd Granston. Lvs 2¾″ x 1″; fls 1¾″
Low   wide, bright pink with dull red throat spotting, 3
Late March   per truss.

Al Jolson
                       (Mars x *haemaleum*), 1969, Seabrook.

Aladdin's Light
                       (Aladdin x Peach Lady), 1966, Lancaster.

Albert Close
Rating 3/3   *(maximum x macrophyllum)*, 1951, Fraser, intrd
Hardy to −10°F   Gable. Lvs blue-green; fls rose pink, throat heavily
Medium   spotted chocolate red, truss conical.
Late May

Albion Ridge
Rating	(selected white clone *macrophyllum*), 1976, layered
Hardy to 15°F	in wild, Drewry, intrd German. Lvs 6½" x 3"; fls
Tall	2½" wide, frilled, white with small green blotch, up
May	to 15 per truss.

Aldham
Rating	(*yakushimanum* x Gable's Flamingo, ARS seed),
Hardy to −5°F	1979, Bagoly, intrd Herbert. Lvs 4¾" x 1½"; fls 3"
Semi-dwarf	wide. 6 lobes, pink with rose red throat, up to 12
Mid-May	per truss.

Alice Franklin, PA 1960
Rating 3/3	(Ole Olson x Loderi King George), 1962, Lem, intrd
Hardy to 0°F	Larson. Lvs 5" x 2½"; fls 4" wide, yellow, throat
Medium	uranium green, truss large.
Late May	

All Beautiful
Rating	(parentage unknown), 1976, Kersey, intrd Freder-
Hardy to −5°F	ick, Jr. Lvs 6½" x 3½"; fls 5" wide, frilled and fra-
Medium	grant, yellow orange in throat shading outward to
Early May	pink, up to 8 per truss.

Allegro
(Azor x Loderi King George), 1958, Lancaster.

Alley Cat, PA 1960
(parentage unknown), 1962, Ostbo.

Amaranthora
(*catawbiense* hybrid), 1958, Parsons. Unknown now.

Amazement
Rating	(*fortunei* x *wardii*), 1978, Hardgrove, intrd Royce.
Hardy to −5°F	Lvs 5" x 2¼"; fls 3" wide, 7 lobes, fragrant, yellow,
Tall	up to 13 per truss.
Late May	

Amazing Grace
Rating	(Mrs. C.S. Sargent x Swansdown), 1979, Pride. Lvs
Hardy to −30°F	4½" x 2"; fls 3½" wide, pink with yellowish green
Semi-dwarf	dorsal spotting, up to 12 per truss.
Early June	

Amber Gem

Rating	(Fawn x Jalisco), 1978, James, intrd Childers. Lvs
Hardy to −5°F	5¾″ x 2″; fls 4½″ wide, 7 lobes, fragrant, pinkish
Medium	orange with reddish orange dorsal spotting, up to
Late May	10 per truss.

Americana

Rating 2/3	(a chimera? Britannia grafted to *discolor* hybrid),
Hardy to −10°F	1958, Lancaster. Lvs 10″ x 2″; fls 3″ wide, frilled,
Medium	cherry red, ball truss.
Mid-May	

Amigo

Rating	(*aberconwayi* x Witch Doctor), 1972, Goheen. Lvs
Hardy to 5°F	5″ x 1½″; fls 3″ wide, saucer-shaped, deep pink edge
Semi-dwarf	shading to yellow center, heavily spotted red, up
Early May	to 15 per truss.

Amy Ann

(parentage unknown), 1964, R. Henny

Anah Kruschke

Rating 2/4	(selected seedling of *ponticum*), 1973, Kruschke,
Hardy to −10°F	intrd Wright, Sr. and Jr. Lvs 4½″ x 1½″; fls 3″ wide,
Medium	deep reddish purple, up to 12 per ball truss.
Late May	

Ananouri, CA 1973

Rating	(Britannia x *discolor*), 1971, Phipps. Lvs 7″ x 2¾″;
Hardy to	fls moderate red, eye inconspicuous, up to 12 per
Semi-dwarf	truss.
Late May	

Angel Falls

Rating	(parentage unknown), 1977, Kersey, intrd Freder-
Hardy to −5°F	ick, Jr. Lvs 7″ x 3½″; fls 4″ wide, 7 lobes, fragrant,
Medium	white with creamy throat and light pink blush, up
Late May	to 12 per ball truss.

Anita Owen

((Fusilier x Jean) x *haemaleum*), 1965, Seabrook.

Ann Carey, PA 1966

Rating	(*keiskei* x *spinuliferum*), 1966, Lem, intrd Anderson.
Hardy to	Lvs 3″ x 1¼″; fls 1″ wide, chartreuse changing to
Low	coral pink, many axillary trusses, develops petaloid
March	stamens in most fls.

36   *Variety Description and Rating*

Ann Luettgen
Rating
Hardy to −15°F
Medium
May

(advanced generation hybrid including *cataw-biense* and *maximum*), 1979, W. Smith. Lvs 6½″ x 1¾″; fls 4″ wide, deep pink with deep red dorsal spotting, up to 17 per truss.

Ann Pascoe

((*apodectum* x *campylocarpum*) x Idealist), 1970, Brandt.

Ann Rutlidge

(*catawbiense* hybrid), 1956, Stokes.

Anna, PA 1952
Rating 3/4
Hardy to 0°F
Tall
Early May

also grex
(Norman Gill x Jean Marie Montague), seed from Rose, (England), 1952, intrd Lem. Lvs 7″ x 2½″; fls 4″ wide, frilled, rose pink fading to pale pink, dark dorsal blotch, up to 12 per truss. More than one form grown.

Anna Baldsiefen
Rating 3/3
Hardy to 0°F
Semi-dwarf
Early April

(Pioneer selfed), 1964, Baldsiefen. Lvs 1″ x ½″; fls 1¼″ wide, phlox pink, in terminal racemes.

Anna H. Hall
Rating 3/3
Hardy to −25°F
Semi-dwarf
May

(*catawbiense* var. *album* Glass x *yakushimanum*), 1962, Leach. Lvs 3½″ x 1½″; fls 2¼″ wide, white from deep pink buds, up to 15 per truss.

Anna Parsons

(*catawbiense* hybrid), 1958, Parsons, Unknown now.

'Isabel Pierce'
Photo by
Lawrence Pierce

Anna Rose Whitney, PA 1954

Rating 4/4 — (*griersonianum* x Countess of Derby), 1954, Van
Hardy to −5°F — Veen, Sr., intrd Whitney. Lvs 8" x 3"; fls 4" wide,
Tall — rose pink, up to 21 per truss.
Late May

Anne Glass   See Mrs. Powell Glass

Anne Hardgrove

Rating — (C.P. Rafill x Moser's Maroon), 1978, Hardgrove,
Hardy to 0°F — intrd Burns. Lvs 6" x 2"; fls 3½" wide, red, up to
Tall — 11 per truss.
Early June

Annie Dalton, AE 1960   synonym Degram

Rating 3/2 — ((*decorum* x *griersonianum*) x America), 1960,
Hardy to −15°F — Gable. Lvs 8¼" x 2¼"; fls 4" wide, apricot pink with
Medium — darker throat, truss lax.
Late May

Annie Dring

(Loderi King George x Corona), 1978, Joslin, intrd
Hodgson.

Antigua

Rating — (Mary Belle x Dexter's Apricot), 1978, Becales,
Hardy to −5°F — intrd Herbert. Lvs 6½" x 2½"; fls 3¼" wide, red
Medium — blending to yellow throat, red blotch and spots on
May — all lobes, up to 10 per lax truss.

Aola

Rating 3/2 — (selected seedling of *valentinianum*), 1962, Lancas-
Hardy to 15°F — ter. Lvs typical of species, fls 3" wide, double and
Semi-dwarf — fimbriated, yellow, up to 5 per truss.
April

Applause

Rating — (*catawbiense* var. *album* x (Adrian Koster x *wil-*
Hardy to −20°F — *liamsianum*)), 1972, Leach. Lvs 4" x 2¼"; fls 2¼"
Medium — wide, white shaded ivory, up to 11 per globular
May — truss.

Apple Dumpling

Rating — ((Catalgla x *yakushimanum* Koichiro Wada) x
Hardy to −5°F — (*lanigerum* Round Wood x *catawbiense*)), 1977,
Semi-dwarf — Yates, intrd M. Yates. Lvs 3" x 1½"; fls 2¾" wide,
Mid-May — 7 lobes, fragrant, pale yellow with greenish yellow
throat, up to 7 per truss.

Apricot Nectar
(unnamed hybrid x Jalisco), 1971, Lyons.

April Blush
Rating   (*carolinianum* var. *album* x *mucronulatum*), 1968,
Hardy to −25°F Nearing. Lvs 1" long, mostly deciduous; fls 1½"
Dwarf   wide, blush pink.
April

April Dream
Rating   (parentage unknown), 1976, Whitney, intrd Sather.
Hardy to −5°F   Initially called April Showers. Lvs 5" x 2"; fls 2½"
Tall   wide, pink, very large red blotch over top 3 lobes,
Early April   up to 12 per truss.

Aristocrat   see Buttermint

Arlene Utz
Rating   (advanced generation hybrid including *cataw-*
Hardy to −15°F *biense* and *maximum*), 1979, W. Smith. Lvs 6" x
Tall   2½"; fls 3" wide, 7 lobes, deep pink with deeper edg-
Late May   ing and throat, up to 11 per truss.

Art Wickens
(Britannia x Jasper), 1967, Seabrook.

Arthur Pride
Rating   (natural hybrid of *maximum* and *catawbiense,* col-
Hardy to −30°F lected wild), 1979, Pride. Lvs 5½" x 2"; fls 2" wide,
Medium   orchid edges, white center, blotch of chartreuse
Mid-June   spots, up to 29 per ball truss.

Artic Moon
(parentage unknown), 1966, Loeb.

Artic Pearl
Rating   (selected seedling of *dauricum* var. *album*), 1971,
Hardy to −25°F Baldsiefen. Lvs typical of species, fls 2" wide, white,
Low   up to 5 per truss.
April

Ashes of Roses
(*fortunei* hybrid), 1958, Dexter.

Atrier   grex
Rating 3/1   (Atrosanguineum x *griersonianum*), 1945, Gable.
Hardy to −10°F Lvs thin; fls red, truss large. Atrier #10, later
Medium   named Redhead, superior.
May

Atroflo, AE 1960 grex

Rating 3/2
Hardy to −5°F
Medium
Late May

(Atrosanguineum x *floccigerum*), 1940, Gable. Lvs indumented; fls rose pink, truss large. More than one form grown.

Atror

(Atrosanguineum x (*orbiculare* x *williamsianum*)), 1945, Gable.

Atsonii

(*thomsonii* x Atrosanguineum), 1937, Gable.

Attar

Rating 4/2
Hardy to 5°F
Tall
Mid-April

(selected seedling of *decorum*, Hu Yu Expedition), 1963, Barto, intrd R. Henny. Lvs typical of species, fls pale rose shaded pale green in throat, truss large.

Aunt Martha

(parentage unknown), 1958, Clark.

Aunty Thora

Rating
Hardy to 10°F
Medium
Mid-May

(Marinus Koster x Pilgrim), 1979, Laxdall. Lvs 7″ x 2¾″; fls 5″ wide, shaded pink, red blotch and some spotting, up to 12 per truss.

Autumn Gold

Rating 4/3
Hardy to 0°F
Medium
Late May

(*discolor* x Fabia), 1956, Van Veen, Sr. Lvs 5″ x 2″; fls 3½″ wide, apricot salmon shaded pink, up to 10 per truss.

Avita

(Margaret Dunn x *occidentale*), 1958, Brandt. Azaleodendron.

Avril

Rating 3/3
Hardy to 5°F
Dwarf
Early April

(*ciliatum* x *imperator*), 1965, Mulligan. Lvs 1¾″ x ¾″; fls 2″ wide, rose, up to 3 per truss.

Award, CA 1974

Rating 4/3
Hardy to 0°F
Medium
Early May

(Anna x Margaret Dunn), 1973, James, intrd Ward. Lvs 7½″ x 2″; fls 4½″ wide, fragrant, white with greenish yellow blotch and spots, margins blushed, up to 15 per truss.

'Scintillation'
Photo by
Cecil Smith

Azonea

(Azor x Catanea), 1973, Nearing.

Aztec Gold

(Indiana x Inca Gold), 1965, Lancaster.

Baby Bonnet

(Rosy Morn x Dido), 1966, R. Henny, intrd L. Henny.

Baby Doll

(Holden x *yakushimanum*), 1972, Lancaster.

Bacher's Gold, PA 1955

Rating 3/3   (Unknown Warrior x Fabia), 1955, Bacher. Lvs 4"
Hardy to 0°F   x 2"; fls pink shading to saffron yellow at center,
Medium   6 lobes, truss upright.
Late May

Ballad

Rating   (Dexter L-1 x America), 1972, Leach. Lvs 4½" x
Hardy to −15°F 2"; fls 2¾" wide, medium pink, dark red dorsal
Medium   blotch, up to 15 per truss.
Late May

Bally Cotton

Rating   (*yakushimanum* Koichiro Wada x *chrysanthum*),
Hardy to −5°F 1979, Reese. Lvs 1¾" x ¾"; fls 2" wide, white with
Semi-dwarf   yellowish green dorsal blotch and spots, up to 7
Mid-April   per ball truss.

Bangkok

Rating	(*catawbiense* var. *album* x (*dichroanthum* x (*grif-*
Hardy to −15°F	*fithianum* x *auriculatum*))), 1973, Leach. Lvs 4″ x
Medium	1½″; fls 3¼″ wide, pink shading to orange yellow
May	at center, reddish orange dorsal spotting, up to 13
	per truss.

Barbara Houston

Rating	(Virginia Scott x Belvedere), 1979, Larson. Lvs 4½″
Hardy to 10°F	x 1¾″; fls 3″ wide, orange buff, large red spots on
Medium	3 dorsal lobes, pink edging, up to 9 per truss.
Early June	

Barbara Tanger

Rating	(advanced generation hybrid including *cataw-*
Hardy to −15°F	*biense* and *maximum*), 1979, W. Smith. Lvs 4½″ x
Tall	2″; fls 3½″ wide, pink with red dorsal spotting, up
May	to 17 per truss.

Barefield's Virginia Anne

Rating	(Vulcan x (Anna x Ole Olson)), 1979, Barefield. Lvs
Hardy to 5°F	8″ x 2¼″; fls 3″ wide, dark pink deepening in throat,
Medium	reverse with darker stripes, up to 12 per truss.
Mid-May	

Barryb

Rating	(*catawbiense* x *maximum,* and perhaps unknown
Hardy to −10°F	hybrids, F_4), 1978, W. Smith. Lvs 4½″ x 2″; fls 2″
Medium	wide, reddish purple with greenish yellow dorsal
Late May	blotch, up to 14 per truss.

Barto Alpine

Rating 3/3	(parentage unknown), 1964, Barto, intrd Greer. Lvs
Hardy to −10°F	1″ x ½″; fls fuchsia purple, 5 per truss.
Semi-dwarf	
Early April	

Barto Blue

Rating 4/3	(selected seedling of *augustinii*), 1958, Barto, intrd
Hardy to 5°F	Phetteplace. Lvs typical of species; fls very good
Tall	blue, 3 per truss.
Late April	

Barto Ivory

(probably *fortunei* hybrid), 1962, Barto, intrd
Greer.

Barto Lavender
                    (parentage unknown), 1962, Barto, Intrd Greer.

Barto Rose
Rating 3/4   (selected seedling of *fargesii*), 1963, Barto, intrd
Hardy to −5°F   Phetteplace. Lvs typical of species; fls 2¼″ wide,
Tall   rose madder with deep purple spotting, up to 14
Late March   per truss.

Basileos
                    (Albescens x *ciliicalyx*), 1972, Strybing Arboretum.

Beatrice Pierce
                    (Charles Dickens x (*decorum* x *griffithianum*)),
                    1958, Nearing.

Beaufort
Rating 3/3   (Boule de Neige x *fortunei*), 1958, Gable. Lvs large,
Hardy to −15°F   fls 2¼″ wide; white tinged mauve, fragrant, up to
Medium   14 per truss.
Early May

Beautiful Day
Rating   (Hotei x Crest), 1975, Whitney, intrd Sather. Lvs
Hardy to −5°F   3¾″ x 1½″; fls 3½″ wide, empire yellow with narrow
Low   stripes of tangerine from throat to edge between
Early June   lobes, up to 12 per truss.

Beautiful Dreamer
Rating   (parentage unknown), 1976, Whitney, intrd Sather.
Hardy to −5°F   Lvs 3¾″ x 2¼″; fls 2½″ wide, yellow with touch of
Medium   orange on each lobe, fading to yellow, up to 12 per
April   truss.

Beckyann
Rating   (*discolor* x *campylocarpum* selfed), 1977, Yates,
Hardy to −10°F   intrd M. Yates. Lvs 4½″ x 2″; fls 2¾″ wide, pale
Low   yellow with brownish dorsal spotting, color intensi-
Late May   fies, up to 12 per ball truss.

Beechwood Pink, AE 1960
Rating   (Atrosanguineum x *fortunei*), 1962, Gable, intrd
Hardy to −15°F   Herbert. Lvs 8″ x 3″; fls 3½″ wide, fuchsine pink,
Medium   truss large.
Early May

Belle Heller

Rating 4/3 (*catawbiense* var. *album* x Madame Carvalho),
Hardy to −10°F 1958, Shammarello. Lvs 5″ x 1¾″; fls 4″ wide, white
Medium with conspicuous golden blotch, truss large.
Mid-May

Bellefontaine

Rating (*fortunei* x *smirnowii*), 1978, Pike, intrd Craig, Can-
Hardy to −15°F ada Dept. of Agric., Research Station, Nova Scotia.
Tall Lvs 7″ x 2″; fls 3½″ wide, 7 lobes, rose shading
Early June lighter in throat, dorsal lobe flecked olive brown,
up to 10 per truss.

Bellvale

Rating (*carolinianum* x *dauricum* var. *album*), 1976, Bald-
Hardy to −25°F siefen. Lvs 2½″ x 1″; fls 2″ wide, light pink with
Low mauve flair.
Early May

Ben Lancaster

(Lackamas Spice x Evening Glow), 1971, Lancaster.

Bengal Rose

(*discolor* x Tally Ho), 1971, Lancaster.

Bergie Larson

Rating (*wardii* x Jasper), 1979, Larson. Lvs 4″ x 1¾″; fls
Hardy to 10°F 3″ wide, light orange, slight red dorsal spotting, re-
Medium verse bright red, up to 12 per truss.
Early June

Bern, PA 1955

(*decorum* x unknown), 1955, Bacher.

Bert Larson

Rating (Diva x *strigillosum*), 1979, Larson. Lvs 6½″ x 1¾″;
Hardy to 10°F fls 3″ wide, red with dark brownish red dorsal spot-
Medium ting, up to 14 per truss.
Mid-April

Bertha Parsons see President Lincoln

Bertie Parsons

(*catawbiense* hybrid), 1958, Parsons. Unknown
now.

Besse Howells

Rating 2/3   (Boule de Neige x red *catawbiense* seedling), 1964,
Hardy to −20°F   Shammarello. Lvs 4″ x 1¾″; fls 2½″ wide, ruffled,
Low   burgundy red with dark red blotch, truss globular.
Late May

Bessie Farmer

Rating   (Olympic Lady x Fawn), 1971, Childers. Lvs 4½″
Hardy to 0°F   x 1½″; fls 4″ wide, flat, pink in bud opening white,
Low   fragrant, up to 7 per truss.
Mid-May

Betsy Balcom

Rating   (Princess Elizabeth x Elizabeth), 1978, McGuire.
Hardy to 0°F   Lvs 3½″x 2¾″; fls 2¾″ wide, red, up to 13 per truss.
Medium
Mid-May

Betsy Kruson

Rating   ((Catalgla x *wardii*) x Mars), 1977, Yates, intrd M.
Hardy to −10°F   Yates. Lvs 7½″ x 2¾″; fls 2¾″ wide, dark rose shad-
Low   ing white in throat, small yellowish flare, up to 10
Late May   per truss.

Betsy Parsons   see President Lincoln.

Betty Arrington

Rating 4/4   (parentage unknown), 1970, Dexter, intrd Arring-
Hardy to −5°F   ton. Lvs 6″ x 2″; fls 3¾″ wide, 7 lobes, fragrant,
Medium   rose madder with prominent ruby red flare, up to
Late May   17 per truss.

Betty Breene

                        (*smirnowii* x Dexter hybrid), 1962, Leach.

Betty Hume

Rating 4/3   (probably *fortunei* hybrid), 1963, Dexter, intrd
Hardy to −10°F   Baldsiefen and Effinger. Lvs 7″ x 2½″; fls 4″ wide,
Tall   ruffled, fragrant, pink.
Late May

Beverly Harvey

                        (parentage unknown), 1966, Coen, intrd Fawcett.

Bewitched

Rating 3/3   (Racil x Cornell Pink), 1969, Guttormsen. Lvs 1½″
Hardy to 0°F   x ½″; fls orchid pink, 5 per ball truss.
Semi-dwarf
Mid-March

Big Girl

Rating   (unnamed white x Avocet), 1973, Phipps. Lvs 6¾"
Hardy to −10°F   x 2½"; fls 4" wide, pale pink with olive green blotch,
Medium   up to 11 per truss.
Late May

Big Mac

Rating   (LaBar's White x *macabeanum*), 1968, Knippen-
Hardy to   berg. Lvs 8" x 3½"; fls 1½" wide, barium yellow,
Low   dark red blotch, up to 12 per flat truss.
Early

Big Savage

(unnamed hybrid x unnamed hybrid), 1972, Yates.

Big Savage Red

Rating   (Mars selfed), 1978, Yates, intrd M. Yates. Lvs 5"
Hardy to −20°F   x 2½"; fls 2½" wide, pink with white flair containing
Medium   few green spots, up to 16 per truss.
Mid-May

Bill Massey

Rating   synonym Nutberger
Rating   (*ciliatum* var. *bergii* x *sinonuttallii*), 1978, Druecker,
Hardy to 20°F   intrd Trillium Lane Nursery. Lvs 4½" x 2½"; fls 3½"
Medium   wide, very fragrant, pink shading paler to edges, re-
Early May   verse striped, up to 6 per truss.

Black Cherry

see Burgundy Cherry

Black Prince

(Romany Chal x *thomsonii*), 1962, Brandt.

Black Prince's Ruby

Rating   (*haemaleum* x *thomsonii*), 1977, Nelson, intrd
Hardy to 10°F   Short. Lvs 3½" x 1½"; fls 2½" wide, very waxy, red
Semi-dwarf   with black veins and nectaries, up to 5 per lax truss.
April

Blackie

(Moser's Maroon x Arthur Osborne), 1962, R.
Henny.

Blaze

(Mars x *catawbiense* var. *rubrum*), 1962, Leach.

Blessed Event

(John Coutts x Sarita Loder), 1962, Lyons.

Blind Date

Rating   (parentage unknown), 1975, Whitney, intrd Sather.
Hardy to −5°F   Lvs 6¾″ x 2½″; fls 4½″ wide, 6 lobes, fragrant, rose
Tall   pink shading to yellowish center, small reddish
Mid-May   brown eye, up to 12 per truss.

Blood Ruby

Rating 3/3   (*forrestii* var. *repens* x Mandalay), 1954, Brandt.
Hardy to 0°F   Lvs 2″ x ¾″; fls 1½″ wide, rich red, up to 5 per
Dwarf   truss.
Early May

Blue Cloud

Rating 4/4   (selected seedling of *augustinii*), 1958, Hansen. Lvs
Hardy to 0°F   typical of species; fls 2½″ wide, powder blue, very
Tall   profuse.
Late April

Blue Frost

Rating   (parentage unknown), 1976, Whitney, intrd Sather.
Hardy to −10°F Lvs 5″ x 2″; fls 2¾″ wide, light purple with shaded
Tall   orange spotting on white throat, up to 20 per truss.
Mid-May

Blue Jay

Rating 4/3   (probably *ponticum* seedling), 1965, Larson. Lvs 5″
Hardy to −5°F   x 1½″; fls lavender blue with brown dorsal blotch.
Medium
Early June

Blue Pacific

Rating   (Purple Splendour x Susan), 1976, Whitney, intrd
Hardy to −5°F   Sather. Lvs 6″ x 2¼″; fls 3¾″ wide, lavender blue
Medium   with dark blotch and spotting, up to 12 per ball
Late May   truss.

Blue Rhapsody

Rating   (A. Bedford x Purple Splendour), 1976 Whitney,
Hardy to −5°F   intrd Sather. Lvs 5½″ x 1½″; fls 3½″ wide, medium
Medium   purple with darker spotting in throat, up to 12 per
Late May   ball truss.

Blue River, AE 1961

Rating 4/4   (Van Nes Sensation x Emperor de Maroc), 1962,
Hardy to 5°F   Lyons. Lvs 6″ x 2″; fls 4″ wide, campanula violet,
Tall   up to 17 per truss.
Early May

Bluette

Rating 3/4	(*impeditum* x augustinii Lackamas Blue), 1958,
Hardy to 0°F	Lancaster. Lvs 1½" x ½"; fls 2" wide, hyacinth blue,
Semi-dwarf	up to 8 per truss, very profuse.
Mid-April	

Blush Button

(C.O.D. x Honeydew), 1967, Knippenberg.

Bob Bovee

Rating	(*yakushimanum* Koichiro Wada x *wardii*), 1976,
Hardy to 0°F	Bovee, intrd Sorensen and Watson. Lvs 5½" x 2½";
Medium	fls 3" wide, yellow, red spot changing to green in
Early June	throat, up to 12 per truss.

Bobbet

(*campylogynum* x *cremastum*), 1966, Caperci.

Bodega Crystal Pink

Rating	(Cilpinense x Cornell Pink), 1975, Heller. Lvs 2½"
Hardy to 5°F	x 1"; fls 2½" wide, pink with darker spots.
Low	
March	

Bodega Ruby Red

Rating	(David x (*haemaleum* x *thomsonii*)), 1975, Heller.
Hardy to 5°F	Lvs 3¾" x 1½"; fls 2" wide, heavy substance, red
Low	with black spots on dorsal lobe, up to 7 per flat
Early May	truss.

Bodega Toreador

Rating	(Vanguard x Matador), 1975, Heller. Lvs 5½" x 1¼";
Hardy to 5°F	fls 2¾" wide, red with darker spots on dorsal lobe,
Low	up to 8 per flat truss.
Early May	

Bodega y Quadra

Rating	(Yvonne Opaline x Loder's White), 1977, hybridizer
Hardy to 10°F	unknown, intrd Heller. Lvs 6" x 2½"; fls 4¼" wide,
Medium	7 lobes, bright pink blending to lighter throat, red
Early May	spot, up to 9 per truss.

Bombay

Rating	(((*scyphocalyx* x *kyawi*) x Catalgla) x (Catalgla x
Hardy to −10°F	*wardii*)), 1972, Leach. Lvs 3¾" x 1¾"; fls 1¾" wide,
Low	greenish yellow with darker spotting, blotch and
Early May	reverse, up to 14 per truss.

Bonnie Brae

Rating

Hardy to −5°F

Tall

Mid-May

(Scintillation x Gable's Red Head), 1978, Herbert. Lvs 7″ x 3″; fls 4″ wide, 7 lobes, fragrant, orchid pink, edges darker, yellowish green blotch, up to 17 per truss.

Bonnie Maid

Rating

Hardy to −10°F

Tall

Early May

(*fortunei* x unknown), 1979, Hall, intrd Brown. Lvs 5½″ x 2″; fls 2¾″ wide, 7 lobes, pink with 2 red dorsal rays, up to 13 per ball truss.

Boule de Rose

(red *catawbiense* hybrid x Boule de Neige), 1962, Leach.

Boulodes

Rating

Hardy to −15°F

Medium

Mid-May

(Boule de Neige x Loderi seedling), 1973, Nearing. Lvs 6″ x 2½″; fls 3½″ wide, fragrant and frilled, pink turning white, up to 10 per truss.

Bowie

Rating

Hardy to 0°F

Medium

Early June

(*chapmani* x *minus*), 1979, Skinner, intrd U.S. National Arboretum. Lvs 3¼″ x 1½″; fls 1½″ wide, pink with brownish blotch, terminal inflorescence up to 3 buds, each up to 14 fls.

Brandywine

Rating 4/2

Hardy to −10°F

Semi-dwarf

Late April

(*pubescens* x *keiskei*), 1950, Nearing. Lvs 3″ x ½″; fls small, cream edged rose, in 2″ balls.

'Anna Baldsiefen'   *Photo by Ted Van Veen*

Bravo

(*catawbiense* var. *album* x (*fortunei* x (*arboreum* x *griffithianum*))), 1974, Leach.

Brenda Lee

Rating
Hardy to −20°F
Low
Late May

(*catawbiense* var. *compactum* x Purple Splendour), 1977, Yates, intrd M. Yates. Lvs 4″ x 1¾″; fls 2¼″ wide, violet with lighter blotch covered with maroon spots, up to 11 per ball truss.

Brickdust

Rating 3/4
Hardy to 0°F
Low
Early May

(Dido x *williamsianum*), 1960, R. Henny. Lvs 2″ x 1″; fls 3″ wide, rose madder shaded red, up to 8 per lax truss.

Bridge North

Rating
Hardy to −5°F
Low
Mid-May

(Henry R. Yates x Boule de Neige), 1977, Herbert, intrd Reese. Lvs 4¼″ x 2¼″; fls 3½″ wide, neyron rose fading lighter with gold spotting in throat, up to 14 per ball truss.

Brinny

Rating
Hardy to
Low
May

((Day Dream x Margaret Dunn) x unnamed seedling), 1964, Graves, intrd Janeck. Lvs 5″ x 1½″; fls 4½″ wide, bright yellow from brown buds, up to 10 per truss.

Britannia's Bells

Rating 4/4
Hardy to 0°F
Low
Mid-April

(*williamsianum* x Britannia), 1967, Lancaster. Lvs 2″ x 1½″; fls 3″ wide, rose red, up to 8 per truss.

Brown Eyes

(*fortunei* hybrid), 1958, Dexter, intrd Bosley.

Bruce Brechtbill

Rating 3/5
Hardy to −5°F
Medium
Late April

(bud sport of Unique), 1974, Brechtbill. Plant identical to Unique except for fl which is pink with some yellow in throat.

Buchanan Simpson

Rating 3/3
Hardy to 0°F
Medium
May

(probably *erubescens* hybrid), 1963, Greig. Lvs 5″ x 2″; fls 3½″ wide, pink, throat speckled reddish olive, truss round.

Buff Lady
Rating 3/3   (Nereid x *discolor*), 1958, Rose, (England), intrd
Hardy to −5°F   Lancaster. Lvs 6″ x 1½″; fls 3½″ wide, buff shaded
Low   coral pink, up to 12 per truss.
June

Bunting
                          (Fabia x Dr. Stocker), 1962, R. Henny.

Burgundy
Rating 3/2   (Britannia x Purple Splendour), 1958 Rose, (Eng-
Hardy to −5°F   land), intrd Lem. Lvs 6″ x 2″; fls 3″ wide, burgundy
Tall   red, up to 15 per dome truss.
May

Burgundy Cherry   synonym Dexter #105, Black Cherry
Rating   (parentage unknown), 1979, Dexter, intrd Knippen-
Hardy to −10°F berg. Lvs 5″ x 2½″; fls 2¼″ wide, carmine with pur-
Medium   ple throat blotch and spots, up to 12 per truss.
Late May

Butterball
                          (*xanthostephanum* x *triflorum*), 1969, Greig.

Buttermint   synonym Compact Yellow, Aristocrat
Rating   (Unique x (Fabia x *apodectum*)), 1979, Mauritsen.
Hardy to 0°F   Lvs 3″ x 1¼″; fls 2¾″ wide, white tinged yellow,
Semi-dwarf   red dorsal spotting and streaks on reverse, up to
Mid-May   10 per lax truss.

Cable Car
                          (Tally Ho x *fortunei*), 1975, Golden. Lvs 5½″ x 1½″;
                          fls 4½″ wide, neyron rose, up to 14 per truss.

Cadis, AE 1959
Rating 4/3   (Caroline x *discolor*), 1958, Gable. Lvs large, light
Hardy to −15°F green, fls large, light pink, fragrant, truss flat.
Medium
Late May

Caernarvon
Rating   (*fortunei* hybrid), 1977, Consolini, intrd Reese. Lvs
Hardy to −5°F   5″ x 2½″; fls 3¼″ wide, fragrant, dark pink with
Semi-dwarf   darker spotting, up to 14 per ball truss.
Mid-May

Cairo

Rating 3/3   ((Catagla x *fortunei*) x (Eldam x *williamsianum*)),
Hardy to −20°F   1973, Leach. Lvs 4½" x 2"; fls 3¼" wide, white, vivid
Medium   greenish yellow blotch and spotting, up to 16 per
Mid-May   truss.

Calcutta

Rating   ((*scyphocalyx* x *kyawi*) x Catalgla), 1972, Leach.
Hardy to −15°F   Lvs 4¼" x 1¾"; fls 1½" wide, yellow edged orange,
Semi-dwarf   up to 13 per truss.
June

California Gold

Rating   (Else Frye x Eldorado), 1976, Bowman. Lvs 4¼" x
Hardy to 15°F   1¾"; fls 3¼" wide, primrose yellow, fragrant, up to
Semi-dwarf   6 per truss.
Late March

Callagold

(*dichroanthum* x *wardii*), 1964, R. Henny.

Camich

(Michael Waterer x *catawbiense*), 1958, Gable.

Canada

Rating   (parentage unknown), 1977, Greig, intrd Caperci.
Hardy to 0°F   Lvs 1½" x ½"; fls bright bluish rose, terminal in-
Dwarf   florescence of 5 buds, each with up to 5 fls.
Mid-May

Canadian Beauty

(Mrs. Horace Fogg x Walloper), 1971, Lofthouse.
Lvs 7" x 2¼"; fls 4½" wide, pink shading to lighter
center, up to 16 per truss.

Canadian Sunset

(*yakushimanum* x Gipsy King, 1974, R. Henny,
intrd Linington.

Candi

Rating 3/3   (*cremastum* x *racemosum*), 1963, Caperci. Lvs 2"
Hardy to 5°F   x ¾"; fls 1" wide, bright rose, up to 6 per axillary
Semi-dwarf   truss.
Late April

Caper

(*williamsianum* x Hiraethlyn), 1964, R. Henny.

Caperci Special

Rating   (parentage and origin unknown), 1977, Caperci. Lvs
Hardy to −15°F 1½″ x ½″; fls 1½″ wide, rosy lilac, few red spots,
Dwarf   up to 7 per truss.
Late April

Caprice

Rating 3/4   (selected seedling of *augustinii*), 1958, Hansen. Lvs
Hardy to −5°F   typical of species, fls bluish lavender.
Medium
April

Captain Jack, PA 1956

Rating 4/2   (Mars x *eriogynum*), 1956, R. Henny. Lvs 8″ x 3″;
Hardy to 5°F   fls 3½″ wide, dark red, up to 15 per truss.
Tall
Late May

Captain Kidd, PA 1960

                (Princess Elizabeth x May Day), 1960, R. Henny.
                Lvs 7″ x 2¼″; fls 3½″ wide, waxy, turkey red, up
                to 15 per truss. Growth contorted.

Carioca

                (Loderi King George x Ostbo Y3), 1963, Bovee.

Carl Phetteplace

Rating   (Naomi Pink Beauty x *fortunei*), 1975, Phetteplace,
Hardy to −10°F intrd Guitteau. Lvs 6″ x 3¾″; fls 4″ wide, heavy
Tall   substance, fragrant, deep pink with variable choco-
Early May   late spotting, up to 13 per truss.

Carlene

                (Lem's Goal x *williamsianum*), 1960, Lem, intrd
                Fawcett.

Carol Amelia

Rating   (Polar Bear x Evening Glow), 1979, Holden. Lvs
Hardy to −5°F   7½″ x 2″; fls 5″ wide, 7 lobes, fragrant, white tinged
Medium   yellow, red dorsal spotting and streaks on reverse,
Mid-June   up to 10 per lax truss.

Carol High

Rating   (Elizabeth x French Creek), 1979, Herbert. Lvs 4¾″
Hardy to −10°F x 2½″; fls 3½″ wide, 6 lobes, fragrant, white with
Medium   chartreuse spotting on dorsal lobe, up to 14 per
Late April   truss.

Carol Jean, PA 1957
> (Vulcan x Robin Hood), 1957, Klupenger.

Carolid
> ((*carolinianum* x *oleofolium*) x *davidsonianum*), 1958, Gable.

Caroline
Rating 3/3   (parentage unknown, probably *decorum* x *bra-*
Hardy to −15°F *chyanthum*), 1956, Gable. Lvs large, wavy margins;
Tall   fls large, scented, pale orchid; truss large.
Mid-May

Caroline Gem
> (Elizabeth x Caroline), 1967, Knippenberg.

Carolyn Grace, AE 1960
Rating 3/3   (*wardii* clone or hybrid), 1962, Grace. Lvs 4½″ x
Hardy to 0°F 2½″; fls 3″ wide, primrose yellow, up to 9 per truss.
Medium
Late April

Carousel
> (*carolinianum* x *saluenense*), 1965, Caperci.

Cary Ann, PA 1961
Rating 3/4   (Corona x Vulcan), 1962, Wright, Sr. and Jr. Lvs
Hardy to 15°F 4½″ x 1½″; fls 2″ wide, coral red, up to 17 per truss.
Low
Early May

Cary's Red
Rating   (parentage unknown), 1974, Cary. Lvs 4″ x 2″; fls
Hardy to −20°F 1¾″ wide, same color as America, up to 22 per truss.
Medium
Late May

Catalgla
Rating 3/3   (selected seedling of *catawbiense* var. *album*), 1959,
Hardy to −25°F Gable, intrd Nearing. Lvs medium green; fls white,
Medium   pale pink in bud, truss large. Much used in hybrid-
Late May   izing.

Catalode, AE 1960   see County of York

Catanea

(selection of *catawbiense*), 1959, Gable, intrd Nearing.

Cathaem #1   see Conoco Cheauge

Cathy

(Corona x Dondis), 1956, R. Henny.

Cathy Carter
Rating   ((*discolor* x Nereid x Tally Ho, exact combination
Hardy to −5°F   unknown), x Autumn Gold), 1977, Jordan. Lvs 4"
Semi-dwarf   x 1¼"; fls 4" wide, 7 lobes, yellow edged rose, some
Early June   dark dorsal spotting, up to 11 per truss.

Cavalier
Rating 4/2   (Pygmalion x Tally Ho), 1958, R. Henny. Lvs 4"
Hardy to 5°F   x 2"; fls large, flame red spotted black in throat,
Low   small but many trusses.
Late May

Cecil Smith
Rating   (King of Shrubs x Crest), 1977, Phetteplace. Lvs
Hardy to 0°F   4" x 2"; fls 4" wide, dresden yellow, up to 11 per
Tall   truss.
Mid-May

Cecil S. Seabrook
Rating   (Fusilier x Jasper), 1967, Seabrook. Lvs 5" x 2"; fls
Hardy to   2½" wide, yellow becoming orange buff, up to 22
Medium   per flat truss.
Early June

Celestial Bells

(Fabia x (*wardii* x *souliei*)), 1965, Wyrens. Lvs 4"
x 1½"; fls 2½" wide, apricot yellow, up to 7 per
truss.

Century Twenty-One
(Cunningham's Sulphur x *discolor*), 1962, Lem.

Ceramic

(*wardii* selfed), 1962, R. Henny.

Chang Tso Lin

((*apodectum* x *campylocarpum*) x Idealist), 1964,
Brandt.

Charlestown
  Rating
  Hardy to −5°F
  Tall
  Mid-May

synonym Everitt #7
(parentage unknown, possibly *fortunei* hybrid), 1976, Dexter, intrd Herbert. Lvs 6″ x 2½″; fls 4½″ wide, fragrant, shades of pink with chartreuse throat, up to 16 per truss.

Charley

(*croceum* x Fabia), 1962, James.

Chartreuse

(*flavidum* x Lady Roseberry), 1962, Brandt.

Chat

(Albatross x *wardii*), 1962, R. Henny.

Chatterbox

(Arthur Osborne x *didymum*), 1962, R. Henny.

Chauncy Alcott

(Purple Splendour x Jasper), 1969, Seabrook.

Cheer
  Rating 2/3
  Hardy to −10°F
  Low
  Early May

(Cunningham's White x red *catawbiense* hybrid) 1958, Shammarello. Lvs 4″ x 1¾″; fls 2½″ wide, shell pink with conspicuous red blotch, truss conical.

Cheerio

(*wardii* x Rosy Morn), 1958, R. Henny.

Cherry Bright

(*thomsonii* x *williamsianum*), 1965, Lancaster. Lvs 2½″ x 2″; fls 2¾″ wide, cherry red, up to 8 per truss.

Cherry Jubilee
  Rating
  Hardy to 0°F
  Semi-dwarf
  May

(Fawn x Lem's Goal), 1971, Childers. Lvs 8″ x 1¾″; fls 5″ wide, blend of yellowish pink and light orange, banded deeper, up to 9 per truss.

Chesapeake
  Rating 3/2
  Hardy to −25°F
  Semi-dwarf
  April

(*pubescens* x *keiskei*), 1958, Nearing. Lvs 2″ x ½″; fls apricot fading to white, all terminals bud.

Chesterland

Rating
Hardy to −25°F
Medium
April

(parentage unknown), 1965, Pot, intrd Leach. Lvs 5¾" x 2¾"; fls 3½" wide, pale pink with bold yellow dorsal spotting, up to 12 per truss.

Cheyenne

Rating 4/3
Hardy to 5°F
Medium
Early May

(Jalisco x Loderi), 1964, Greer. Lvs 5" x 2"; fls 4½" wide, yellow with slight brown marking in throat, up to 9 per truss.

Chief Joseph

(*scyphocalyx* x (Rubina x Fabia)), 1969, Witt.

Chief Paulina, PA 1954

Rating 4/3
Hardy to 5°F
Medium
April

(selected seedling of *concinnum*), 1958, James. Lvs typical of species, fls royal purple spotted dark brown, in small trusses.

'Epoch'
Photo by
Cecil Smith

Chiffon

Rating	(parentage unknown), 1976, Whitney, intrd Sather.
Hardy to 5°F	Lvs 3″ x 2″; fls 2½″ wide, flat, 7 lobes, shaded pink
Semi-dwarf	tones deeper in throat, minor red spotting, up to
Mid-April	8 per truss.

Cindy

(*calostrotum* x *ciliatum* var. *bergii*), 1958, Larson.

C.I.S., PA 1952

AM from RHS, 1975

Rating 4/2 (Fabia x Loder's White), 1958, R. Henny. Lvs 6″
Hardy to 10°F x 2¼″; fls 4″ wide, calyx petaloid, biscuit with bril-
Medium liant orange red throat, reverse flushed same, up
Mid-May to 11 per loose truss.

Citation

(*williamsianum* x Diane), 1965, R. Henny.

Clara

(*decorum* x Loderi King George), 1962, Slonecker.
Lvs 5″ x 2″; fls 5″ wide, white, up to 12 per truss.

Clara Curry

Rating (Vulcan x America), 1977, Hughes. Lvs 5″ x 1½″;
Hardy to 0°F fls 3″ wide, maroon red with no marking, up to 14
Semi-dwarf per ball truss.
Early May

Clara Raustein

Rating ((*decorum* x *discolor*) x ((*wardii* x *dichroanthum*)
Hardy to −5°F x *fortunei*)), 1972, Raustein. Lvs 5½″ x 2″; fls 3″
Tall wide, apricot fading to yellow, up to 13 per truss.
Mid-May

Claribel

(Earl of Athlone x *haematodes*), 1965, Seabrook.

Clatsop Belle

(Bow Bells x Earl of Athlone), 1967, Baker.

Cliff Garland

Rating 4/4 (Bric-a-Brac x *mucronulatum*-pink form), 1972
Hardy to −20°F Nearing. Lvs 2″, nearly circular; fls 2″ wide, shell
Dwarf pink, up to 4 per cluster.
Early April

Cliff Spangle

Rating 4/4 (Bric-a-Brac x *mucronulatum*-pink form), 1972
Hardy to −20°F Nearing. Lvs 1″, evergreen; fls 2½″ wide, deep pink,
Dwarf clusters of 5.
Early April

C.O.D.

(probably *fortunei* hybrid), 1958, Dexter, intrd
Everitt. Fls pale yellow shading deeper to throat,
deep yellow blotch, pink tinting on reverse.

Codorus grex
(*minus* x *racemosum*), 1934, Gable.

Colonel Coen

(parentage unknown), 1958, Ostbo.

Columbia Sunset

(*griersonianum* x Azor), 1968, Baker.

Compact Yellow see Buttermint

Comstock

Rating (Jalisco x Jasper), 1979, James, intrd Greer. Lvs 5″
Hardy to −5°F x 3″; fls 3½″ wide, pale orange yellow deepening
Semi-dwarf in throat, pink streaks on reverse, up to 8 per lax
Early May truss.

Conchita

Rating (*ciliicalyx* x *moupinense*), 1976, Druecker. Lvs 3¾″
Hardy to 20°F x 1½″; fls 4″ wide, phlox pink spotted crimson.
Low
March

Conemaugh grex
Rating 3/3 (*racemosum* x *mucronulatum*), 1958, Gable. Small
Hardy to −15°F leafed twiggy plant, star-shaped fls, lavender pink,
Low in 2″ balls.
Early April

Conestoga grex
(*racemosum* x *carolinianum*), 1955, Gable.

Conewago grex
Rating 3/2 (*carolianum* x *mucronulatum*), 1958, Gable. Small
Hardy to −25°F leafed twiggy plant, fls rosy lavender.
Low
April

Conewingo   grex
(diphrocalyx x *haematodes)*, 1934, Gable.

Confection, PA 1956
Rating 3/3   (Corona x Dondis), 1967, R. Henny. Lvs 8" x 2½";
Hardy to 0°F   fls 3½" wide, rose madder, up to 16 per truss.
Medium
Mid-May

Connie Hatton
Rating   *(kyawi* x *discolor*), 1975, Short. Lvs 8" x 2¼"; fls
Hardy to 5°F   3½" wide, fragrant, dark pink shading paler in
Tall   throat, up to 12 per truss.
Early July

Connie Stanton
(Princess Elizabeth x Boule de Neige), 1969, Stanton.

Connie Yates
Rating   (Mars x *yakushimanum* Koichiro Wada), 1977,
Hardy to −10°F   Yates, intrd M. Yates. Lvs 4¾" x 2¼"; fls 2½" wide,
Semi-dwarf   dark pink with white flare and gold spots, up to
Late May   14 per truss.

Conoco Cheauge   synonym Cathaem #1
(catawbiense x *haematodes*), 1934, Gable.

Cookie
Rating   (Queen o' the May x Fawn), 1979, James. Lvs 6"
Hardy to −10°F   x 2¼"; fls 6" wide, fragrant, rose with maroon spot-
Tall   ting on dorsal lobe, up to 10 per truss.
Early May

Coplen's White
(catawbiense hybrid), 1958, Coplen, intrd Gable.

Coral, PA 1956
(discolor x *(neriiflorum* x *dichroanthum*))*, 1958,
Ostbo.

Coral Velvet
Rating 3/3   *(yakushimanum* hybrid, seedling from Japan), 1970,
Hardy to −10°F   Greer. Lvs 2¼" x ¾"; fls 2" wide, coral pink fading
Low   to light salmon.
Early May

Cordy Wagner
    (Goldsworth Orange x Loderi King George), 1966, Brandt.

Corinne
    (Vulcan selfed), 1955, Lem.

Cornell Pink
Rating 4/3   (selected seedling of *mucronulatum*), 1961, Skinner.
Hardy to −25°F Lvs typical of species, fl largest of pink forms, lumi-
Medium   nous color.
Early

Cornwallis   synonym Acadia
Rating   (*fortunei*, open pollinated), 1978, Schumacker, intrd
Hardy to −15°F Craig, Canada Dept. of Agric., Research Station,
Semi-dwarf   Nova Scotia. Lvs 5½″ x 2″; fls 2½″ wide, fragrant,
Mid-June   dawn pink with heavy red spotting on 3 upper
                        lobes, up to 11 per truss.

Cotillion
    (Fabia x Naomi), 1962, R. Henny.

Cotton Candy
Rating 4/4   (Marinus Koster x Loderi Venus), 1962, J. Henny.
Hardy to 5°F   Lvs 6″ x 3″; fls 5″ wide, soft pink, up to 12 per
Tall   truss.
Early May

County of York, AE 1960   synonym Catalode
Rating 3/3   (*catawbiense* var. *album* x Loderi King George),
Hardy to −15°F 1936, Gable. Lvs 10″ x 4″, convex; fls 4″ wide, white
Tall   with olive throat, up to 13 per truss.
Mid-May

Crackerjack
    (*dichroanthum* x *wardii*), 1965, R. Henny.

Craswell
Rating   (Mars x *yakushimanum* Koichiro Wada), 1977,
Hardy to −5°F   Reese. Lvs 5″ x 2″; fls 2″ wide, carmine rose, up
Semi-dwarf   to 14 per ball truss.
Early May

Crater Lake, CA 1975
Rating   (*augustinii* Barto Blue x Bluebird), 1976, Phette-
Hardy to −5°F   place. Lvs 2″ x 1″; fls 2″ wide, brilliant violet, no
Tall   spotting, 3 per truss.
Early May

Cream Crest
Rating 3/3   (*chryseum* x Cilpinense), 1963, Wright, Sr. and Jr.
Hardy to 0°F   Lvs small; fls 1″ wide, cup-shaped, yellow, up to
Dwarf   8 per tight truss.
Early April

Cream Glory
Rating   (Comstock x Cheyenne), 1979, Greer. Lvs 5″ x 2½″;
Hardy to −5°F   fls 4½″ wide, 7 lobes, fragrant, yellow shading
Medium   darker to throat, slight red streaking in throat, up
Early May   to 9 per truss.

Creeping Fire
                              (Jaipur x May Day), 1960, Brandt.

Crimson Bells
                              (F.C. Puddle x *williamsianum*), 1967, Lancaster.

Crimson Queen
                              (Azor x Moser's Maroon), 1963, Lancaster.

Crimson Star
                              (Britannia x Unknown Warrior), 1958, Hardgrove.

Crosspatch
Rating   (parentage unknown), 1975, Nelson, intrd
Hardy to 5°F   McLaren. Lvs 6″ x 2¼″; fls 3½″ wide, pink shading
Tall   to red in throat, up to 16 per truss.
Early June

Crown of Gold
Rating   (parentage unknown), 1978, Frederick, Jr. Lvs 6″
Hardy to −5°F   x 2″; fls 4″ wide, 7 lobes, fragrant, pink with darker
Semi-dwarf   striping and chartreuse throat, up to 8 per truss.
Mid-May

Currant Bells
                              (*thomsonii* x *williamsianum*), 1967, Lancaster.

Custard
                              (China x *decorum*), 1963, R. Henny.

Cutie, AE 1962
Rating 3/3   (*calostrotum* hybrid), 1960, Greig, intrd Larson. Lvs
Hardy to −15°F   and fls typical of calostrotum, purplish pink, heavy
Semi-dwarf   bloom.
Early May

Cyril Berkeley

(selected seedling of *forrestii* var. *tumescens*), 1965, Greig.

Czech Beauty
Rating   (Goldsworth Yellow x unknown), 1979, Hindla. Lvs
Hardy to −10°F 5″ x 1¾″; fls 3½″ wide, yellow with dull orange spot-
Tall   ting, up to 11 per truss.
Late May

Dainty Jean
Rating   (*williamsianum* x Helene Schiffner), 1963, Bovee.
Hardy to   Lvs 2″ x 1½″; fls 3″ wide, flat, ruffled, white flushed
Dwarf   pink on reverse, up to 6 per loose truss.
Mid-May

Daisy Rand

(*catawbiense* hybrid), 1958, Parsons.

Dan Laxdall
Rating   (Elizabeth x Mrs. G.W. Leak), 1976, Laxdall. Lvs
Hardy to 10°F 4″ x 1¼″; fls 3½″ wide, rose, deeper color in throat
Semi-dwarf   extending up center of lobes as narrow stripes, up
Mid-May   to 10 per truss.

Dark Eyes

(Kettledrum x (*detonsum* x *griersonianum*)), 1972, Nearing.

Darlene, PA 1952

(Armistice Day x *griersonianum*), 1958, Lem.

David Forsythe

(*catawbiense* var. *compactum* x Mars), 1972, Baldanza.

David Gable, AE 1960 synonym Gable's Pink #1
Rating 4/4   (Atrosanguineum x *fortunei*), 1962, Gable. Lvs
Hardy to −15°F large; fls large, pink with red throat, truss large.
Medium
Early May

Debbie

(May Day x Carmen), 1963, Henny and Wennekamp.

Debijoe

(carolinianum x saluenense), 1966, Caperci.

Debutante   see White Mustang

Decalgla

(Catalgla x *decorum*), 1973, Gable, intrd Nearing.

Degram   see Annie Dalton

Del

(*croceum* x Fabia), 1962, James, intrd Thompson.

Del James
Rating 5/2   (selected form of *taggianum*), 1966, James, intrd
Hardy to 20°F Bowman. Lvs 6″ x 1½″; fls 3½″ wide, fragrant,
Tall   white with chrome yellow blotch, up to 5 per truss.
Very early

Delaware
Rating 3/2   (*pubescens* x *keiskei*), 1958, Nearing. Lvs small; fls
Hardy to −10°F small, apricot fading to white.
Semi-dwarf
Late April

Dextanea

(Catanea x white Dexter hybrid), 1973, Hess, intrd
Nearing.

Dexter's Appleblossom synonym DE #631
Rating   (parentage unknown), 1978, Dexter, named Cowles,
Hardy to 0°F   rgstrd Heritage Plantation. Lvs 6″ x 2½″; fls 3″
Tall   wide, 6 lobes, fragrant, white with edging of pink,
Late May   yellowish green blotch and spots, up to 15 per flat
              truss.

Dexter's Apricot synonym DE #225
Rating   (parentage unknown), 1978, Dexter, named Cowles,
Hardy to 0°F   rgstrd Heritage Plantation. Lvs 6½″ x 2½″; fls 4″
Tall   wide, 6 lobes, fragrant, pink with darker edging and
Late May   yellow green central blotch, up to 15 per flat truss.

Dexter's Big Red see Dexter's Giant Red

Dexter's Brandy-Green synonym DE #491
Rating   (parentage unknown), 1978, Dexter, named Cowles,
Hardy to 0°F   rgstrd Heritage Plantation. Lvs 6½″ x 2½″; fls 4″
Tall   wide, 6 lobes, fragrant, pink with heavy green spot-
Late May   ting on top lobes, up to 8 per flat truss.

Dexter's Brick Red   synonym DE #427

Rating
Hardy to 0°F
Semi-dwarf
Late May

(parentage unknown), 1978, Dexter, named Cowles, rgstrd Heritage Plantation. Lvs 3½" x 1½"; fls 3½" wide, 7 lobes, pink with red blotch on top 3 lobes, up to 12 per lax truss.

Dexter's Cream   synonym DE #437

Rating
Hardy to 0°F
Semi-dwarf
Late May

(parentage unknown), 1978, Dexter, named Cowles, rgstrd Heritage Plantation. Lvs 3½" x 1½"; fls 3½" wide, 6 lobes, fragrant, cream shaded pink, pale yellow blotch and stripes, up to 8 per lax truss.

Dexter's Crown Pink   synonym DE #600

Rating
Hardy to 0°F
Tall
Early June

(parentage unknown), 1978, Dexter, named Cowles, rgstrd Heritage Plantation. Lvs 6" x 2"; fls 3" wide, 6 lobes, pink with olive green blotch, up to 10 per truss.

Dexter's Favorite   synonym DE #123

(parentage unknown), 1958, Dexter, intrd Amateis.

Dexter's Giant Red   synonym DE #431, Dexter's Big Red

Rating
Hardy to 0°F
Tall
Early June

(parentage unknown), 1978, Dexter, named Cowles, rgstrd Heritage Plantation. Lvs 6½" x 3"; fls 4" wide, 7 lobes, pink with dark red throat blotch, light red spots over entire corolla, up to 15 per truss.

Dexter's Glow   synonym DE #317

Rating
Hardy to 0°F
Tall
Early June

(parentage unknown), 1978, Dexter, named Cowles, rgstrd Heritage Plantation. Lvs 4½" x 2¼"; fls 3½" wide, fragrant, strong pink, paler throat, dark red ring around base of corolla, up to 10 per lax truss.

Dexter's Horizon   synonym DE #480

Rating
Hardy to 0°F
Medium
Early June

(parentage unknown), 1978, Dexter, named Cowles, rgstrd Heritage Plantation. Lvs 6½" x 2½"; fls 3½" wide, 6 lobes, a bicolor, central area white, edges deep pink, yellow green blotch, up to 12 per ball truss.

Dexter's Orange   synonym DE #296

Rating
Hardy to 0°F
Semi-dwarf
Late May

(parentage unknown), 1978, Dexter, named Cowles, rgstrd Heritage Plantation. Lvs 4½" x 2"; fls 3" wide, 7 lobes, pink with brownish orange blotch, up to 8 per lax truss.

Dexter's Peppermint synonym DE #215

Rating	(parentage unknown), 1978, Dexter, named Cowles,
Hardy to 0°F	rgstrd Heritage Plantation. Lvs 4½″ x 2¼″; fls 3½″
Semi-dwarf	wide, 7 lobes, fragrant, light pink with yellow green
Late May	blotch deep in throat, up to 15 per ball truss.

Dexter's Pink Glory synonym DE #219

Rating	(parentage unknown), 1978, Dexter, named Cowles,
Hardy to 0°F	rgstrd Heritage Plantation. Lvs 6½″ x 2½″; fls 4½″
Medium	wide, 6 lobes, fragrant, deep pink with spotting of
Early June	yellow green and red blend over center, up to 8 per flat truss.

Dexter's Spice synonym DE #968

Rating	(parentage unknown), 1978, Dexter, named Cowles,
Hardy to 0°F	rgstrd Heritage Plantation. Lvs 5″ x 2¼″; fls 5″
Medium	wide, 7 lobes, fragrant, white with pale yellow green
Early June	spotting in throat, up to 7 per lax truss.

Dexter's Springtime synonym DE #314

Rating	(parentage unknown), 1978, Dexter, named Cowles,
Hardy to 0°F	˙rgstrd Heritage Plantation. Lvs 5″ x 2″; fls 3½″
Semi-dwarf	wide, 6 lobes, fragrant, a bicolor, cream edged deep
Early June	pink, reddish brown rays of spots in throat, up to 10 per flat truss.

Dexter's Vanilla synonym DE #997

Rating	(parentage unknown), 1978, Dexter, named Cowles,
Hardy to 0°F	rgstrd Heritage Plantation. Lvs 5″ x 2¼″; fls 3½″
Semi-dwarf	wide, 7 lobes, fragrant, cream white with deep pink
Late May	edges and central veins, small reddish brown blotch, up to 8 per lax truss.

Dexter's Victoria synonym DE #441

Rating	(parentage unknown), 1978, Dexter, named Cowles,
Hardy to 0°F	rgstrd Heritage Plantation. Lvs 4″ x 1¾″; fls 3″
Medium	wide, deep pink with large greenish brown blotch,
Early June	up to 15 per truss.

DE #9   see Skyglow

DE #105   see Burgundy Cherry

DE #123   see Dexter's Favorite

DE #215   See Dexter's Peppermint

DE # 219   see Dexter's Pink Glory

DE # 225   see Dexter's Apricot

DE # 296   see Dexter's Orange

DE # 314   see Dexter's Springtime

DE # 317   see Dexter's Glow

DE # 427   see Dexter's Brick Red

DE # 431   see Dexter's Giant Red

DE # 437   see Dexter's Cream

DE # 441   see Dexter's Victoria

DE # 480   see Dexter's Horizon

DE # 491   see Dexter's Brandy-Green

DE # 600   see Dexter's Crown Pink

DE # 631   see Dexter's Appleblossom

DE # 968   see Dexter's Spice

DE # 997   see Dexter's Vanilla

Diane Titcomb, PA 1958

Rating 3/3   (Marinus Koster x Snow Queen), 1958, Larson. Lvs
Hardy to 0°F   6″ x 2½″; fls 4″ wide, white margined blush pink,
Tall   up to 16 per truss.
Mid-May

Disca

Rating 3/3   (*discolor* x Caroline), 1958, Gable. Lvs large; fls
Hardy to −5°F   large, frilled and fragrant, white tinged pink in
Medium   large dome truss.
Late May

Display

Rating   (parentage unknown), 1976, Kersey, intrd Freder-
Hardy to −5°F   ick, Jr. Lvs 6″ x 3″; fls 4″ wide, 7 lobes, fragrant,
Medium   orchid rose with brownish green blotch, up to 12
Early May   per truss.

Dixy Lee Ray

Rating	(Zuiderzee x Naomi Pink Beauty), 1979, Larson.
Hardy to 10°F	Lvs 5″ x 2½″; fls 4½″ wide, 7 lobes, orchid pink
Tall	with slight red dorsal spotting, white star-shaped
Mid-April	throat, up to 17 per truss.

Doctor Richard Anderson

Rating	(Else Frye x *johnstoneanum*), 1979, Anderson, intrd
Hardy to 15°F	Braafladt. Lvs 3¾″ x 1¼″; fls 4¼″ wide, white
Semi-dwarf	blushed pink on edges, orange blotch, fragrant, up
Late March	to 6 per truss.

Doll

(Corona x Dondis), 1956, R. Henny.

Dolly Madison

Rating	(*catawbiense* var. *album* x (*fortunei* x (*arboreum*
Hardy to −20°F	x *griffithianum*))), 1972, Leach. Lvs 6″ x 2½″; fls
Medium	3¼″ wide, white, up to 13 per truss.
May	

Donna Hardgrove

Rating	(*fortunei* x (*wardii* x *dichroanthum*)), 1978, Hard-
Hardy to −5°F	grove, intrd Burns. Lvs 3½″ x 1½″; fls 2½″ wide,
Semi-dwarf	apricot pink flushed yellow, up to 8 per truss.
Mid-May	

Dora Amateis, AE 19

Rating 4/4	(*carolinianum* x *ciliatum*), 1958, Amateis. Lvs 5″
Hardy to −15°F	x 1″; fls 2″ wide, white lightly spotted green, in clus-
Semi-dwarf	ters of 5, very profuse.
Late April	

Doris Bigler

Rating	(advanced generation hybrid including *cataw-*
Hardy to −15°F	*biense* and *maximum*), 1979, W. Smith. Lvs 4½″ x
Tall	1¾″; fls 2″ wide, light purple with reddish purple
May	edging and yellow blotch, up to 17 per ball truss.

Doris Caroline, PA 1960

(Loderi x Lady Bligh), 1962, R. Henny.

Dorothy Amateis

(America x Purple Splendour), 1971, Amateis, intrd
Baldsiefen.

Dorothy Lee

(Jean Marie Montague x *haemaleum*), 1965, Seabrook.

Dorothy Robbins
(*campylocarpum* x Margaret Dunn), 1970, Brandt.

Double Date
Rating
Hardy to −5°F
Medium
Mid-May

synonym Toandos Rose, Whitney's Double Pink (parentage unknown), 1975, Whitney, intrd Sather. Lvs 4¾" x 1¼"; fls 2½" wide, double with 6 outer lobes and 3 frilled inner petals, rose pink, up to 10 per truss.

Doubloons
Rating 3/3
Hardy to 5°F
Semi-dwarf
Early April

(Carolyn Grace x Moonstone), 1963, Wright Sr. and Jr. Lvs 3" x 2"; fls 5" wide, yellow, up to 10 per loose truss.

Douglas R. Stephens
(Jean Marie Montague x unnamed white hybrid), 1973, Stephens.

Doug's Green Eyes
(King of Shrubs x Flame), 1972, Lem.

Dream Girl
also grex
(Day Dream x Margaret Dunn), 1958, Brandt.

Dream of Kings
Rating
Hardy to 0°F
Semi-dwarf
Late May

(A. Bedford x Purple Splendour), 1977, Frederick, Jr. Lvs 6" x 2¼"; fls 3½" wide, lavender with large purple dorsal blotch, up to 20 per truss.

Dress Parade
Rating
Hardy to −10°F
Medium
Mid-May

(parentage unknown), 1978, Kersey, intrd Frederick, Jr. Lvs 6" x 2¼"; fls 3½" wide, 7 lobes, fragrant, pink with chartreuse throat, up to 9 per truss.

Dress Up
(Mars x Tally Ho), 1965, R. Henny.

Dr. Ross
Rating 3/2
Hardy to 0°F
Medium
Mid-May

(*griersonianum* x Borde Hill), 1958, R. Henny. Lvs 6" x 2"; fls 4" wide, geranium lake, up to 18 per truss.

Duet

> (*catawbiense* var. *album* x ((*dichroanthum* x *griffithianum*) x *auriculatum*)), 1962, Leach.

Earl Moore

> (Earl of Athlone x Jean Marie Montague), 1965, Seabrook.

Earlene

Rating
Hardy to −15°F
Semi-dwarf
Late May

> (Shaazam x *yakushimanum* Koichiro Wada), 1977, Yates, intrd M. Yates. Lvs 4½" x 1½"; fls 2" wide, salmon, no blotch, reverse claret rose, up to 14 per ball truss.

Early Bird

> (*williamsianum* x *fargesii*), 1960, R. Henny.

Easter Bells

> (*williamsianum* x China), 1967, Lancaster.

Ebony

Rating
Hardy to −10°F
Dwarf
Late April

> (*carolinianum* var. *album* x P.J.M.), 1979, Mezitt, intrd Weston Nurseries. Lvs 1¾" x 1", deep shiny maroon in winter; fls light purple, up to 10 per truss.

Edith Berkeley

> (*consanguineum* x (*auriculatum* x Loderi King George)), 1958, Greig.

Edith Pride

Rating
Hardy to −25°F
Tall
Mid-June

> (English Roseum x *maximum*), 1979, Pride. Lvs 5½" x 1¾"; fls 2" wide, pink with small white blotch and yellow spots, up to 22 per truss.

Edmond Amateis

Rating 4/4
Hardy to −15°F
Tall
Early May

> (*catawbiense* var. *album* x Dexter seedling), 1969, Amateis, intrd Leach. Lvs 5" x 2¼"; fls 3¼" wide, white with bold twin-rayed red dorsal blotch, up to 13 per truss.

Edna McCarty, PA 1959 synonym Lily #3

> (Alice x *auriculatum*), 1962, Ostbo. Lvs large; fls large, white, fragrant. A mule.

Edward Dunn, PA 1958

Rating 4/4 ((*neriiflorum* x *dichroanthum*) x *discolor*), 1958,
Hardy to −5°F Ostbo. Lvs 6″ x 2½″; fls 3″ wide, rich apricot pink,
Medium up to 10 per truss. Formerly Apricot #5.
Late May

Edward Long

(Fabia x *fortunei*), 1964, James.

Edwin Beinecke

(*fortunei* seedling), 1963, Dexter, intrd Young and
Effinger.

Edwin O. Weber

Rating (Purpureum Elegans x Madame Albert Moser),
Hardy to −5°F 1974, Weber. Lvs 6½″ x 2″; fls 3½″ wide, imperial
Tall purple with large blotch of uranium green, up to
Late May 28 per truss.

Edwin Parker

Rating (Day Dream x Albatross), 1968, R. Henny, intrd
Hardy to L. Henny. Lvs 5″ x 1½″; fls 4″ wide, flat, pink to
Medium peach with creamy center, up to 16 per truss.
June

Egbert Van Alstyne

(May Day x *haematodes*), 1965, Seabrook.

El Camino

Rating (parentage unknown), 1976, Lem?, Whitney, intrd
Hardy to −5°F Sather. Lvs 5½″ x 2¾″; fls 5″ wide, dark pink with
Tall darker blotch and spotting, up to 13 per truss.
Early May

Elam

Rating (Chesapeake seedling), 1972, Nearing. Lvs 1″ x ¼″;
Hardy to −20°F fls 1½″ wide, deep rose, in clusters.
Dwarf
Early May

Electra's Son

Rating (seedling of Electra), 1977, Parker. Lvs 4″ x 1½″;
Hardy to 10°F fls 3″ wide, orchid with yellow green blotch, reverse
Tall a redder shade, terminal inflorescence of 4 trusses,
Mid-May each up to 4 fls.

Elfin Hill

(Jock x *haematodes*), 1968, Wyatt.

Elie

Rating 2/2   (Cunningham's White x red *catawbiense* seedling),
Hardy to −10°F 1958, Shammarello. Lvs 4″ x 1½″; fls 2½″ wide,
Medium   cerise pink with deep blotch, truss conical.
Early May

Elise Whipple

Rating   (Vulcan x Boule de Neige), 1973, Kruse, intrd
Hardy to −5°F Whipple, Lvs 4″ x 1½″; fls 2½″ wide, white suffused
Semi-dwarf   red, up to 15 per flat truss.
Late May

Elizabeth Blackford

(parentage unknown), 1958, Ostbo.

Elizabeth Sidamon-Eristoff

Rating   (parentage unknown), 1973, Phipps. Lvs 5¼″ x 2½″;
Hardy to −10°F fls 4″ wide, orchid pink, 2 red blotches, up to 12
Medium   per truss.
Late May

Elizabeth Titcomb, PA 1958

Rating 4/4   (Marinus Koster x Snow Queen), 1958, Larson. Lvs
Hardy to 0°F 5″ x 2½″; fls 4½″ wide, heavy substance, white, up
Tall   to 16 per truss.
Late April

Ella

Rating 4/3   (*dichroanthum* x *wardii*), 1958, R. Henny. Lvs 3″
Hardy to 10°F x 1½″; fls 3″ wide, yellow, up to 9 per truss.
Low
Late May

Elsa Reid

(form of *souliei* from wild collected seed), 1970,
Berry, intrd Bovee.

Else Frye

Rating 4/3   (*ciliicalyx* hybrid), 1963, Bowman. Lvs 3″ x 1½″;
Hardy to 15°F fls 4″ wide, white flushed rose outside, chrome yel-
Medium   low throat, up to 6 per loose truss, very fragrant.
April

Elsmere
Rating   (Chesapeake seedling), 1972, Nearing. Lvs 2"; fls
Hardy to −25°F less than 1" wide, definitely yellow, scattered rath-
Low   er than clustered.
Early May

Emett Adams
(May Day x *haematodes*), 1969, Seabrook.

Enchanted Evening
Rating   (parentage unknown), 1976, Whitney, intrd Sather.
Hardy to −5°F Lvs 4¾" x 2"; fls 4" wide, peach, throat yellow, edge
Medium   darker peach, yellowish green spotting on dorsal
Late May   lobe, up to 12 per lax truss.

Endre Ostbo, PA 1954
Rating 3/3   (*souliei* x *discolor*), 1962, Ostbo. Lvs 4" x 2½"; fls
Hardy to 0°F   4" wide, pink fringed deeper, some red spotting, up
Medium   to 8 per truss.
Late May

Epoch
Rating 3/3   (grown from colchicine treated seed of *carolinian-*
Hardy to −10°F *um* var. *album*), 1972, Kehr. Lvs 4" x 2"; fls 2½"
Semi-dwarf   wide, reflexed, saucer-shaped, heavy substance,
Early May   white turning blush, up to 12 per ball truss.

Erchless
(unnamed hybrid x Mrs. Furnival), 1972, Phipps.

Ermine
Rating 4/4   (Britannia x Mrs. A.T. de la Mare), 1962, R. Henny.
Hardy to 0°F   Lvs 6" x 1½"; fls 3½" wide, pure white, up to 11
Medium   per truss.
Late May

Ernest R. Ball
(Britannia x Jasper), 1969, Seabrook.

Ernie Dee
Rating   (*dauricum* x *racemosum*), 1977, Caperci. Lvs ¾" x
Hardy to 0°F   ¼"; fls 1" wide, lavender spotted red, terminal in-
Dwarf   florescence up to 8 trusses, each with 2 fls.
Mid-April

'Sugar Pink'   'Dora Amateis'

Photos by Harold Greer

Esquire

Rating 4/3	(probably *griersonianum* hybrid), 1958, Barto,
Hardy to 5°F	intrd James. Lvs 5½" x 2"; fls 4" wide, deep pink,
Medium	truss loose.
Early May	

Estelle Gatke

(Loderi Venus x Tally Ho), 1956, Gatke.

Esther Grace

(Countess of Derby x White Swan), 1972, Bovee.

Esther Packard

(Mars x unnamed Loderi hybrid), 1965, Lyons.

Ethel Dupar

(parentage unknown), 1968, Whitney.

Ethel-Mae

Rating	(*chapmani* x *mucronulatum*), 1965, Herbert. Lvs 2"
Hardy to	x ¾"; fls 1½" wide, bell-shaped, orchid pink, termi-
Low	nal inflorescence of 4 trusses, each up to 10 fls.
Early April	

Ethel Roupe

(*catawbiense* hybrid), 1958, Stokes.

Ethel V. Cary

Rating   (*brachycarpum* x Mrs. C.S. Sargent), 1974, Cary.
Hardy to −20°F   Lvs medium; fls 2½″ wide, orchid edge fading to
Semi-dwarf   white, reverse solid orchid, up to 20 per truss.
Late May

Etta Burrows

Rating 4/4   (Fusilier x *strigillosum*), 1965, Larson. Lvs 9″ x 2″;
Hardy to 0°F   fls 3″ wide, blood red slightly spotted, up to 30 per
Tall   truss.
April

Eulalie Wagner, PA 1963

Rating   (J.H. Van Nes x Loderi King George), 1964, Lem,
Hardy to   intrd Fawcett. Lvs 5″ x 2½″; fls 4½″ wide, pink with
Medium   darker veins, up to 12 per truss.
Late April

Eva Rebecca

Rating   (Polar Bear x Autumn Gold), 1979, Holden. Lvs
Hardy to −5°F   7½″ x 2″; fls 4″ wide, 7 lobes, fragrant, orange shad-
Semi-dwarf   ing to yellow, dull orange spotting, up to 10 per
Mid-June   lax truss.

Evangeline

see Fundy

Evelyn

(Britannia x Loderi Venus), 1958, R. Henny.

Evening Glow

Rating 3/3   (*discolor* x Fabia), 1958, Van Veen, Sr. Lvs 5″ x
Hardy to −5°F   2″; fls 3″ wide, light yellow, prominent calyx, up
Medium   to 6 per lax truss.
Late May

Everitt's Hardy Mauve

(*fortunei* hybrid), 1958, Dexter.

Everitt # 7

see Charlestown

Exalted Ruler

(parentage unknown), 1972, Lyons.

Exotic, PA 1961

Rating 4/3   (Loderi King George x Ostbo Y3), 1962, Bovee. Lvs
Hardy to 5°F   8″ x 2½″; fls 4½″ wide, red blended with pink and
Tall   yellow, up to 11 per truss.
Early May

Fair Lady, PA 1959

Rating 4/3   (*arboreum* var. *roseum* x Loderi Venus), 1959, R.
Hardy to 0°F   Henny. Lvs 8″ x 3″; fls 3½″ wide, rose shaded
Tall   darker, up to 15 per truss.
Early May

Fair Sky

Rating   (selected seedling of *augustinii*), 1976, Barto, intrd
Hardy to −5°F   Phetteplace. Lvs typical of species, fls flat and
Tall   square, purplish blue with greenish yellow spots,
Early May   often 2 terminal buds.

Fairweather

Rating   ((Fabia x *yakushimanum*) x Hello Dolly), 1974,
Hardy to 10°F   Brockenbrough. Lvs 5″ x 1½″; fls 2″ wide, salmon
Semi-dwarf   orange fading to creamy yellow, up to 16 per truss.
Early May

Fairy Tale

                   (Loderi x *arboreum* var. *roseum*), 1965, R. Henny.
                   Lvs 7″ x 2½″; fls 4″ wide, fuchsine pink, up to 11
                   per truss.

Fake   See Purple Fake

Fanfare

Rating 3/2   (America x Kettledrum), 1958, Leach. Lvs 5¼″ x
Hardy to −20°F 1¾″; fls unfading bright red, dome truss.
Medium
Mid-May

Farewell Party

Rating   (parentage unknown), 1976, Kersey, intrd Fred-
Hardy to −5°F   erick, Jr. Lvs 5½″ x 3″; fls 4½″ wide, fragrant, white
Medium   with yellow green spotting in throat, up to 12 per
Mid-June   flat truss.

Farquhar's Pink

                   (*catawbiense* hybrid), 1958, Farquhar.

Farquhar's Red

                   (*catawbiense* hybrid), 1958, Farquhar.

Fawn, PA 1959

Rating 4/4   (*fortunei* x Fabia), 1958, James. Lvs 4″ x 1½″; fls
Hardy to 5°F   4½″ wide, flat, salmon pink shaded orange, yellow
Tall   in throat, up to 9 per truss.
Early May

Fayetta

(Tally Ho x Golden Horn), 1958, Whitney.

Fifth Avenue Red

(Diane x *haematodes*), 1965, R. Henny, intrd L. Henny. Lvs 3¾" x 2"; fls 2½" wide, glossy rose red with lighter streaks, up to 10 per truss.

Finch
Rating 3/2
Hardy to 0°F
Tall
Mid-April

(selected seedling of *desquamatum*), 1958, Barto, intrd R. Henny. Lvs typical of species, fls 1¾" wide, mallow purple with crimson spots.

Finesse

(*souliei* x Bow Bells), 1958, R. Henny. Lvs 2½" x 1½"; fls 2½" wide, persian rose, up to 7 per truss.

Finlandia
Rating
Hardy to −15°F
Semi-dwarf
Early April

(Catalgla x (Adrian Koster x *williamsianum*)), 1974, Leach. Lvs 3½" x 2¼"; fls 3" wide, white from pink buds, up to 12 per truss.

Fiona

(Bow Bells x Loderi Pink Diamond), 1962, Brandt.

Fire Wine
Rating
Hardy to 0°F
Semi-dwarf
Mid-May

(Purple Splendour x Fire Bird), 1979, Greer. Lvs 4" x 1¼"; fls 3" wide, purplish red with deeper spotting on dorsal lobe, up to 16 per truss.

Fireman Jeff
Rating
Hardy to 5°F
Semi-dwarf
Early May

(Jean Marie Montague x Grosclaude), 1977, Brandt, intrd Eichelser. Lvs 3" x 1¼"; fls 2½" wide, bright red with some brown spotting on 3 dorsal lobes, up to 10 per truss.

First Love

(*oreotrephes* x Royal Flush), 1966, R. Henny, intrd L. Henny. Lvs 2½" x 1"; fls pink with maroon eye, up to 8 per truss.

Flair
Rating
Hardy to −15°F
Low
April

(Catalgla x (Adrian Koster x *williamsianum*)), 1974, Leach. Lvs 3½" x 2"; fls 2¾" wide, white with ivory shading on dorsal lobe, up to 12 per truss.

Flame

((Corona x Loderi) x *griersonianum*), 1958, Lem.

Flame Tips

((Day Dream x Margaret Dunn) x unnamed seedling), 1965, Graves, intrd Janeck.

Flatterer, PA 1957

(Corona x Day Dream), 1958, R. Henny. Lvs medium; fls 3½" wide, carmine rose, up to 15 per truss.

Flora Markeeta, PA 1967

Rating 3/4   (*thomsonii* x (Unique x Luscombei var. Leonards-
Hardy to −5°F   lee)), 1967, Markeeta Nursery. Lvs 4" x 1½"; fls
Semi-dwarf   3" wide, coral pink bud opening ivory white blushed
Early April   coral, up to 10 per truss.

Florence Archer

Rating   (*wardii* x Marcia), 1979, Larson. Lvs 3¾" x 2½";
Hardy to 10°F   fls 3¾" wide, yellow diffused with red, yellowish
Semi-dwarf   green dorsal spotting, red edging, up to 8 per truss.
Early June

Flushing

(*catawbiense* hybrid), 1958, Parsons.

Forrest Fire

(Tally Ho x Britannia), 1958, R. Henny.

Fortwilliam

Rating   (*fortunei* x *williamsianum*), 1967, Herbert. Lvs 4½"
Hardy to −5°F   x 2¼"; fls 4" wide, light pink striped darker, yellow
Semi-dwarf   throat, fragrant, up to 12 per truss.
Late May

Fran Labera

Rating   (Helen Everitt x Dexter's Honeydew), 1978, Fuller.
Hardy to −15°F Lvs 5¼" x 2¼"; fls 4" wide, 7 lobes, fragrant, white
Tall   to cream, chartreuse throat, up to 11 per truss.
Mid-May

Francesca

(Britannia x Dexter #202), 1972, Consolini.

Frank Baum

(Mars x Jasper), 1969, Seabrook.

Franz Lehar

(Glamour x Jester), 1965, Seabrook.

Fred Robbins
  (Carmen x Choremia), 1965, Brandt.

Fred Hamilton   synonym Orange Cross
  Rating 3/3   ((*neriiflorum* x *griersonianum*) x *dichroanthum*),
  Hardy to −5°F   1972, Lem, intrd Van Veen, Jr. Lvs 4″ x 1½″; fls
  Medium   2½″ wide, yellow with yellowish pink tones at edges
  Late May   of lobes and stripes inside and outside of corolla,
                     concentrated yellowish green spotting on 3 upper
                     lobes, up to 12 per truss.

Freeman R. Stephens
  Rating   (Jean Marie Montague x unnamed white), 1973,
  Hardy to −10°F   Stephens. Lvs 6½″ x 3″; fls 4″ wide, cherry red with
  Medium   dark dorsal spotting, up to 15 per truss.
  Late April

French Creek
  Rating   (parentage unknown), 1970, Herbert. Lvs 4½″ x
  Hardy to −15°F   1¾″; fls 3½″ wide, ruffled, pink fading to white,
  Medium   green spotted throat, up to 20 per truss.
  Mid-May

Frontier
  Rating   (Letty Edwards x Crest), 1978, J. Elliott. Lvs 4½″
  Hardy to 10°F   x 2″; fls 4″ wide, 7 lobes, rose shading yellow to
  Medium   center, up to 14 per ball truss.
  Mid-May

Full Moon, PA 1955
  Rating 4/3   (Crest x Harvest Moon), 1958, J. Henny. Lvs 3½″
  Hardy to −5°F   x 2½″; fls 3½″ wide, canary yellow, up to 11 per
  Low   ball truss.
  Mid-May

Fundy   synonym Evangeline
  Rating   (*fortunei* x *smirnowii*), 1978, Hancock, intrd Swain,
  Hardy to −15°F   Canada Dept. of Agric., Research Station, Nova
  Tall   Scotia. Lvs 6″ x 2″; fls 3½″ wide, 7 lobes, fragrant,
  Mid-June   rose at edge fading lighter to center, olive brown
                     dorsal blotch, up to 10 per truss.

Gable's Pink #1   see David Gable

Gable's Pink #2   see Robert Allison

Gabriel

Rating	(Dr. H.C. Dresselhuys x *smirnowii*), 1978, Swain,
Hardy to −15°F	intrd Craig, Dept. of Agric., Research Station,
Medium	Nova Scotia. Lvs 5½″ x 2″; fls 2¾″ wide, pink with
Mid-June	olive brown flecks on dorsal lobe, up to 18 per truss.

Gary Herbert

Rating	(parentage uncertain, believed selfed seedling of
Hardy to −5°F	*vernicosum* aff., R. 18139, or F$_2$ seedling of *verni-*
Tall	*cosum* #1 and #2), 1976, Gable, intrd Herbert. Lvs
Early May	5½″ x 3″; fls 3″ wide, 7 lobes, frilled and fragrant, shaded salmon tones, up to 7 per flat truss.

Gay Hostess

Rating	(parentage unknown), 1976, Kersey, intrd Freder-
Hardy to −5°F	ick, Jr. Lvs 6½ ″ x 2½″; fls 3″ wide, rose pink spotted
Medium	light green, up to 14 per truss.
Mid-May	

Gay Princess

synonym Pink Princess

Rating	(Atroflo open pollinated), 1979, Herbert. Lvs 7½″
Hardy to −5°F	x 1¾″; fls 3″ wide, pink, lighter edging, throat and
Medium	reverse, up to 18 per truss.
Mid-May	

Gayblade

(Azma x Mars), 1972, Wright, Sr. and Jr., intrd Lindsley, Sr.

Gene

Rating 4/2	*(ciliatum* x *spiciferum)*, 1962, R.B.G. seed intrd
Hardy to 5°F	Mulligan. Lvs 2¼″ long; fls 1¼″ wide, cyclamen
Low	purple in spherical trusses.
Early April	

General Anthony Wayne

Rating	(Scintillation x Atrier), 1976, Herbert. Lvs 7″ x 3″;
Hardy to −5°F	fls 4″ wide, fragrant, pink with light green throat,
Tall	some spotting, up to 17 per truss.
Mid-May	

General Grant

(parentage unknown), 1958, Parsons.

Geneva, PA 1955

(Unknown Warrior x Fabia), 1958, Bacher.

Genghis Khan

(Britannia x Felis), 1969, Brandt. Lvs 5″ x 1½″; fls 3″ wide, red, up to 15 per truss.

George Budgen

Rating
Hardy to 25°F
Medium
Winter

(*laetum* x *zoelleri*), 1977, Lelliot, (Australia), intrd Strybing Arobretum. Lvs 4″ x 2½″; fls 3″ wide, shades of yellow and orange, up to 5 per truss.

George Grace, PA 1952

(Loderi x Borde Hill), 1958, R. Henny. Lvs 6½″ long; fls 4½″ wide, pink, slightly recurved, up to 15 per truss.

George M. Cohan

(May Day x Jasper), 1968, Seabrook.

George Ritter

Rating
Hardy to 15°F
Low
Early June

(*griersonianum* x unknown), 1976, Frye, intrd Druecker. Lvs 7¼″ x 2¼″; fls 4¼″ wide, pink, throat crimson, up to 6 per lax truss.

Georgia May

(parentage unknown), 1964, Core.

Gertrude Bovee

Rating
Hardy to −5°F
Medium
Late May

(Loderi King George x Ostbo Y3), 1972. Bovee. Lvs 8″ x 3″; fls 4½″ wide, ruffled cream blending outwards to pink, some dark spots, up to 12 per truss.

'Queen Anne's'
Photo by
Henry T. Skinner

Gi-Gi, AE 1973

Rating 4/3   (parentage unknown), 1973, Dexter, intrd Burns.
Hardy to −5°F   Lvs 4½" x 2"; fls 3¼" wide, rose red with deep red
Medium   spots all over, up to 18 per truss.
Late May

Ginny Beale

Rating   (*metternichii* x *adenopodum*), 1979, Gable, intrd
Hardy to −10°F   Davis. Lvs 4½" x 1"; fls 2" wide, rose with faint
Semi-dwarf   pink stripes on reverse, no marks, up to 16 per truss.
Early May

Ginny Gee

Rating   (*keiskei*-prostrate form x *racemosum*), 1979, Berg.
Hardy to 0°F   Lvs 1¼" x ½"; fls 1" wide, white with pink mottling
Dwarf   within and without, terminal inflorescence up to
Mid-April   11 buds, each up to 5 fls.

Glad Tidings

Rating 3/3   (China x *williamsianum*), 1965, Lancaster. Lvs 6"
Hardy to 0°F   x 2½"; fls 4" wide, blend of cream and pink with
Medium   red flair, up to 12 per truss.
April

Gladys Johnson, PA 1958

(Diva x *fortunei*), 1958, purchased as seedling, intrd
Johnson. Lvs 7" x 3"; fls 4" wide, rose pink fading
paler, fragrant, up to 15 per truss.

Glow

(*griersonianum* x Armistice Day), 1958, Bovee.

Glowing Embers

Rating 3/2   (*griersonianum* x Romany Chal), 1958, J. Henny.
Hardy to 5°F   Lvs 5" x 2"; fls 2½" wide, geranium red, truss coni-
Medium   cal.
June

Glowing Star

(*fortunei* x C.P. Rafill), 1958, Hardgrove.

Gloxineum

(*fortunei* hybrid), 1958, Dexter, intrd deWilde.

Gold Braid

(Fabia x Dondis), 1958, R. Henny.

Gold Mohur, PA 1955 Dream Girl grex

Rating 3/3   (Day Dream x Margaret Dunn), 1955, Brandt. Lvs
Hardy to 0°F   6" x 2"; fls 3" wide, yellow spotted green, up to
Medium   12 per loose truss.
Late May

Gold Moon

Rating   (Goldfort x Full Moon), 1976, Bagoly, intrd Tiet-
Hardy to −10°F   jens. Lvs 6" x 2¾"; fls 4" wide, 7 lobes, fragrant,
Semi-dwarf   white, throat brushed yellowish green, up to 11 per
Late April   truss.

Goldbug

Rating 3/3   (*croceum* x Fabia), 1958, R. Henny. Lvs 4" x 1¾";
Hardy to 5°F   fls 1½" wide, scarlet changing to orange then yel-
Semi-dwarf   low, spotted all over with maroon dots, up to 9 per
Early May   truss.

Goldstrike

Rating 4/4   (*oreotrephes* x Royal Flush F_2 selfed), 1962, R.
Hardy to 0°F   Henny. Lvs 4" x 1"; fls 2" wide, yellow, up to 8
Medium   per truss.
May

Golden Anniversary

                   (*chlorops* x (Golden West x Mariloo)), 1971, Lan-
                   caster.

Golden Belle   Margaret Dunn grex

Rating 4/3   (*discolor* x Fabia), 1958, J. Henny. Lvs 4½" x 1½";
Hardy to 0°F   fls 3" wide, yellow centers with deep pink margins,
Medium   up to 11 per truss.
Late May

Golden Days

Rating 3/3   (Dondis x *dichroanthum*), 1972, R. Henny. Lvs 5½"
Hardy to 0°F   x 1¾"; fls 3" wide, yellow, edges carrot red, up to
Medium   10 per truss.
Early May

Golden Fantasy

Rating   (parentage unknown), 1979, Frederick, Jr. Lvs 6¼"
Hardy to 0°F   x 3"; fls 5" wide, 7 lobes, fragrant, cream, yellow
Tall   center, greenish blotch, up to 8 per truss.
Late May

Golden Folly

                   (Fabia x Moonstone), 1964, Larson.

Golden Gate

(selected form of *zoelleri*), 1972, Strybing Arboretum.

Golden Gift

(*chryseum* x *leucaspis*), 1962, Wright, Sr. and Jr.

Golden Glow

(Fabia x Azor), 1958, Lancaster.

Golden Pheasant

(Day Dream x Margaret Dunn), 1966, Brandt.

Golden Salmon

Rating
Hardy to −15°F
Medium
Mid-May

(Atrosanguineum x *griersonianum* x same, probably a sibling cross, not a self), 1973, Gable, intrd Nearing. Lvs 5″ x 2″; fls 3½″ wide, 7 lobes, heavy substance, fragrant, salmon with darker blotch of radiating stripes, up to 10 per lax truss.

Golden Star

Rating
Hardy to 0°F
Medium
Late May

(*fortunei* x *wardii*), 1978, Hardgrove, intrd Burns. Lvs 5″ x 2″; fls 3″ wide, 7 lobes, yellow, up to 7 per truss.

Golden West

(*fortunei* x *campylocarpum*), 1958, James.

Golden Witt

Rating
Hardy to
Low
Early May

(*scyphocalyx* x (Moonstone x Adrastia)), 1966, Witt, intrd Michaud. Lvs 3″ x 1½″; fls 3″ wide, yellow with throat blotch jasper red, up to 9 per truss.

Goldendale

Rating
Hardy to −5°F
Medium
Late May

(((Loderi x *wardii*) x *campylocarpum*) x Skipper), 1974, McNew. Lvs 3″ x 1″; fls 3″ wide, butter yellow with dark red center, up to 14 per truss.

Good News

Rating 3/3
Hardy to −5°F
Medium
June

(Britannia x Romany Chal), 1974, J. Henny. Lvs 6″ x 2″; fls 2½″ wide, scarlet, up to 12 per ball truss.

Grace Seabrook

Rating
Hardy to 5°F
Medium
Early April

(Jean Marie Montague x *strigillosum*), 1965, Seabrook. Lvs 7" x 2"; fls 3" wide, blood red to currant red, ball truss.

Great Lakes, PA 1960

Rating 3/4
Hardy to −25°F
Semi-dwarf
Mid-May

(Catalgla x *yakushimanum* Koichiro Wada), 1960, Leach. Lvs 3½" x 1½"; fls 2½" wide, pink in bud opening white, up to 15 per truss.

Great Scott

Rating
Hardy to −5°F
Medium
Mid-May

(Mrs. J.G. Millais x Cheyenne), 1979, Greer. Lvs 6" x 2¼"; fls 4½" wide, 7 lobes, pink with prominent dark red dorsal flare, up to 14 per truss.

Greeley

Rating 3/3
Hardy to 5°F
Medium
May

(Fawn x (*elliottii* x Umpqua Chief)), 1961, Greer. Lvs 6" x 2"; fls 4" wide, watermelon pink, up to 13 per truss.

Green Goddess

Rating
Hardy to
Medium
Mid-May

(Mrs. Lindsay Smith x (*fortunei* x Fabia)), 1971, Lyons. Lvs 7½" x 3"; fls 3¾" wide, chartreuse with green blotch, up to 12 per ball truss.

Gretchen

Rating 4/4
Hardy to −15°F
Medium
Mid-May

((*decorum* x *griffithianum*) x Kettledrum), 1958, Nearing, intrd Gable. Good foliage and plant habit. Fls pink with red throat, truss a large dome.

Gretchen Gossler

Rating
Hardy to −5°F
Tall
Mid-May

(Idealist x Crest), 1977, Phetteplace. Lvs 4" x 2¼"; fls 4½" wide, yellow green with red blotch, up to 12 per truss.

Gretchen Medlar

(Boule de Neige x Henrietta Sargent), 1958, Skinner.

Griselda
(Fabia x Margaret Dunn), 1958, R. Henny.

Guardian Fir, CA 1975
Rating (Albatross x (*discolor* x Tally Ho)), 1974, Lem,
Hardy to 0°F intrd Butler. Lvs 7″ x 1½″; fls 5″ wide, heavy sub-
Tall stance, medium pink shading to light yellowish
Mid-June pink on upper lobes, small red blotch and speckling, up to 10 per truss.

Guy Bradour
Rating (Mrs. C.S. Sargent x Purple Splendour), 1977, Yates,
Hardy to −15°F intrd M. Yates. Lvs 4½″ x 2″; fls 3½″ wide, fragrant,
Semi-dwarf violet with black blotch, up to 10 per truss.
Mid-May

Guy Nearing
Rating (*detonsum* x Gilian), 1973, Nearing, intrd Raustein.
Hardy to −10°F Lvs 5¼″ x 2¼″; fls 2″ wide, reddish purple with
Medium maroon blotch, up to 25 per truss.
Late May

H. Phipps #2   see Wheatley

Halesite Maiden
Rating (parentage unknown), 1974, Dexter, intrd Sch-
Hardy to −5°F laikjer. Lvs 5½″ x 2¾″; fls 3½″ wide, fragrant, light
Medium red, up to 12 per truss.
Late May

Halfdan Lem
Rating (Jean Marie Montague x Red Loderi), 1974, Lem,
Hardy to 10°F intrd Seattle Chapter, Lvs 8″ x 3″; fls 3½″ wide,
Medium heavy substance, red with darker spots on dorsal
Early May lobe, up to 13 per truss.

Half Penny
Rating (Anna x Margaret Dunn), 1960, James. Lvs 8″ x
Hardy to 2½″; fls 5″ wide, pink buds opening primrose yellow
Medium with large red blotches entirely around center of
Late May corolla, up to 14 per truss.

Hallelujah, CA 1975
Rating 4/4 (Jean Marie Montague x Kimberly), 1976, Greer.
Hardy to −15°F Lvs 4½″ x 2½″; fls 4″ wide, red, up to 10 per truss.
Medium
Early May

Hamma Hamma
Rating   (Fabia x unknown), 1979, Clark. Lvs 5" x 1¾", fls
Hardy to 15°F   2¾" wide, red with heavy black spotting on dorsal
Medium   lobe and black nectaries, up to 18 per truss.
Mid-May

Happy Day
                          (Lady Clementine Mitford x Ladybird), 1971,
                          Lyons.

Hardy Giant
Rating   (*fortunei* x *fictolacteum*), 1967, Knippenberg. Lvs 9"
Hardy to   x 3"; fls 3½" wide, creamy white with raspberry
Tall   blotch, up to 14 per truss.
Mid-May

Harnden's White
Rating   (Albatross x Hawk), 1979, Greer. Lvs 5" x 2¼"; fls
Hardy to 0°F   4½" wide, almost white, up to 10 per truss.
Tall
Mid-May

Harold Amateis
Rating   (*maximum* x *strigillosum*), 1967, Amateis, intrd
Hardy to   Baldsiefen. Lvs 6" x 1½"; fls 2¼" wide, cardinal red
Medium   with deep maroon throat, up to 20 per truss.
May

Harry Von Tilzer
                          (May Day x *haematodes*), 1967, Seabrook.

Hazel
Rating 3/4   (*bureavii* hybrid), 1979, origin unknown, intrd
Hardy to −15°F   Greer. Lvs 5½" x 2"; fls 3" wide, light pink with
Medium   deep pink stripes, ball truss.
Mid-April

Hazle Smith
                          (*occidentale* x Corona), 1965, Wyatt. Azaleoden-
                          dron. Lvs 4" x 1¼"; fls 2" wide, white with crimson
                          blotch, up to 18 per truss.

Helen
                          (*decorum* x Souldis), 1958, Brandt.

Helen Child

Rating	(*fortunei* hybrid x *williamsianum*), 1977, Larson.
Hardy to 10°F	Lvs 3" x 2"; fls 3" wide, bright pink with spotting
Semi-dwarf	in throat, up to 9 per truss.
Mid-April	

Helen Druecker

(*elliottii* x Betty Wormald), 1964, Druecker. Lvs 8" x 4"; fls 4½" wide, pink shading deeper at edges, up to 16 per truss.

Helen Everitt

Rating	(unknown Dexter x unknown Dexter), 1975,
Hardy to −15°F	Everitt, intrd Fuller. Lvs 4" x 2"; fls 5" wide, 5-7
Tall	overlapping lobes, fragrant, pure white, up to 9 per
Mid-May	truss. Stamens vestigial.

Helen Johnson, PA 1956

(Mrs. Furnival x Mrs. Donald Graham), 1956, Ostbo.

Helen Scott Richey

Rating	((*racemosum* x *moupinense*) x *mucronulatum* Cor-
Hardy to	nell Pink), 1977, Scott. Lvs 1" x ¼"; fls 1¼" wide,
Semi-dwarf	pink with darker spotting, inflorescence up to 5 ter-
Early February	minal buds, each with 2 fls.

Helene Huber

Rating	(probably *fortunei* hybrid), 1978, Dexter, intrd Her-
Hardy to −5°F	bert. Lvs 4½" x 2"; fls 3" wide, fragrant, pink with
Tall	dull yellow blotch and spotting, up to 16 per ball
Mid-May	truss.

Helios

Rating	((*decorum* x *discolor*) x (*fortunei* x (*wardii* x
Hardy to −5°F	*dichroanthum*))), 1979, Raustein. Lvs 4½" x 1¾";
Semi-dwarf	fls 3½" wide, 6 lobes, fragrant, a bicolor, pink shad-
Mid-May	ing to yellow throat, up to 10 per truss.

Hello Dolly

Rating 3/3	(Fabia x *smirnowii*), 1974, Lem, intrd J. Elliott. Lvs
Hardy to 0°F	4" x 1¼"; fls 2¾" wide, porcelain rose blending to
Medium	yellow in throat, few light green spots, up to 10
Late April	per lax truss.

Hendrick's Park

Rating	(Jalisco Elect x Fawn), 1979, James. Lvs 4" x 2";
Hardy to −10°F	fls 2½" wide, fragrant, pink with darker throat, up
Tall	to 12 per ball truss.
Late April	

Henry R. Yates

Rating   (*litiense* x unknown), 1971, Gable. Lvs 6" x 2¼";
Hardy to   fls 2½" wide, ivory with bold flare, up to 11 per
Low   truss.
April

Herbert Parsons   see President Lincoln

Highnoon

(Earl of Athlone x Fabia), 1958, R. Henny.

Hockessin

Rating 3/2   (*pubescens* x *keiskei*), 1958, Nearing. Identical to
Hardy to −25°F Chesapeake, but larger.
Semi-dwarf
April

Holden

Rating 3/4   (Cunningham's White x red *catawbiense* hybrid),
Hardy to −15°F 1958, Shammarello. Lvs 4" x 2"; fls 2½" wide, lumi-
Semi-dwarf   nous red with dark red blotch, conical truss.
Mid-May

Honeydew

(Carolyn Grace x Moonstone), 1962, Wright Sr. and
Jr.

Honeymoon

Rating 4/4   ((*wardii* x Devonshire Cream) x *croceum*), 1976,
Hardy to −5°F Whitney, intrd Sather. Lvs 3¾" x 2¼"; fls 2" wide,
Medium   yellow, throat greenish, small orange blotch, up to
Late April   14 per flat truss.

'Noyo Brave'
Photo by
Cecil Smith

Honore Hocanson
(Carmen x Choremia), 1965, Brandt.

Hoopskirt
(Rosy Morn x Dido), 1958, R. Henny.

Hope Braafladt
Rating   (*lindleyi* x Countess of Haddington), 1979, Braa-
Hardy to 20°F   fladt. Lvs 3¾" x 1¼"; fls 3¼" wide, white with dull
Semi-dwarf   orchid blotch and faint stripes, fragrant, up to 5
April   per lax truss.

Hotei, PA 1964   AM RHS 1974
Rating 4/3   (Goldsworth Orange x (*souliei* x *wardii*)), 1968, Sif-
Hardy to −5°F   ferman, intrd Nelson. Lvs 4" x 1½"; fls 2½" wide,
Medium   prominent calyx, canary yellow, up to 12 per ball
May   truss.

Hotshot
(*eriogynum* x Mars), 1958, R. Henny.

HS #10   see Nathan Hale

Hulagu Khan
(*xanthocodon* x Lady Roseberry), 1969, Brandt.

Humboldt Sunrise
Rating   (Else Frye x *johnstoneanum*), 1979, Anderson, intrd
Hardy to   Braafladt. Lvs 3¼" x 1½"; fls 3¼" wide, fragrant,
Semi-dwarf   yellow, darker blotch, up to 6 per truss.
Late April

Ice Cube
Rating 4/3   (Catalgla x Belle Heller), 1973, Shammarello. Lvs
Hardy to −20°F 5" x 2"; fls 2½" wide, ivory white with lemon blotch,
Medium   truss conical.
Mid-May

Ida Bradour
Rating   (Mary Belle x *vernicosum* aff., R. 18139, #2), 1978
Hardy to −10°F Gable, intrd M. Yates. Lvs 5¾" x 1¾"; fls 3½" wide,
Medium   pink shades with yellowish green throat, up to 14
Late May   per ball truss.

Idol, PA 1957
Rating 4/4   (Loderi King George x Britannia), 1958, R. Henny.
Hardy to −5°F   Lvs 2" long; fls 3½" wide, tyrian rose with lighter
Tall   center, up to 12 per truss.
Late April

Illahee

Rating (Mrs. Furnival x Evening Glow), 1977, A. Van Veen.
Hardy to −5°F Lvs 6″ x 2″; fls 3″ wide, orchid pink, throat yel-
Semi-dwarf lowish pink, orange yellow flare, calyx streaked or-
Mid-May chid pink, up to 12 per flat truss.

Improved Parson's Grandiflorum

(*catawbiense* hybrid), 1958, Stokes.

Inca Chief

Rating (Mars x (Mars x *catawbiense* var. *rubrum*)), 1972,
Hardy to −20°F Leach. Lvs 5″ x 2¼″; fls 3″ wide, purplish red with
Medium deeper arch-shaped dorsal blotch on lighter ground,
Mid-May up to 18 per globular truss.

Inca Gold, PA 1961

Rating 4/4 (*chlorops* x unknown), 1962, Lancaster. Lvs 4″ x
Hardy to −5°F 2″; fls 3″ wide, barium yellow slightly rayed mahog-
Semi-dwarf any, up to 12 per truss.
Early May

Indian Chief

(*catawbiense* hybrid), 1958, Stokes.

Isabel Pierce

Rating (Anna x Lem's Goal), 1975, Lem, intrd Pierce. Lvs
Hardy to 15°F 5¼″ x 2¾″; fls 3¾″ wide, medium pink lightening
Medium to center, prominent brown blotch and spots in
Mid-May throat, internal and external narrow stripes of deep
pink from base to lobe edges, up to 10 per truss.

Island Gem

Rating (selected seedling of *oreotrephes*) RHS seed, 1978,
Hardy to 10°F Short. Lvs typical of species, fls orchid with reddish
Medium blotch, terminal inflorescence of 3 buds, each up
Mid-April to 4 fls.

Ivory Bells

Rating 4/4 (*chlorops* x *williamsianum*), 1966, Lancaster. Lvs
Hardy to −5°F 2½″ x 1½″; fls 3″ wide, flat, Chinese yellow fading
Semi-dwarf lighter, up to 10 per truss.
Early May

Ivory Tower

Rating (*catawbiense* var. *album* x (*wardii* x *fortunei*)),
Hardy to −25°F 1964, Leach. Lvs 4½″ x 1¾″; fls 3″ wide, ivory with
Medium dorsal suffusion and dual discontinuous stripes of
Early May greenish yellow, up to 13 per globular truss.

J. Edgar Hoover

(Ivery's Scarlet x Francis Hanger), 1967, Seabrook.

Jack Lyons

(Borde Hill x Rose Red), 1972, Lyons.

Jack Owen Yates

Rating
Hardy to −10°F
Semi-dwarf
Mid-May

((Catalgla x *wardii*) x Mars), 1977, Yates, intrd M. Yates. Lvs 6¾" x 2½"; fls 2½" wide, magenta shading to white center, 2 yellow rays, up to 13 per truss.

Jade

Rating 3/3
Hardy to 5°F
Semi-dwarf
Early May

(Fabia x Corona), 1958, R. Henny. Lvs 3½" x 2"; fls 2" wide, combination of pink, orange and later greenish yellow, tight truss.

J'aime

(Jaipur x May Day), 1964, Brandt.

Jalipeño

Rating
Hardy to 5°F
Semi-dwarf
Mid-April

(((Fabia x *haematodes*) x Earl of Athlone) x Jean Marie Montague), 1977, Goheen. Lvs 5" x 1¾"; fls 2" wide, bright red with few brown spots and dark brown nectaries, up to 18 per truss.

James Barto, PA 1953

Rating 3/4
Hardy to −5°F
Low
Early May

(probably *williamsianum* x *orbiculare*), 1958, Barto, intrd Prentice. Lvs 3" x 2"; fls 2" wide, fuchsine pink, up to 5 per truss

James C. Stephens

(Jean Marie Montague x unnamed white), 1973, Stephens.

Jan-di-lyn, PA 1961

((*lacteum* x Mary Swaythling) x Ole Olson), 1963, Wyrens.

Jane Henny

Rating
Hardy to −10°F
Tall
Late May

synonym Rosebud
(Lady Bligh x Loderi Venus), 1978, R. Henny, intrd L. Henny. Lvs 6" x 2"; fls 4" wide, white with pink shading and mottling, up to 13 per truss.

Jane Holden

Rating
Hardy to −5°F
Medium
Early June

(Polar Bear x Autumn Gold), 1979, Holden. Lvs 7½" x 2"; fls 4" wide, 7 lobes, fragrant, rose with red dorsal flare, up to 10 per lax truss.

Jane Rice

Rating
Hardy to −15°F
Tall
May

(advanced generation hybrid including *cataw-biense* and *maximum*), 1979, W. Smith. Lvs 4½" x 2"; fls 3½" wide, pink with yellowish green spotting, up to 10 per truss.

Jane Rogers

(Mrs. Donald Graham x Mrs. R.S. Holford), 1957, Ostbo.

'Riplet'   *Photo by Gwen Bell*

Janet Blair   synonym John Wister

Rating 4/4
Hardy to −15°F
Tall
Early May

(Dexter hybrid x unknown), 1962, Leach. Lvs 4½" x 2½"; fls 3" wide, frilled, pinkish mauve, golden brown dorsal blotch, up to 9 per tall truss.

Janet Scroggs

Rating
Hardy to 10°F
Medium
Mid-May

(Virginia Scott x Jasper), 1979, Larson. Lvs 5¼" x 2¼"; fls 2¾" wide, yellow with dull orange dorsal spotting, up to 9 per truss.

Janielle
(unnamed yellow x Marcia), 1962, Greer.

Jason's Maxim
Rating
Hardy to −25°F
Medium
Mid-June

(*maximum* hybrid), 1977, Bowers, intrd Miller. Lvs 4¼″ x 1¾″; fls 1¾″ wide, white with yellow spots on dorsal lobe, reverse has pink tube, up to 16 per truss.

Jay McMartin
Rating 4/3
Hardy to 10°F
Tall
Late May

(C.P. Rafill x Moser's Maroon), 1962, Bowman. Lvs 8″ x 1½″; fls 3″ wide, crimson spotted black, up to 18 per truss.

Jean Leppo
Rating
Hardy to −15°F
Medium
Mid-May

(advanced generation hybrid including *cataw-biense* and *maximum*), 1978, W. Smith. Lvs 4¼″ x 1¾″; fls 2½″ wide, pink with slight yellow blotch, up to 17 per truss.

Jennice Coffey
Rating
Hardy to 10°F
Semi-dwarf
Early June

(Marinus Koster x Pilgrim), 1979, Laxdall. Lvs 5″ x 1¾″; fls 2½″ wide, pink with red star-shaped blotch in throat, deeper stripes on reverse, up to 16 per ball truss.

Jennie Dosser
(Britannia x Trilby), 1965, Dosser.

Jennie Lewis
(Britannia x Trilby), 1965, Dosser.

Jerome Kern
(Jean Marie Montague x *haemaleum*), 1967, Seabrook.

Jezebel
(Fabia x unknown), 1958, Clark

Jim Drewry
(Ruby F. Bowman x *elliottii*), 1971, Druecker.

Jiminy Cricket
(*euchaites* x *gymnocarpum*), 1962, James.

Jimmy
(Carolyn Grace x *wardii*), 1972, Bovee.

Jingle Bells

Rating 4/4   (Fabia x Ole Olson), 1974, Lem, intrd J. Elliott. Lvs
Hardy to −5°F   3½″ x 1½″; fls 3″ wide, orange with red throat, fad-
Semi-dwarf   ing to yellow but retaining red throat, 2 red rays
Mid-May   on dorsal lobe, up to 10 per lax truss.

Jodi

Rating   (*racemosum* x *moupinense*), 1977, Lem, intrd Gran-
Hardy to 0°F   ston. Lvs 1½″ x ¾″; fls 1½″ wide, pink with minor
Dwarf   spotting, terminal inflorescense of 6 buds, each with
Late March   4 fls.

Joe Gable

                  (Catalgla x *wardii*), 1972, Gable.

Joe Kruson

                  (Vulcan's Flame x Mars), 1972, Yates.

John Skrentny

Rating 4/3   (selected seedling of *arboreum* from wild collected
Hardy to 10°F   seed by Skrentny), 1966, Lancaster. Lvs 8″ x 1¾″;
Medium   fls 2″ wide, clear cherry red, up to 18 per truss.
Mid-April

John Wister   see Janet Blair

Josephine Everitt

                  (*fortunei* hybrid), 1958, Dexter.

Joy Ride

Rating   (parentage unknown), 1976, Whitney, intrd Sather.
Hardy to −10°F   Lvs 5½″ x 2¼″; fls 2″ wide, pale pink with orange
Tall   blotch in upper throat, up to 15 per truss.
Early May

Juan De Fuca

Rating   (Blue Ensign x *ponticum*), 1977, Larson, intrd
Hardy to 10°F   Northwest Ornamental Horticultural Society. Lvs
Tall   6″ x 2″; fls 3″ wide, lavender with dark red blotch
Mid-June   and spots, up to 12 per truss.

Judy

                  (*fortunei* x *campylocarpum*), 1958, James.

Julia Grothaus, CA 1975

Rating   (Albatross x Golden Belle), 1975, Grothaus. Lvs
Hardy to 0°F   6¼″ x 3¼″; fls 5″ wide, 7 lobes, frilled and fragrant,
Tall   peach with white edge that widens as fl ages, small
Early June   brownish blotch, up to 12 per flat truss.

Julie Titcomb, PA 1958

Rating 3/3   (Marinus Koster x Snow Queen), 1958, Larson. Lvs
Hardy to 0°F   7″ x 2¼″; fls 4½″ wide, carmine outside, flushed
Tall   pink on upper part within, some crimson spots, up
Early May   to 16 per truss.

Karl Hoschna

(Bow Bells x Jasper), 1967, Seabrook.

Katherine Dalton

Rating 3/4   (*fortunei* x *smirnowii*), 1958, Gable. Lvs slightly in-
Hardy to −15°F dumented; fls very pale pink from bright buds.
Medium
May

Kathleen Jane

Rating   (parentage unknown), 1975, Stephens. Lvs 4½″ x
Hardy to −10°F 1½″; fls 2½″ wide, scarlet with black spotting, up
Tall   to 12 per truss.
Early May

Kathryn Reboul

Rating   (*spinuliferum* x *racemosum*), 1975, Hardgrove,
Hardy to −5°F   intrd Reboul. Lvs 2½″ x 1″; fls 1″ wide, pale yellow
Semi-dwarf   flushed salmon, up to 14 per truss.
Mid-April

Kathryna

Rating   (advanced generation hybrid of *catawbiense* and
Hardy to −15°F *maximum*), 1978, W. Smith. Lvs 4¼″ x 1¾″; fls 2½″
Tall   wide, pink with slight yellow blotch, up to 17 per
Mid-May   truss.

Kathy Doll

(Corona x Dondis), 1964, R. Henny.

Katja

Rating   ((*catawbiense* var. *album* x *discolor*) x Madame de
Hardy to −10°F Bruin), 1976, Raustein. Lvs 6″ x 2″; fls 2″ wide,
Low   heavy substance, vivid pink, paler in throat, up to
Mid-May   16 per ball truss.

Kay

(Britannia x Loderi King George), 1972, Yates.

Kay Logan

(Romany Chai x Elizabeth), 1969, Seabrook.

Kenhelen

((Day Dream x Margaret Dunn) x unnamed seedling), 1965, Graves, intrd Janeck.

Ken Janeck, AE 1969

Rating 4/4 (selected seedling of *yakushimanum*), 1965, Janeck.
Hardy to −10°F Lvs 5″ x 1″, heavy indumentum; fls 2½″ wide, fuchsine pink fading to white with fern green stippling
Low
Early May on upper lobe, up to 17 per truss.

Kentucky Cardinal synonym The Cardinal

Rating 2/3 (*brachycarpum* x Essex Scarlet), 1958, Gable. Foliage dark and good; fls small, very dark red.
Hardy to −15°F
Low
Late May

Kevin

Rating (*yakushimanum* Koichiro Wada x Jade), 1975,
Hardy to 0°F Bovee, intrd Sorensen and Watson. Lvs 5″ x 2″,
Low indumented and convex; fls 2¼″ wide, deep pink
Early May fading to yellowish pink; edging and reverse a
darker version of fl color, up to 14 per truss.

Kim, AE 1973

Rating 3/4 (*campylogynum* x *cremastum*), 1966, Caperci. Lvs
Hardy to 5°F 1″ x ½″; fls ¾″ wide, pink turning to yellow, up
Dwarf to 4 per truss.
Late May

Kimberly, PA 1963

Rating 3/4 (*williamsianum* x *fortunei*), 1964, Greer. Lvs 3″ x
Hardy to 0°F 2″; fls 3½″ wide, pink turning to white, open truss.
Semi-dwarf
April

Kimberton

Rating (unknown x Crest), 1979, Bagoly, intrd Herbert.
Hardy to −5°F Lvs 5¾″ x 2¼″; fls 3½″ wide, fragrant, pink with
Medium chartreuse blotch, up to 12 per truss.
Mid-May

Kimbeth

Rating (Kimberly x Elizabeth), 1979, Greer. Lvs 2¾″ x 1½″;
Hardy to 0°F fls 2½″ wide, deep pink, up to 5 per flat truss.
Semi-dwarf
Late April

King of Jordan

Rating	(Nereid x Tally Ho x *discolor,* exact combination
Hardy to −5°F	unknown), 1977, probably Frye, intrd Jordan. Lvs
Semi-dwarf	6½" x 1¾"; fls 4" wide, yellow center shading to
Early June	pink edges, greenish spots in throat, up to 10 per
	truss.

King of Shrubs, PA 1950   synonym Orange Azor

Rating 4/2	(*discolor* x Fabia), 1958, Ostbo. Lvs 5½" x 2" wide;
Hardy to 0°F	fls 3" wide, apricot yellow base, wide margin of por-
Medium	celain rose, truss lax.
Late May	

King Tut

Rating 3/3	((*smirnowii* x America) x red *catawbiense* seed-
Hardy to −20°F	ling), 1958, Shammarello. Lvs 5" x 2½"; fls 2½"
Medium	wide, deep pink with yellowish brown blotch, truss
Mid-May	conical.

Kinglet

(*racemosum* x Finch), 1964, R. Henny.

King's Destiny

Rating	(unknown x Purple Splendour), 1978, Frederick, Jr.
Hardy to −10°F	Lvs 6" x 2"; fls 4½" wide, dark lavender with dark
Semi-dwarf	purple blotch and spotting, up to 11 per truss.
Mid-May	

King's Favor

Rating	(Purple Splendour x A. Bedford), 1978, Frederick, Jr.
Hardy to −10°F	Lvs 8" x 2"; fls 3¼" wide, orchid with golden yellow
Semi-dwarf	spotted blotch, up to 12 per ball truss.
Mid-May	

King's Ransom

(*campylocarpum* x unknown), 1974, Irvine, intrd McCuaig.

Kismet

(Grenadier x Pygmalion), 1958, R. Henny.

Kissena

(*catawbiense* hybrid), 1958, Parsons. Unknown now.

Klassy's Pride

Rating   ((*neriiflorum* x *strigillosum*) x (Loderi x *thomson-*
Hardy to −10°F *ii*)), 1979, Nelson, intrd Heller. Lvs 5″ x 1¾″; fls
Medium   2″ wide, red with black dorsal spotting, up to 14
Late April   per truss.

Koster's Choice synonym Peter Koster
                          (*fortunei* hybrid), 1958, Dexter.

Kristin

Rating   (*yakushimanum* Koichiro Wada x Bow Bells), 1975,
Hardy to 0°F   Bovee, intrd Sorensen and Watson. Lvs 3″ x 2″;
Low   fls 2½″ wide, pale pink with faint red spotting, up
Early May   to 14 per truss.

Kubla Khan

                          (Britannia x Goldsworth Orange), 1962, Brandt.

Kulu

Rating   (natural hybrid of *vernicosum* aff., Rock 18139),
Hardy to −10°F 1979, Gable, intrd C. Gable. Known as *vernicosum*
Medium   #2. Lvs 4½″ x 1¾″; fls 4″ wide, 7 lobes, fragrant,
Early May   pink blending deeper in throat, indistinct blotch,
                          up to 10 per truss.

Kurt Herbert Adler

Rating   (*phaeopeplum* x *lochae*), 1974, Lelliot (Australia),
Hardy to 25°F   intrd Strybing Arboretum. Lvs 3¼″ x 2″, new
Dwarf   growth brown from density of scales; fls 1½″ wide,
Winter   fragrant, mandarin red.

Kyoto Coral

Rating   ((*discolor* x Nereid x Tally Ho, exact combination
Hardy to −5°F   unknown) x unknown), 1977, Jordan. Lvs 5″ x 2″;
Semi-dwarf   fls 4½″ wide, texture of crepe, light to dark shades
Late May   of coral, up to 11 per flat truss.

La Verne

Rating   (Vulcan x Mrs. Furnival), 1975, Stephens. Lvs 4¾″
Hardy to −10°F x 1¾″; fls 4″ wide, rose bengal with deep red blotch,
Semi-dwarf   up to 11 per truss.
Late April

LaBar's White

                          (clone or natural hybrid of *catawbiense*), 1959,
                          found and intrd LaBar's Nursery. Resembles *ca-*
                          tawbiense except white with yellowish markings in
                          throat.

Lackamas Blue, PA 1963

Rating 2/4   (selected seedling of *augustinii* from Kerr Estate),
Hardy to −5°F   1964, Lancaster. Lvs typical of species, fls 3¼" wide,
Tall   flat, good bluish lavender, up to 4 per truss.
Late April

Lackamas Cream, PA 1962

Rating 3/3   (selected seedling of *chlorops*), 1963, Lancaster. Lvs
Hardy to −5°F   typical of species; fls 3½" wide, 7 lobes, primrose
Medium   yellow rayed mahogany, up to 12 per truss.
April

Lackamas Firebrand

(Essex Scarlet x *griersonianum*), 1967, Lancaster.

Lackamas Glory

(Earl of Athlone x *thomsonii*), 1963, Lancaster.

Lackamas Gold, PA 1962

(*chlorops* x *wardii*), 1963, Lancaster.

Lackamas Ruby

(Earl of Athlone x *thomsonii),* 1963, Lancaster.

Lackamas Sovereign

(Purple Splendour x Tally Ho), 1963, Lancaster.

Lackamas Spice, PA, 1962

Rating 3/3   (*chlorops* x *diaprepes*), 1963, Lancaster. Lvs 7" x
Hardy to 0°F   2¼"; fls 4" wide, spicy fragrance, pale yellow to
Medium   cream, up to 12 per truss.
Early May

Ladifor

(Lady Clementine Mitford x *fortunei*), 1958, Gable.

Lady April

Rating   (Dido x *williamsianum*), 1978, Childers. Lvs 2" x
Hardy to −10°F 1¼"; fls 2¾" wide, pink fading almost white, trans-
Semi-dwarf   lucent, up to 5 per lax truss.
Mid-April

Lady Rae

(*souliei* x Robert Allison), 1969, Gable, named Andrews.

Lagoon

(*augustinii* hybrid), 1958, Wright Sr. and Jr.

Lake Labish, PA 1955

Rating 4/2   (Lady Bligh x Loderi Venus), 1958, R. Henny. Lvs
Hardy to 5°F   5″ x 2½″; fls 3½″ wide, strawberry red, stamens not
Medium   fully formed, up to 17 per truss.
Mid-May

Lake Ozette

(*griersonianum* x Loderi Venus), 1958, Clark.

Lartag

Rating 4/4   (probably *taggianum* hybrid), 1966, Bowman. Lvs
Hardy to 15°F   5″ x 1½″; fls 3″ wide, narrow tubular, fragrant,
Tall   white, up to 4 per loose truss.
February-March

Last Chance, PA 1957

Rating 3/3   (Mar x *eriogynum*), 1958, R. Henny. Lvs 6″ x 2″;
Hardy to −5°F   fls 3½″ wide, claret rose shaded delft rose at center,
Tall   up to 14 per truss. Confusion exists between this
Late May   and Witchery which has never been registered.

Last Rose

(*discolor* x Tally Ho), 1963, Greig.

Laura Marie

(Countess of Athlone x *ponticum*), 1971, Lancaster.

Laurel Pink

Rating 4/4   (Boule de Neige x F.C. Puddle), 1967, Knippenberg.
Hardy to −20°F Lvs 2¼″ x 1¼″; fls 1¼″ wide, carmine rose, up to
Semi-dwarf   12 per globular truss.
Late April

Lavender Charm

Rating   ((*decorum* x *griffithianum*) x Purpureum Elegans),
Hardy to −5°F   1976, Gable, intrd Herbert. Lvs 7″ x 2½″; fls 4½″
Tall   wide, pale pink with lavender cast, small blotch,
Mid-May   reverse much darker, up to 14 per truss.

Lavender Princess

(*fortunei* hybrid), 1958, Dexter, intrd Bosley.

Lawton's Chinese Red

Rating   (parentage unknown), 1979, Lawton, intrd Hoogen-
Hardy to −5°F   doorn Nurseries. Lvs 4″ x 1½″; fls 2¾″ wide, red
Semi-dwarf   with no markings, up to 15 per truss.
Mid-May

'Windbeam'
Photo by
Dr. Herbert
Spady

Leaburg, PA 1956

Rating 4/3
Hardy to 5°F
Semi-dwarf
Mid-April

(*dichroanthum* x Penjerrick), 1958, Phetteplace. Lvs 2″ x 1″; fls 3″ wide, brilliant waxy red, truss flat.

Leah Yates

Rating
Hardy to −15°F
Semi-dwarf
Late May

(Mars selfed), 1977, Yates, intrd M. Yates. Lvs 7½″ x 2½″; fls 2¾″ wide, cerise with white dorsal flare containing 2 tan rays of spots, truss tall.

Leeann

Rating
Hardy to 10°F
Semi-dwarf
Early April

(Carmen x Choremia), 1979, Heller. Lvs 3¾″ x 1½″; fls 4″ wide, red, light maroon blotch, up to 8 per lax truss.

Leilie

(Jaipur x May Day), 1966, Brandt.

Lemon Bells

(*decorum* x Fabia), 1958, R. Henny.

Lemon Drop

(Moonstone seedling), 1962, Bovee.

Lemon Mist, AE 1969

Rating 3/3
Hardy to 15°F
Dwarf
March

(*xanthostephanum* x *leucaspis*), 1968, Scott. Lvs 2¾″ x 1¼″; fls 1½″ wide, yellow, up to 3 per terminal and axillary buds.

Lem's Cameo, SPA 1971

Rating 5/3   (Dido x Anna), 1975, Lem. Lvs 5¼" x 2¼"; fls 3¾"
Hardy to 5°F   wide, heavy substance, pale peach throat shading
Tall   to pink outer edge, red dorsal blotch, up to 20 per
Early May   dome truss.

Lem's Goal, PA 1952

(Lady Bessborough x Azor), 1958, Lem.

Lenape

Rating 3/4   (*pubescens* x *keiskei*), 1958, Nearing. Lvs 3" x 1½";
Hardy to −10°F fls small, light yellow, golf-ball size trusses.
Semi-dwarf
Early April

Leo Friedman

(Bow Bells x *strigillosum)* 1969, Seabrook.

Leona

Rating 3/3   (Corona x Dondis), 1958, R. Henny. Lvs 5" x 2";
Hardy to 0°F   fls 3" wide, rich pink, slightly spotted, darker base,
Medium   domed truss.
Mid-May

Lilacina

(*catawbiense* hybrid), 1958, Parsons. Unknown
now.

Lily #3   see Edna McCarty

Lily Maid

Rating   (*discolor* x unknown), 1975, Nelson, named Putney.
Hardy to 5°F   Lvs 8¾" x 3"; fls 3½" wide, frilled and fragrant,
Tall   pale pink, throat yellow, blotch a brown stripe, up
Early June   to 16 per truss.

Limelight

Rating   (*catawbiense* var. *album* x (*fortunei* x *wardii*)),
Hardy to −25°F 1963, Leach. Lvs 5" x 2½"; fls 3½" wide, 7 lobes,
Medium   pale yellow, strong yellow green dorsal blotch, up
Mid-May   to 15 per globular truss.

Lionel

(*catawbiense* hybrid), 1958, Parsons. Unknown
now.

Lipstick

(Fabia x Dondis), 1958, R. Henny.

Lisa, PA 1962

Rating 3/3   (Catalgla x Madonna), 1964, Gable. Lvs 8″ x 4″;
Hardy to −15°F   fls 4″ wide, white with sap green blotch, up to 18
Tall   per truss.
Late May

Little Amy

Rating   (*cremastum* x *campylogynum*), 1977, Caperci. Lvs
Hardy to 0°F   1½″ x 1″; fls 1¾″ wide, orient pink, up to 6 nodding
Dwarf   fls to truss.
Late May

Little Birdie

(Hummingbird x *forrestii* var. *repens*), 1958, R.
Henny.

Little Bobbie

(*forrestii* var. *repens* x Hummingbird), 1958, R.
Henny.

Little Dragon

(Fabia x *venator*), 1958, Lancaster.

Little Ernie

(*forrestii* var. *repens* x May Day), 1962, Allen.

Little Gem, PA 1962

Rating   (Carmen x *elliottii*), 1976, Whitney, intrd Sather.
Hardy to 5°F   Lvs 3″ x 1″; fls 2″ wide, heavy substance, red, up
Dwarf   to 8 per lax truss.
Early May

Little Janet

(*forrestii* var. *repens* x Hummingbird), 1958, R.
Henny.

Little Joe

Rating 3/3   (*forrestii* var. *repens* x May Day), 1958, Brandt. Lvs
Hardy to 5°F   1½″ x 1″; fls 2″ wide, red, truss lax.
Dwarf
Late April

Little Lou, PA 1963

(Lucy Lou x *valentinianum*), 1964, Sumner.

Little Minx

(*haematodes* x Jock), 1966, Wyatt.

Little Nemo

(Carmen x Choremia), 1965, Brandt.

Little Patty

(*forrestii* var. *repens* x Hummingbird), 1962, R. Henny.

Little Peep

((Earl of Athlone x Fabia) x *forrestii* var. *repens*), 1958, R. Henny.

Little Pudding, PA 1963

Rating 3/3   (*decorum* x Fabia), 1958, R. Henny. Lvs 3½" long,
Hardy to 5°F   fls 4" wide, coral pink to tan, deeper in throat, up
Low   to 13 per loose truss.
Mid-May

Little Sheba, PA 1954

Rating 3/4   ((Earl of Athlone x Fabia) x *forrestii* var. *repens*),
Hardy to 5°F   1958, R. Henny. Lvs 2¼" long; fls 2" wide, blood
Dwarf   red, up to 3 per terminal bud.
Early May

Little Trooper

(Arthur Osborne x Fabia), 1969, Baker.

Little White Dove

Rating   (*fortunei* x *yakushimanum*), 1974, Lancaster, intrd
Hardy to 5°F   J. Elliott. Lvs 2½" x 1"; fls 2¼" wide, white, up
Semi-dwarf   to 12 per ball truss.
Early May

Livonia Lindsley

(Loderi King George x Mars), 1969, Wright, Sr. and Jr., intrd Lindsley. Lvs 5" x 2"; fls 3" wide, orchid pink fading slightly, up to 24 per truss.

Loderi Olga

(Loderi Pink Diamond x Loderi King George), 1967, Brandt.

Lodestar

Rating   (*catawbiense* var. *album* x Belle Heller), 1965,
Hardy to −20°F Leach. Lvs 5" x 2"; fls 3¼" wide, usually white,
Medium   variable to very pale lavender, with bold spotted
Mid-May   dark greenish yellow dorsal blotch, up to 15 per truss.

Loeb's Moonlight
(parentage unknown), 1966, Loeb.

Lollipop
(Loderi x *williamsianum*), 1965, Ostbo, intrd Wright, Sr. and Jr.

Longwood
Rating
Hardy to 0°F
Low
Early May

(Vernus x Olympic Lady), 1976, Leach, intrd Longwood Gardens. Lvs 2½″ x 1¾″; fls 2½″ wide, lavender pink with dark red spots in throat, up to 7 per truss.

Lonny
Rating
Hardy to −10°F
Medium
Late April

(Charley x (Fawn x Damaris)), 1979, James. Lvs 8″ x 3¼″; fls 5″ wide, chartreuse green throat shading outward to pink edging, up to 10 per flat truss.

Lori Eichelser
Rating 4/4
Hardy to 0°F
Semi-dwarf
Early April

(*forrestii* var. *repens* x Bow Bells), 1967, Brandt, intrd Janeck. Lvs 2½″ x 1½″; fls 2½″ wide, cherry pink, up to 4 per truss.

Louis Amateis
(*carolinianum* x *bullatum*), 1958, Amateis.

Louise P. Delano
(*fortunei hybrid*), 1958, Dexter.

Love Story
Rating
Hardy to −5°F
Medium
Early May

(parentage unknown), 1976, Whitney, intrd Sather. Lvs 4″ x 1¾″; fls 3½″ wide, pale peach fading to pale yellow, deeper yellow blotch and orange red spotting in throat, edging deep peach, up to 10 per truss.

Lucky Strike
Rating 4/3
Hardy to 5°F
Medium
Late May

(*griersonianum* x Countess of Derby), 1958, Van Veen, Sr. Lvs 6″ x 2″; fls 3″ wide, deep salmon pink, up to 9 per truss.

Lucy Lou
((*ciliatum* x *leucaspis*) x leucaspis), 1958, Larson.

Lucy's Good Pink

Rating   (Ruby F. Bowman x *griersonianum*), 1976,
Hardy to −15°F   Druecker Lvs 6¾" x 2"; fls 4½" wide, 7 lobes, tyrian
Tall   rose, red calyx, up to 7 per lax truss.
Early June

Lurline

                    (*yakushimanum* x Unknown Warrior), 1969, Bry-
                    don.

Lydia, CA 1972

Rating 3/3   (Antoon van Welie x Day Dream), 1964, Greer. Lvs
Hardy to 0°F   6" x 2½"; fls 4" wide, china rose slightly marked
Medium   cardinal red on upper lobes, up to 14 per truss.
Late May

Mabel Parsons

                    (*catawbiense* hybrid), 1958, Parsons. Unknown
                    now.

Macopin

Rating   (chance seedling of *racemosum*), 1963, Nearing. Lvs
Hardy to −20°F   typical of species, fls pale lilac in globular clusters.
Semi-dwarf
Early May

Madame Pompidou

                    (parentage unknown), 1972, Kordus.

Madonna

                    ((*decorum* x *griersonianum*) x America), 1958,
                    Gable. Almost extinct.

Maggie Stoeffel

Rating 4/4   (parentage unknown), 1969, Whitney, intrd Ruth-
Hardy to 0°F   erford. Lvs 4½" x 1¾"; fls 3½" wide, double, pale
Medium   rose with crimson brown markings, up to 19 per
Mid-May   truss.

Magnagloss

Rating   ((*wardii* x *discolor*) x unknown), 1973, Nearing. Lvs
Hardy to −15°F   3" x 1½"; fls 2½" wide, orchid with conspicuous
Medium   blotch extending into spots, up to 12 per truss.
Early June

Malemute
Rating
Hardy to 10°F
Medium
Late April

(Loderi King George x unnamed orange Lem hybrid), 1978, J. Elliott. Lvs 6" x 2"; fls 5" wide, 7 lobes, fragrant, pink with darker edging, flare and reverse, up to 11 per lax truss.

Maletta
Rating
Hardy to
Medium
Mid-May

((*auriculatum* x *discolor*) x *ungernii* hybrid), 1972, Yates. Lvs 6" x 2½"; fls 3¼" wide, creamy center with edge of old gold, up to 15 per truss.

Mamie

(*souliei* x Bow Bells), 1963, R. Henny. Lvs 3½" x 2"; fls 3" wide, pink, up to 11 per truss.

Mamie Doud Eisenhower

(parentage unknown), 1972, Kordus.

Manda Sue
Rating 4/3
Hardy to 0°F
Semi-dwarf
May

(Vulcan x Elspeth), 1971, Baker. Lvs 4" x 1¾"; fls 2½" wide, shell pink with red edges and yellowish center, up to 14 per truss.

Man of War

(Britannia x Loderi King George), 1972, Lyons.

Mannie Weber
Rating
Hardy to −5°F
Medium
Late May

(*catawbiense* Boursault x Madame Albert Moser), 1974, Weber. Lvs 6½" x 2½"; fls 3½" wide, imperial purple, upper lobe spotted fern green, up to 14 per truss.

March Sun, PA 1963
Rating
Hardy to
Dwarf
March

(*caucasicum citrinum* x Moonstone), 1965, Wyrens. Lvs 2½" x 1¾"; fls 2½" wide, lemon yellow with small crimson blotch, up to 12 per tight truss.

Mardi Gras
Rating
Hardy to 0°F
Semi-dwarf
May

(*yakushimanum* Koichiro Wada x Vanessa), 1976, Bovee. Lvs 6" x 2"; fls 3" wide, pink and white blend, no spotting, up to 12 per truss.

Margaret Alice

Rating
Hardy to −10°F
Semi-dwarf
Late April

(unnamed dwarf pink x Elizabeth), 1973, Stephens. Lvs 3½" x 1½"; fls 3¼" wide, tyrian rose with small red streaks in throat, up to 8 per ball truss.

Margaret Einarson

Rating
Hardy to 5°F
Semi-dwarf
Mid-June

(Vulcan x Azor), 1977, Laxdall. Lvs 5¼" x 1½"; fls 2½" wide, 6 lobes, geranium lake, up to 12 per ball truss.

Margaret Knight

(pink Dexter x Purple Splendour), 1971, Loeb.

Marguerite

(*catawbiense* hybrid), 1958, Bosley.

Maricee, AE 1959

Rating 4/4
Hardy to 5°F
Dwarf
Early May

(selected seedling of *sargentianum*), 1962, Caperci. Lvs typical of species, fls small, creamy white in few fld truss, many trusses.

Marie Tietjens

Rating
Hardy to −10°F
Semi-dwarf
Late May

(*vernicosum* x Full Moon), 1976, Bagoly, intrd Tietjens. Lvs 6½" x 2¼'; fls 3½" wide, 7 lobes, pink shading darker at margins, no markings, up to 7 per truss.

Marilyn

(Fusalier x Fabia), 1965, R. Henny.

Marine, PA 1960

Rating 3/3
Hardy to 10°F
Tall
Late April

(selection of *augustinii*), 1962, Bovee. Lvs typical of species, fls deep lavender blue, out-facing, 3 to truss.

Marjorie Baird

(Iviza x *campylocarpum*), 1965, Larson.

Mark Henny

(Diane x *williamsianum*), 1965, R. Henny, intrd L. Henny. Lvs 3½" long, fls 1¾" wide, cherry red, up to 8 per truss.

Mark Twain
(Jean Marie Montague x Indiana), 1965, Seabrook.

Markeeta's Flame   synonym Markeeta's Prize #2
Rating   (Loderi Venus x Anna), 1978, Beck, intrd North.
Hardy to −5°F   Lvs 5½" x 2¾"; fls 5" wide, bright dark pink, darker
Medium   spotting on dorsal lobe, up to 13 per ball truss.
Early May

Markeeta's Prize
Rating 4/4   (Loderi Venus x Anna), 1967, Markeeta Nursery.
Hardy to −5°F   Lvs 6" x 2½"; fls 5" wide, scarlet red, up to 12 per
Low   truss.
Early May

Marshall Lyons
(Ole Olson x Loderi King George), 1972, Lyons

Martha Isaacson, PA 1956
(*occidentale* x Ostbo seedling #70), 1958, Ostbo.
Azaleodendron.

Martha May
(Mars x Tally Ho), 1965, R. Henny, intrd L. Henny.

Martha Phipps
Rating   (parentage unknown), 1973, Phipps. Lvs 5¼" x 1¾";
Hardy to −10°F   fls 4" wide, pale yellow suffused pink, inside manda-
Medium   rin orange at margins, up to 10 per compact truss.
Mid-May

Martha Robbins
(*forrestii* var. *repens* x *sperabile*), 1971, Brandt.

Blue Pacific   *Photo by Harold Greer*

Martha Wright

(*burmanicum* x Fragrantissimum), 1968, Sumner.

Marvellous

(Countess of Derby x unknown), 1962, Greer. Extinct.

Mary Ann

(Corona x Dondis), 1958, R. Henny.

Mary Belle, PA 1962

Rating 4/4   (Atrier x Dechaem), 1964, Gable. Lvs 5½″ x 2½″;
Hardy to −15°F fls 4″ wide, salmon pink fading to buff yellow, flat
Medium   truss.
Late May

Mary Briggs

(*haematodes* x Elizabeth), 1968, Wyatt. Lvs 3″ x 1″; fls 2″ wide, blood red, up to 10 per truss.

Mary D. Black

(*fortunei* x Madame Fr. J. Chauvin), 1958, Larson. Extinct.

Mary Fleming, AE 1973

Rating 4/3   ((racemosum x keiskei) x keiskei), 1972, Nearing.
Hardy to −25°F Lvs small; fls small, bisque yellow with streaks of
Semi-dwarf   salmon, very abundant.
Late April

Mary Francis Hawkins

(parentage unknown), 1958, Gable.

Mary Greig

(*euchaites* x *souliei*), 1962, Greig. Extinct.

Mary Harmon, AE 1958

(Mrs. Donald Graham x *occidentale*), 1958, Ostbo. Azaleodendron.

Mary Jane

Rating   (*yakushimanum* x Leo), 1974, Freimann. Lvs 4″ x
Hardy to 0°F   1½″; fls 2″ wide, carmine rose fading to white, up
Semi-dwarf   to 12 per ball truss.
Mid-May

Mary Lucille

Rating	(Mrs. A.T. de la Mare x Earl of Donoughmore),
Hardy to −10°F	1975, Stephens. Lvs 6″ x 2″; fls 4½″ wide, rose opal
Medium	with dark red dorsal blotch and spots, up to 15 per
Late April	ball truss.

Mary Mayo, PA 1960

Rating	(Loderi King George x Ostbo Y3), 1962, Bovee. Lvs
Hardy to	6½″ x 2½″; fls 4½″ wide, frilled, blend of pink shades
Medium	and yellow, up to 11 per truss.
Mid-May	

Mary Tranquillia

Rating	((*discolor* x Nereid x Tally Ho, exact combination
Hardy to −5°F	unknown) x Autumn Gold), 1977, Jordan. Lvs 4½″
Semi-dwarf	x 1½″; fls 4¼″ wide, yellow center, rose edging, fine
Early June	peppering of red spots on dorsal lobe, reverse
	pinker, flourescent effect, up to 11 per flat truss.

Mary Yates

Rating	(Pink Twins x Leah Yates), 1977, Yates, intrd M.
Hardy to −10°F	Yates. Lvs 5½″ x 2½″; fls 2½″ wide, 7 lobes, orchid
Low	pink shading lighter to center, few gold spots, up
Mid-May	to 10 per ball truss.

Maryke

Rating 4/4	(*discolor* x Fabia), 1955, Van Veen, Sr. Lvs 6″ x
Hardy to 0°F	2½″; fls 3½″ wide, blend of pink and yellow, up to
Medium	9 per lax truss.
Late May	

Maureen

(*williamsianum* x Lem's Goal), 1973, Lem.

Maxdis

(*maximum* x *discolor*), 1958, Gable.

Maxie

(*maximum* x *macrophyllum*), 1958, Gable.

Maxine Childers

Rating	(*strigillosum* x Elizabeth), 1977, Childers, intrd
Hardy to −5°F	Phetteplace. Lvs 4″ x 1″; fls 2¼″ wide, cardinal red,
Low	up to 10 per flat truss.
Early April	

Maxine Margaret

Rating   (*strigillosum* x Elizabeth), 1977, Childers. Lvs 3½″
Hardy to −15°F   x 1″; 2″ wide, currant red with black nectaries,
Semi-dwarf   up to 11 per flat truss.
Early April

Maximum Superbum

                        (*maximum* hybrid or clone), 1958, Parsons. Un-
                        known now.

May Schwarz

Rating   (Candi x *tephropeplum*), 1977, Scott. Lvs 1½″ x ½″;
Hardy to   fls 1¼″ wide, pink with darker streaks and reverse,
Dwarf   up to 6 per truss.
Late March

May Song

                        (Bow Bells x Day Dream), 1963, Grace, intrd
                        Bovee. Lvs 2½″ long; fls 3½″ wide, pink flushed
                        deeper, up to 11 per truss.

May Time

                        (*catawbiense* var. *album* x *yakushimanum* Koi-
                        chiro Wada), 1973, Leach. Lvs 4¼″ x 1¾″; fls 2½″
                        wide, white, exterior faintly flushed orchid pink on
                        ribs, up to 14 per truss.

Mayflower

                        (*racemosum* x *carolinianum*), 1958, Gable.

Meadowbrook, AE 1973

Rating 3/3   (Mrs. C.S. Sargent x Everestianum), 1958, Voss-
Hardy to −15°F   berg. Lvs 5″ x 2″; fls 2¼″ wide, frilled, bright pink
Medium   with white blotch and green spots, up to 22 per
Late May   truss.

Meadowgold

Rating   (*burmanicum* x Lemon Mist), 1976, Scott. Lvs 1½″
Hardy to   x ¾″; fls 1½″ wide, sulphur yellow with aureolin
Semi-dwarf   spots on dorsal lobe, terminal inflorescence up to
Late March   3 buds, each up to 6 fls.

Meath

Rating   (Boule de Neige x *yakushimanum* Koichro Wada),
Hardy to −5°F   1979, Reese. Lvs 4¼″ x 2¼″; fls 3¾″ wide, 7 lobes,
Dwarf   fragrant, shaded pink with yellow green dorsal
Mid-May   blotch and spotting, up to 9 per truss.

Meliz

Rating
Hardy to 0°F
Dwarf
Late May

(*kotschyi* hybrid), 1977, Caperci. Lvs 1¼" x ½"; fls ¾" wide, pink spotted darker, inflorescence of 4 buds, each up to 8 fls.

Mellow Gold

(*wardii* x *campylocarpum*), 1958, Lancaster.

Merle Lee, PA 1954

(Azor selfed), 1958, Esch.

Merry Mae White

Rating
Hardy to −10°F
Semi-dwarf
Mid-May.

(parentage unknown), 1978, Hardgrove, intrd Royce. Lvs 4½" x 2"; fls 3" wide, 6 lobes, white with 2 small purplish rays, up to 11 per truss.

'Mary Fleming'
Photo by Dr. Herbert Spady

Meta

Rating
Hardy to 10°F
Tall
Early May

(Lady Berry x Ivy), 1979, Heller. Lvs 3½" x 1¼"; fls 2¾" wide, funnel-shaped, dull red, up to 4 per lax truss.

Mi Amor, CA 1969 AM RHS 1975

(*lindleyi* x *nuttallii*), 1962, Sumner.

Michael Rice

Rating
Hardy to −15°F
Tall
May

(advanced generation hybrid including *cataw-biense* and *maximum*), 1979, W. Smith. Lvs 4¼" x 1¾"; fls 3" wide, pink with deeper spotting and edging, up to 15 per ball truss.

Midget
                (selected seedling of *leucaspis*), Bovee. As species, but tiny.

Mildred Amateis
                (*carolinianum* x *edgeworthii*), 1958, Amateis.

Mildred Fawcett, PA 1960

Rating	(Faggetter's Favourite x Mrs. Donald Graham),
Hardy to	1962, Fawcett. Lvs 6¼" x 2"; fls 3" wide, blush pink
Tall	with orange pink blotch, truss large.
Early May	

Millard Kepner

Rating	(Decatros x *yakushimanum*), 1975, Schumacher,
Hardy to −5°F	intrd Byrkit. Lvs 5½" x 1"; fls 3½" wide, dark pink
Medium	fading lighter with lavender undertone, incon-
Mid-April	spicuous blotch, up to 15 per ball truss.

Millicent Scott

Rating	(*racemosum* x Saffron Queen), 1977, Scott. Lvs 1½"
Hardy to	x ½"; fls 1" wide, buff with light red markings, in-
Semi-dwarf	florescence of 7 terminal and axillary buds, each
Mid-March	with 3 fls.

Minas Maid

Rating	(Nova Zembla x *yakushimanum*), 1979, Swain,
Hardy to −15°F	intrd Craig, Dept. of Agric., Research Station Sta-
Semi-dwarf	tion, Nova Scotia. Lvs 3¾" x 1¾"; fls 2¼" wide,
Early June	pink with dorsal ruby fleck, up to 15 per ball truss.

Ming
                (Albatross x *wardii*), 1962, R. Henny. Lvs 6" x 3"; fls 4" wide, uranium green with reddish blotch on dorsal lobe.

Ming Toy

Rating	(Medusa x Crest), 1978, Childers. Lvs 4" x 1½"; fls
Hardy to −10°F	2½" wide, yellow slightly shaded orange, up to 9
Semi-dwarf	per lax truss.
Early May	

Mini Bell
                (*tephropeplum* x unknown), 1974, Irvine, intrd Mc-Cuaig. fls pink, 35 to truss.

Mini White

(*maximum* x *chrysanthum*), 1972, Potter.

Mirage

(Fabia x Margaret Dunn), 1958, R. Henny.

Mira-Mi Linda

(Bow Bells x Hawk), 1966, Heineman.

Mirelle Vernimb

(selected seedling of *hemitrichotum*), 1971, Vernimb.

Miss Jack

Rating   (Ole Olson x (*lacteum* x Mary Swaythling)), 1963,
Hardy to   James. Lvs 4½" x 2½"; fls 4" wide, ivory with small
Medium   area of red spots on upper lobe, up to 12 per truss.
Early May

Miss Olympia, PA 1960

Rating 4/4   (Loderi King George x *williamsianum*), 1962,
Hardy to 0°F   Ostbo, intrd Clark. Lvs 5" long; fls 4" wide, blush
Low   pink with darker throat.
Mid-April

Miss Prim

Rating 3/3   (*decorum* x *irroratum*), 1960, Bovee. Lvs 4" long;
Hardy to −5°F   fls 4" wide, white blotched brilliant yellow green,
Medium   up to 15 per truss.
Late March

Mission Bells

Rating 3/4   (*williamsianum* x *orbiculare*), 1958, Lancaster. Lvs
Hardy to −5°F   4" x 1½"; fls 2½" wide, fragrant, white flushed pink,
Low   up to 8 per lax truss.
Early May

Misty Morn

Rating   (unknown x Purple Splendour), 1976, Frederick, Jr.
Hardy to −5°F   Lvs 6" x 2¼"; fls 3½" wide, violet with yellowish
Medium   green rays, reverse darker, up to 14 per flat truss.
Mid-May

Mitzi

(*croceum* x Fabia), 1958, R. Henny.

'Springfield'
Photo by
Harold Greer

Mobur
Rating 4/3   (Burgundy x Moser's Maroon), 1962, Bowman. Lvs
Hardy to 10°F   5" x 1¾"; fls 3" wide, dahlia purple spotted maroon,
Medium   up to 15 per truss.
Late May

Mohur, PA 1955 Dream Girl grex
                (Day Dream x Margaret Dunn), 1958, Brandt. Extinct.

Molly Ann
Rating   (Elizabeth x unnamed seedling), 1974, Freimann.
Hardy to 0°F   Lvs 2¾" x 1¾"; fls 2" wide, crimson with small
Semi-dwarf   spots, up to 7 per lax truss.
Mid-April

Monique
                (Britannia x Purple Splendour), 1972, Nelson.

Montchanin
Rating 2/2   (*pubescens* x *keiskei*), 1958, Nearing. Lvs small; fls
Hardy to −25°F small, white, very profusely borne.
Medium
Late April

Moon Mist
                (*fortunei* x Lackamas Cream), 1965, Lancaster.

Moonlight Tango
                (Mars x Diva), 1965, R. Henny, intrd L. Henny.

Moonrise

(Loderi King George x Souvenir of W.C. Slocock),
1958, Wright Sr. and Jr.

Moontide, PA 1955

Rating 3/2
Hardy to 0°F
Low
Late April

(*wardii* x Loder's White), 1958, R. Henny. Lvs 6″
x 2″; fls 3½″ wide, white, up to 16 per truss.

'Odee Wright'   *Photo by Cecil Smith*

Morning Sunshine

Rating
Hardy to 0°F
Medium
Mid-April

(parentage unknown), 1977, Whitney, intrd Sather.
Lvs 4½″ x 2″; fls 4″ wide, 7 lobes, primrose yellow,
up to 14 per ball truss.

Moukoense

(*pemakoense* x *moupinense*), 1958, Brandt.

Mount Hood

Rating
Hardy to −5°F
Tall
Early May

(Fawn x Crest), 1975, Phetteplace. Lvs 5½" x 2"; fls 3½" wide, white with chartreuse shading deep in throat, fragrant, up to 13 per truss.

Mount Mazama

Rating
Hardy to 0°F
Medium
Late April

(Britannia x Loderi, or reverse), 1979, Grace, intrd Grothaus. Lvs 6" x 2½"; fls 4½" wide, red, darker red nectaries and stripes on reverse, up to 15 per ball truss.

Mount Mitchell

Rating 3/3
Hardy to −25°F
Medium
May

(selected seedling of red *maximum*), 1965, Leach. Lvs 6" x 2"; fls 2" wide, strong pink with yellowish green dorsal blotch, exterior and bud red, up to 15 per ball truss.

Mount Siga

Rating
Hardy to −5°F
Medium
Early May

(natural hybrid of *vernicosum* aff., Rock 18139), 1979, Gable, intrd C. Gable. Known as *vernicosum* #1. Lvs 4½" x 1¾"; fls 4" wide, 8 lobes, pink blending deeper in throat, dull red dorsal blotch and spotting, up to 12 per truss.

Mountain Aura

Rating 4/4
Hardy to −15°F
Low
Late May

(Dorothea x red hybrid), 1968, Nearing. Lvs 6" x 3"; fls 4" wide, flax blue with white center, round truss.

Mountain Flare

Rating
Hardy to −15°F
Medium
Mid-May

(Boule de Neige x Loderi King George), 1973, Nearing. Lvs 7" x 2"; fls 4½" wide, fragrant, red with darker speckling, up to 15 per truss.

Mountain Glow

Rating 4/4
Hardy to −15°F
Low
Late May

(Dorothea x red hybrid), 1968, Nearing. Lvs 6" x 3"; fls 4" wide, reddish purple, round truss.

Mountain Queen

Rating 4/4
Hardy to −15°F
Low
Late May

(Dorothea x red hybrid), 1968, Nearing. Lvs 7" x 3"; fls 4" wide, slight fragrance, rose with pale center, ball truss.

Mrs. A.J. Holden

Rating
Hardy to −5°F
Medium
Mid-June

(Polar Bear x Evening Glow), 1979, Holden. Lvs 7½″ x 2″; fls 5¼″ wide, 7 lobes, fragrant, yellow with light green spotting, pink edging, up to 10 per truss.

Mrs. A.R. McEwan, AE 1956

Rating 3/3
Hardy to −5°F
Tall
Early May

(selected seedling of Loderi), 1958, Ihrig, intrd University of Washington. Lvs 7½″ x 2½″; fls 5″ wide, persian rose with white throat, dome truss.

Mrs. Bernice Baker

Rating 4/4
Hardy to −10°F
Tall
Late May

(Dawn's Delight x *fortunei*), 1958, Larson. Lvs 6″ x 2″; fls deep pink fading to white, tall truss.

Mrs. Betty Hager

Rating
Hardy to 0°F
Medium
Early May

((*decorum* x *discolor*) x Madame de Bruin), 1974, Raustein. Lvs 5½″ x 2¼″; fls 3″ wide, dark pink with blotch and spotting of red, up to 15 per ball truss.

Mrs. Byron Scott

(*souliei* hybrid), 1958, Larson.
Possibly identical to Mrs. Powell Glass.

Mrs. Carter Glass

(Catagla x *decorum*), 1958, Gable. Possibly identical to Mrs. Powell Glass.

Mrs. Donald Graham, AE 1958

Rating 4/2
Hardy to 5°F
Medium
Early June

((Corona x *griersonianum*) x Loderi), 1958, seed Rose (England), intrd Ostbo. Lvs 7″ x 2¼″; fls 4½″ wide, deep salmon pink, up to 9 per flat truss.

Mrs. Elizabeth Titcomb   see Elizabeth Titcomb

Mrs. Erna Heyderhoff

Rating
Hardy to −10°F
Medium
Late May

(Mrs. Furnival x Catalgla), 1976, Beury, intrd Heyderhoff. Lvs 6½″ x 2½″; fls 3″ wide, white shading to pale pink at edges, prominent red blotch, up to 21 per ball truss.

Mrs. Frank S. Baker

(*fortunei* x Dawn's Delight), 1958, Larson.

Mrs. H. B. Gardner
(*fortunei* hybrid), 1958, Dexter. Unknown now.

Mrs. H. T. Krug
Rating — (*fortunei,* open pollinated), 1979, Krug. Lvs 7½″ x
Hardy to −15°F — 2½″; fls 4″ wide, 7 lobes, fragrant, pink shading in-
Tall — ward to yellow green, red deep in throat, up to 12
Late April — per truss.

Mrs. Helen Weyerhaeuser
(Fusilier x Jean), 1958, Larson.

Mrs. Horace Fogg, PA 1964
Rating 4/3 — (*griersonianum* x Loderi Venus), 1958, Larson. Lvs
Hardy to 0°F — 6″ x 2″; fls 4½″ wide, medium pink, frosted effect,
Medium — throat nearly red, dome truss.
May

Mrs. Howard Phipps
(unknown hybrid x Naomi), 1971, Phipps. Lvs 7″
x 2½″, mat; fls moderate orchid pink, no eye, up
to 14 per truss.

Mrs. Lammot Copeland
Rating — (*wardii* x Virginia Scott), 1971, Larson. Lvs 6″ x 2″;
Hardy to 0°F — fls 3½″ wide, yellow, up to 15 per truss.
Tall
June

Mrs. Muriel Carfrae
Rating — (*yakushimanum* hybrid), 1975, Berg, intrd Trainor.
Hardy to −15°F — Lvs 4″ x 1½″; fls 2″ wide, pale pink blending to
Semi-dwarf — cream throat, up to 15 per truss.
Early May

'Hotei'
Photo by
Harold Greer.

Mrs. Paul B. Smith
> (Albatross x Pygmalion), 1958, Larson.

Mrs. Powell Glass synonym Anne Glass
Rating 3/2   (Catalgla x *decorum*), 1958, Gable. Fls pure white,
Hardy to −20°F lvs dark green, truss lax. Plant is called Anne Glass;
Medium   should have been so registered.
Late May

Mrs. W.R. Coe
Rating 3/4   (*fortunei* hybrid), 1958, Dexter. Lvs very large; fls
Hardy to −5°F 4″ wide, brilliant pink with crimson throat, very
Medium   large truss.
Mid-May

Mrs. Wayne W. Keyes
> (Earl of Athlone x *fortunei*), 1958, Larson. Extinct.

Mt. Mitchell
> (*maximum* x *catawbiense*), 1958, Gable.

Mucram
> (*mucronulatum* x *ambiguum*), 1958, Gable.

Mucronulatum Pink
> (chance *mucronulatum* hybrid), 1958, Gable.

Mumtaz-I-Mahal
> (Day Dream x Margaret Dunn), 1966, Brandt. Extinct.

Muriel Pearce
Rating   (Anna x Fusilier), 1973, Lem, intrd Pearce. Lvs 4″
Hardy to 15°F x 1½″; fls 3½″ wide, shaded rose madder with plen-
Tall   tiful red spots, up to 15 per truss.
Early May

My Lady
> (Forsterianum selfed), 1972, Sumner.

My Pet
Rating   (parentage unknown), 1976, Whitney, intrd Sather.
Hardy to 0°F   Lvs 2½″ x 1¼″; fls 2″ wide, pale yellow with small
Dwarf   red blotch, up to 10 per truss.
Early April

My Pretty One

Rating 3/4   (*carneum* x *moupinense*), 1964, James, intrd
Hardy to   Childers. Lvs 2½" x 1"; fls 3½" wide, shallow, pink
Dwarf   fading white, up to 3 per truss. Mahogany peeling
Early March   bark at all seasons.

Nancy Read

                   (*pemakoense* x Racil), 1958, Larson. Clusters of
                   bluish pink fls on dwarf plant.

Nancy Sue

Rating   (parentage unknown), 1975, Stephens. Lvs 5½" x
Hardy to −10°F   2"; fls 4" wide, magenta rose with dark gold spots,
Medium   up to 17 per truss.
Early May

Naranja

                   (Margaret Dunn x Tally Ho), 1963, Brandt. Ex-
                   tinct.

Narnia

Rating   (*aurigeranum* x *zoelleri*), 1978, seed Lelliot (Aus-
Hardy to 30°F   tralia), intrd Moynier. Lvs 5" x 2½"; fls 3" wide,
Medium   yellow to orange bicolor, up to 10 per flat truss.
Year-round

Nathan Hale   synonym HS #10

Rating   (parentage unknown), 1973, Dexter, intrd Sch-
Hardy to −5°F   laikjer. Lvs 5½" x 2½"; fls 3½" wide, 7 lobes, fra-
Medium   grant, rose with darker blotch, ball truss.
Late May

Nectarine

                   ((Coronis x *griersonianum*) x Margaret Dunn),
                   1958, Brandt.

Nestucca, PA 1950

Rating 4/4   (*fortunei* x *yakushimanum*), 1960, seed Hanger
Hardy to −10°F   (England), intrd C. Smith. Lvs 5" x 1½"; fls 5" wide,
Semi-dwarf   bowl-shaped, white with brown traces in throat, up
Early May   to 15 per truss.

New Hope

Rating   (*yakushimanum* x Kiev), 1976, Bovee, intrd Her-
Hardy to −5°F   bert. Lvs 5" x 1¾"; fls 3¼" wide, dark pink shading
Semi-dwarf   lighter to throat, spots and reverse darker pink, up
Early May   to 10 per ball truss.

New Romance

(Lady Bligh x Loderi Venus), 1966, R. Henny, intrd L. Henny. Lvs 5″ x 1¼″; fls 2½″ wide, rose pink, opening white.

Newport

(*catawbiense* hybrid), 1958, Stokes.

Nez Perce Chief see The Chief

Nina

Rating
Hardy to −20°F
Medium
Mid-May

(parentage unknown), 1979, Wytovich. Lvs 5″ x 2½″; fls 3½″ wide, fragrant, pink fading lighter, dark red throat blotch, up to 10 per truss.

Norseman

Rating
Hardy to 0°F
Low
Early June

(parentage unknown), 1974, Lem, intrd J. Elliott. Lvs 5¼″ x 1½″; fls 2½″ wide, carmine with scarlet throat, up to 15 per flat truss.

Noyo Brave

Rating
Hardy to 0°F
Semi-dwarf
Early May

(Noyo Chief x *yakushimanum* Koichiro Wada), 1978, C. Smith. Lvs 5″ x 2″; fls 2½″ wide, mandarin red, fading with age, very small radiant red blotch, up to 22 per ball truss.

Noyo Chief, CA 1971

Rating 4/5
Hardy to 15°F
Tall
Late March

(hybrid of *arboreum* subsp. *nilagricum*), 1965, Reuthe (England), imported by Brandt, intrd Bowman. Lvs 7″ x 2½″, parsley green, highly glossy; fls 2½″ wide, clear rose red, up to 16 per compact truss. Has been sold as *kingianum* and *zeylanicum*.

Nuance

Rating
Hardy to −15°F
Medium
Late May

((*catawbiense* var. *album* x (*neriiflorum* x *dichroanthum*)) x *discolor*), 1973, Leach. Lvs 4″ x 2″; fls 2¾″ wide, heavy substance, pale orange yellow suffused purplish pink, greenish yellow dorsal spotting, up to 14 per truss.

Nugget

(Cowslip x *chamaethomsonii* var. *chamaethauma*), 1962, Brandt.

Nutberger   see Bill Massey

Nuthatch

(parentage unknown), 1965, R. Henny, intrd L. Henny. Lvs 6″ x 2″; fls 2″ wide, azalea pink, up to 7 per open truss.

Oasis

(Fawn x Dido), 1972, James.

Oceanlake

Rating 4/4
Hardy to −5°F
Dwarf
Late April

(Blue Diamond x Sapphire), 1966, Wright, Sr. and Jr. Lvs 1″ x ½″; fls 1″ wide, flat, deep violet blue, 8 per truss.

Odee Wright, PA 1966

Rating 4/4
Hardy to 0°F
Medium
Early May

(Idealist x Mrs. Betty Robertson), 1965, Wright, Sr. and Jr. Lvs 3½″ x 1½″; fls 4½″ wide, peach buds opening chartreuse with carmine throat spots, up to 15 per truss.

Oh-Too

Rating
Hardy to −5°F
Medium
Early May

(China x Goldbug), 1976, W. Elliot, intrd Sather. Lvs 5″ x 2½″; fls 2½″ wide, pale red maturing to yellow, salmon throat with red spots, up to 14 per ball truss.

Old Copper

Rating 4/3
Hardy to 0°F
Medium
Late May

(Fabia x Vulcan), 1958, Van Veen, Sr. Lvs 4″ x 1½″; fls 2½″ wide, old copper color, up to 5 per loose truss.

Old Spice

Rating 3/3
Hardy to −5°F
Medium
Mid-May

(Azor x *decorum*), 1963, Lancaster. Lvs 7″ x 2″; fls 3½″ wide, fragrant, phlox pink blending to apricot, up to 12 per truss.

Ole Olson

Rating 3/3
Hardy to 0°F
Medium
Mid-May

Old Olsen is presumed to be same plant. (*campylocarpum* var. *elatum* x *discolor*), 1958, Gable, intrd Lem. Lvs 4″ x 2″; fls 3½″ wide, pale yellow, truss loose.

Olin O. Dobbs

Rating 3/3
Hardy to −15°F
Medium
Late May

(Mars x Purple Splendour, or reverse), 1979, Dobbs, intrd Greer. Lvs 5″ x 2″; fls 2½″ wide, heavy substance, deep reddish purple, up to 15 per truss.

Oliver Twist

(Charles Dickens x *yakushimanum*), 1969, Lancaster. Lvs 4½″ x 2″; fls 2½″ wide, clear fuchsine pink, up to 20 per truss.

Olympic Blondie

(Fabia x unknown), 1958, Clark. Extinct.

Olympic Brave

(Fabia x unknown), 1958, Clark. Extinct.

Olympic Brownie

(Fabia x unknown), 1958, Clark. Extinct.

Olympic Chimes

(Fabia x unknown), 1958, Clark.

Olympic Chinook

(Fabia x unknown), 1958, Clark.

Olympic Hose-in-Hose

(Fabia x unknown), 1958, Clark.

Olympic Hunter

(Fabia x unknown), 1958, Clark. Extinct.

Olympic Knight

(Fabia x unknown), 1958, Clark.

Olympic Lady, PA 1960   synonym White Olympic Lady

Rating 3/3   (Loderi King George x *williamsianum*), 1958,
Hardy to 0°F   Ostbo, intrd Clark. Lvs 3″ x 2¼″; fls 3″ wide, pink
Low   turning white, up to 8 per truss.
Early April

Olympic Maid

(Fabia x unknown), 1958, Clark. Extinct.

Olympic Miss

(Fabia x unknown), 1958, Clark. Extinct.

Olympic Quinault

(*griersonianum* hybrid), 1958, Layritz Nursery, intrd Clark.

Olympic Sweetheart

(Romany Chai x *discolor*), 1958, Clark.

Opal Fawcett, AE 1958

(parentage unknown), 1958, Ostbo, intrd Fawcett. Lvs 8″ x 2½″; fls 3½″ wide, very pale pink fading to white, opalescent, up to 16 per truss.

Ophir

Dream Girl grex
(Day Dream x Margaret Dunn), 1958, Brandt. Extinct.

Orange Azor   see King of Shrubs

Orange Cross   see Fred Hamilton

Orange Delight

Rating   ((Lady Berry x *xanthocodon*) x Lady Roseberry),
Hardy to 10°F   1979, Heller. Lvs 2½″ x 1¼″; fls 2″ wide, funnel-
Tall   shaped, shades of orange, up to 6 per lax truss.
Early May

Oregon Queen

(*macrophyllum* x *occidentale,* natural hybrid), 1958. Azaleodendron.

Osceola

(*catawbiense* hybrid), 1958, Parsons. Unknown now.

Ostbo's Copper

(Fabia x Mrs. W. C. Slocock), 1958, Ostbo.

Ostbo's Low Yellow, PA 1960

(parentage unknown), 1960, Ostbo. Lvs 4″ x 2″; fls 4½″ wide, creamy yellow.

Othello

((Armistice Day x *griersonianum*) x Carmen), 1954, Brandt.

Otis Hyde

Rating   (Fabia x Albatross), 1964, Larson. Lvs 6″ x 2½″;
Hardy to   fls 4″ wide, red, streaking, spots and throat currant
Medium   red, orange overlay over all, up to 12 per truss.
Late May

Otto Holmdahl

(Butterfly x *ponticum*), 1969, Ostbo. Lvs 4″ x 1¾″; fls 3″ wide, creamy yellow, crimson flecks, up to 11 per truss.

Ouro Puro

(Francis Hanger selfed), 1965, Brandt. Extinct.

Owen Pierce

(Saffron Queen x *burmanicum*), 1972, Sumner.

Pacific Glow
Rating
Hardy to 10°F
Medium
Mid-April

(Loderi Venus x *strigillosum*), 1979, Larson, regstrd Jack. Lvs 5½" x 2"; fls 3¼" wide, 6 lobes, pink, throat darker, no markings, up to 17 per ball truss.

Painted Star

(Meadowbrook x Anita), 1958, Hardgrove.

Pale Perfection
Rating 2/4
Hardy to −15°F
Medium
Mid-May

(*catawbiense* hybrid), 1967, Wyman, intrd Ticknor. Lvs 4¼" x 1¾"; fls 2½" wide, rose with dark greenish blotch, up to 13 per truss.

Pamela Love

(unnamed *thomsonii* hybrid x unnamed Loderi seedling), 1965, Love.

Paricutin

(Britannia x Tally Ho), 1968, Brandt.

Parker's Pink, AE 1973   synonym Parker's #1
Rating 2/3
Hardy to −25°F
Medium
Late May

(parentage unknown), 1973, Dexter and Parker, intrd Vossberg. Lvs 6½" x 2¾"; fls 3½" wide, fragrant, dark pink fading to white in throat with dense red spots, up to 12 per truss.

Parker's #1   see Parker's Pink

Party Pink
Rating
Hardy to −20°F
Medium
Mid-May

(Mrs. Furnival x *catawbiense* var. *album*), 1973, Leach. Lvs 4¾" x 2½"; fls 3" wide, purplish pink shading to paler center, conspicuous yellow spotting, up to 18 per ball truss.

Pastel Star

(*catawbiense* var. *rubrum* x *discolor*), 1958, Hardgrove.

'Shamrock'
Photo by
Cecil Smith

Pastor Dunker

Rating
Hardy to 0°F
Semi-dwarf
Early May

((*(decorum* x *discolor)* x *(fortunei* x *(wardii* x *dichroanthum)))* x Jean Marie Montague), 1979 Raustein. Lvs 5″ x 2″; fls 3″ wide, fragrant, pink, throat faintly yellow, up to 15 per truss.

Patricia

Rating 3/3
Hardy to 5°F
Dwarf
Late May

(selected seedling of *campylogynum* var. *charopeum*), 1960, Caperci. Lvs typical of species, fls magenta purple.

Patty Bee

Rating
Hardy to 15°F
Dwarf
Mid-April

(*keiskei* Yaku Fairy x *fletcherianum*), 1978, Berg. Lvs 1¼″ x ½″; fls 2″ wide, yellow, up to 6 per truss.

Paul Detlefsen

(May Day x *haematodes*), 1967, Seabrook.

Paul Lincke

(Glamour x *strigillosum*), 1965, Seabrook.

Peach Lady

Rating 3/3
Hardy to −5°F
Low
Late May

(Neried x *discolor*), 1958, seed Rose (England), intrd Lancaster. Lvs 6″ x 1½″; fls 4″ wide, peach, edged rose, yellow eye, up to 12 per rounded truss.

Peach Loderi

(Apricot #3 x Loderi King George), 1965, Wyrens. Lvs 6″ x 2½″; fls 4½″ wide, pink spotted maroon in throat, up to 11 per flat truss.

Peachblow

(parentage unknown), 1958, Barto, intrd Wright Sr. and Jr.

Peeping Tom

Rating 4/3
Hardy to 0°F
Low
May

(*wardii* x Mrs. Furnival), 1965, Wright, Sr. and Jr. Lvs 3" x 1½"; fls 2½" wide, white with dark purple blotch, up to 12 per compact truss.

Peking

Rating
Hardy to −15°F
Medium
Mid-May

((*catawbiense* var. *album* x Hawk) x (LaBar's White x Crest)), 1973, Leach. Lvs 4" x 1¾"; fls 2½" wide, brilliant greenish yellow with dark red blotch and spots, up to 15 per truss.

Pele

(Glory of Keston x Mandalay), 1965, Brandt.

Penny

(Sarita Loder x Idealist), 1958, James.

Pennywise

Rating
Hardy to −5°F
Low
Mid-May

(Mars x *yakushimanum* Koichiro Wada), 1977, Reese. Lvs 4¾" x 2¼"; fls 2" wide, carmine rose, up to 17 per ball truss.

Peppermint Stick, CA 1974

Rating
Hardy to 0°F
Semi-dwarf
Late May

(Moser's Maroon x *yakushimanum*), 1973, Lancaster, intrd McGuire. Lvs 6" x 1¼"; fls 2½" wide, white star-shaped center with red edges, yellow brown spots, up to 21 per truss.

Pepperpot

Rating
Hardy to 15°F
Semi-dwarf
Late April

(Goldbug x unnamed orange Lem hybrid), 1978, J. Elliott. Lvs 3" x 1½"; fls 1½" wide, yellow heavily spotted red inside, some outside, up to 10 per lax truss.

Pera

Rating 3/3
Hardy to −5°F
Dwarf
April

grex also
(*pemakoense* x *racemosum*), 1958, Lem. Lvs small, plant twiggy, fls 1½" wide, lilac pink, up to 6 per truss. Heavy bloomer.

Peter Koster

see Koster's Choice

Phyllis Ballard, PA 1956
(*discolor* x (*neriiflorum* x *dichroanthum*)), 1958, Ostbo.

Pickering
Rating
Hardy to −5°F
Medium
Mid-May

(Catalgla x (*fortunei* x *campylocarpum*)), 1967, Herbert. Lvs 5″ x 2″; fls 3″ wide, cream flushed pink, yellow throat, up to 10 per truss.

Pieces of Eight
Rating
Hardy to 0°F
Medium
Early May

(Virginia Richards x unknown), 1977, Kersey, intrd Frederick, Jr. Lvs 5″ x 2½″; fls 4½″ wide, 7 lobes, fragrant, pale yellow with pale orange spotting on 3 dorsal lobes, up to 10 per truss.

Pieces of Gold
Rating
Hardy to 0°F
Semi-dwarf
Early May

(parentage unknown), 1978, Frederick, Jr. Lvs 7″ x 2¾″; fls 4″ wide, 7 lobes, fragrant, cream, throat chartreuse, brownish spotting on dorsal lobe, up to 10 per ball truss.

Pikeland
Rating
Hardy to −5°F
Dwarf
Mid-April

(*keiskei* x *campylogynum*), 1976, Herbert. Lvs 2¼″ x ¾″; fls 1¼″ wide, pink with darker spotting and edging, terminal inflorescence of 6 buds, each up to 7 fls.

Pink Cameo
Rating 3/3
Hardy to −20°F
Medium
Late May

(Boule de Neige x red *catawbiense* seedling), 1958, Shammarello. Lvs 4½″ x 1½″; fls 2½″ wide, clear pink with pinkish yellow blotch, compact truss.

Pink Chiffon
Rating 3/3
Hardy to −5°F
Tall
Mid-May

(selected seedling of *fortunei*, Rock seed), 1967, Hansen. Lvs and fls typical of species, fls very good pink.

Pink Cloud
Rating
Hardy to −10°F
Medium
Early May

(parentage unknown), 1976, Whitney, intrd Sather. Lvs 4½″ x 2″; fls 3½″ wide, frilled and fragrant, medium pink with dull yellow blotch, up to 16 per ball truss.

Pink Crepe
(Fawn x Lem's Goal), 1972, Childers.

Pink Divinity
(Fawn x Lem's Goal), 1972, Childers.

Pink Flair
Rating 3/3   (Boule de Neige x red *catawbiense* seedling), 1973,
Hardy to −20°F   Shammarello. Lvs 3½" x 1¾"; fls 2½" wide, pastel
Medium   pink with conspicuous red blotch, globular truss.
Late May

Pink Flourish
(*catawbiense* var. *album* x ((*decorum* x *griffithian-um*) x *catawbiense* hybrid)), 1962, Leach. Lvs 5" x 2¼"; fls 3½" wide, pale pink, darker edging and reverse, small yellowish brown blotch, up to 15 per truss.

Pink Frosting
(*catawbiense* var. *album* x *yakushimanum*), 1963, Leach. Lvs 4" x 1¾"; fls 2" wide, pale pink with darker reverse, up to 14 per truss.

Pink Globe
Rating   (*catawbiense*-Gable's red selection x (*griersonian-um* x *fortunei*)), 1973, Nearing. Lvs 6" x 2"; fls 3½"
Hardy to −15°F
Tall   wide, rose pink with small blotch, up to 12 per truss.
Late May

Pink Mermaid, PA 1954
(Azor selfed), 1958, Esch. Lvs 6" x 1¾"; fls 4½" wide, dawn pink, edges and throat deeper, up to 9 per truss.

Pink Panther
Rating   (Unnamed pink selection of *mucronulatum* selfed),
Hardy to −10°F   1977, Egan, intrd Lewis. Lvs typical of species, fls
Tall   2" wide, good rose pink, inflorescence of 5 buds,
Late March   each single fld.

Pink Parasol
Rating   (selected seedling of *yakushimanum*), 1969, Leach.
Hardy to −15°F   Lvs typical of species, fls white from very deep pink
Semi-dwarf   buds.
Early May

Pink Parfait, PA 1961
(parentage unknown), 1962, Senko. Azaleodendron.

Pink Petticoats, CA 1971

Rating 4/4	(Jan Dekens Selfed), 1966, Lofthouse. Lvs 8″ x 2¾″;
Hardy to 0°F	fls 2½″ wide, china rose, frilled picotee edge, up to
Medium	32 in high truss.
Mid-May	

Pink Princess   see Gay Princess

Pink Punch

(Catalgla x *fortunei*), 1972, Yates.

Pink Snowflakes

(*racemosum* x *moupinense*), 1969, Scott.

Pinkie Price

Rating	((Meadowbrook x *fortunei*, or reverse) x sibling of
Hardy to −10°F	same cross), 1973, Phipps. Lvs 4¾″ x 2″; fls 3¾″
Tall	wide, very deep pink shading outward to white, 2
Late May	green blotches, up to 10 per truss.

Pinnacle

Rating 4/3	(pink *catawbiense* seedling x pink *catawbiense*
Hardy to −20°F	seedling), 1958, Shammarello. Lvs 4½″ x 2″; fls 2½″
Medium	wide, pure pink with citron yellow blotch, truss
Late May	conical.

Pinwheel

(parentage unknown), 1964, R. Henny, intrd L. Henny.

Pirouette

(*yakushimanum* Koichiro Wada x Pink Petticoats), 1973, Lofthouse.

Pleasant Dream

Rating	(parentage unknown), 1975, Whitney, intrd Sather.
Hardy to 0°F	Lvs 5½″ x 2″; fls 5″ wide, frilled and fragrant, pink
Tall	with shading of yellow, small orange blotch, up to
Early June	10 per truss.

Pocahontas

(*catawbiense* hybrid), 1958, Parsons. Unknown now.

Point Defiance   Walloper grex

Rating 4/4	(Anna x Marinus Koster), 1970, Lem, intrd Tacoma
Hardy to 0°F	Park Department. Lvs 7¼″ x 3″, mat; fls 4½″ wide,
Tall	fleshy, white, edged initially on all lobes with red,
May	no markings, up to 17 per truss.

Polynesian Sunset

Rating	(parentage unknown), 1976, Whitney, intrd Sather.
Hardy to 0°F	Lvs 5″ x 1½″, with half-twist; fls 4″ wide, 7 lobes,
Medium	orange with spotting, edging and reverse of red, up
Late May	to 12 per lax truss.

Pomo Princess

Rating	(probably *grande* x *arboreum*. Wisley seed), 1978,
Hardy to 15°F	Druecker, intrd German. Lvs 5½″ x 1½″; fls 2¼″
Tall	wide, carmine fading to white in throat, up to 13
Very early	per truss.

Poppinjay

((*maximum* x *catawbiense*) x Jasper), 1972, Leach.

'Taurus'
*Photo by
Cecil Smith*

Portent

(*mucronulatum* x *ciliatum*), 1958, Leach.

Powder Mill Run

Rating	(*yakushimanum* x Mars), 1976, Bagoly, intrd Her-
Hardy to −5°F	bert. Lvs 5½″ x 1¾″; fls 2½″ wide, dark pink shading
Semi-dwarf	to white in throat, up to 24 per ball truss.
Mid-May	

Powell Glass

(natural white variant of *catawbiense*), 1962, Amateis. Origin — Catalgla seed from Gable in 1947. Third generation broke into white, pinks and varying shades of lavender. Fourth generation showed a majority of whites. Powell Glass, the fifth generation, has bloomed all white, can be presumed to be stabilized. As best white to best white has always been crossed, there has been no lessening in the vitality of the plant.

Pow Wow

(Earl of Athlone x Fabia), 1958, R. Henny.

Prairie Gold

Rating   ((Eldorado x *leucaspis*) x Lemon Mist), 1976, Scott.
Hardy to   Lvs 1¼" x ½"; fls 1½" wide, yellow, terminal inflore-
Dwarf   scence of 3 buds, each with 4 fls.
Mid-March

President Kennedy

(*maximum* x Pink Pearl), 1965, Fenicchia.

President Lincoln   synonym Herbert Parsons, Betsy Parsons, Bertha Parsons
(*catawbiense* hybrid), 1958, Parsons.

Pride of Kings

Rating   (A. Bedford x Purple Splendour), 1978, Frederick, Jr.
Hardy to −10°F Lvs 6" x 2¼"; fls 3¾" wide, light purple with purple
Medium   throat and heavy brown dorsal blotch, up to 9 per
Early May   truss.

Prize

Rating 3/2   (Boule de Neige x red *catawbiense* seedling), 1958,
Hardy to −20°F Shammarello. Lvs 4" x 1¾"; fls 2" wide, shrimp pink
Medium   with yellowish brown blotch, truss globular.
Late May

Professor Amateis

(Everestianum x Van Nes Sensation), 1972, Baldsiefen.

Promise of Spring

(*strigillosum* x unknown), 1973, Lofthouse.

Puck

(*racemosum* x *spiciferum*), 1958, Wright Sr. and Jr.

Puget Sound
Rating 4/4   (Loderi King George x Van Nes Sensation), 1958,
Hardy to −5°F   Clark. Lvs 6" x 2½"; fls 5" wide, pink slightly tinged
Tall   lilac, truss large.
Early May

Purple Fake   synonym Fake
                          (selected seedling of *concinnum* var. *pseudoyanth-*
                          inum), 1962, R. Henny. Lvs typical of species, fls
                          2" wide, orchid with crimson spots.

Purple Gem
Rating 3/4   (*carolinianum* x *fastigiatum*), 1958, Hardgrove. Lvs
Hardy to −20°F small; fls small, purplish violet, ball truss.
Dwarf
Mid-April

Purpureum Crispum
                          (*catawbiense* hybrid), 1958, Parsons.

Quala-A-Wa-Loo
Rating   (Else Frye x *johnstoneanum*), 1979, Anderson, intrd
Hardy to 15°F   Braafladt. Lvs 2¾" x 1¼"; fls 3¼" wide, yellow with
Semi-dwarf   red dorsal blotch, up to 5 per truss.
Mid-March

Quasar
Rating   (Wardii x Idealist, ARS seed), 1978, Short. Lvs 4¼"
Hardy to 20°F   x 2¼"; fls 2¾" wide, yellow with dark red throat
Medium   blotch, up to 8 per truss.
Late April

Queen Anne's
Rating   ((*brachycarpum* x *catawbiense*) x unnamed white
Hardy to 0°F   *fortunei* hybrid), 1979, Skinner. Lvs 5½" x 2"; fls
Medium   2½" wide, pale violet fading to clear white, no
Early May   markings, petaloid stamens, up to 13 per truss.

Queen Bee
                          (*dichroanthum* x unknown), 1962, Corbin.

Queen Mab
                          (Corona x *souliei*), 1962, Brandt.

Queen Nefertiti
Rating   (Loderi Venus x Anna), 1978, Beck, rgstrd North.
Hardy to 15°F   Lvs 5¾" x 2¼"; fls 5" wide, pink with darker edging,
Medium   reverse and dorsal spotting, up to 13 per ball truss.
Early May

'Henry Yates'
Photo by
R.L. Ticknor

Quinella

(Britannia x May Day), 1958, R. Henny. Fls geranium red, have appearance of double fl as calyx is as large as fl itself.

Rae Berry

Rating 4/4
Hardy to 5°F
Dwarf
Early May

(selected seedling of *trichostomum*), 1972, Berry, intrd Bovee. Lvs and fls typical of species, but fls deep pink.

Rain of Gold

Rating
Hardy to −10°F
Tall
Early May

(parentage unknown), 1977, Kersey, intrd Frederick, Jr. Lvs 5½" x 2¼"; fls 3½" wide, 8 lobes, fragrant, very pale yellow, chartreuse blotch and spotting, reverse pale peach, no stamens, up to 9 per ball truss.

Rainier Pink

Rating
Hardy to −5°F
Medium
Early June

(parentage unknown), 1977, Jordan. Lvs 6" x 1¾"; fls 4¾" wide, yellow with overlay of neyron rose, small red spots in throat, reverse all pink, up to 9 per flat truss.

Ramapo

Rating 4/4
Hardy to −20°F
Dwarf
April

(*fastigiatum* x *carolinianum*), 1958, Nearing. Lvs 1", nearly circular, frosty blue-gray new growth; fls 1" wide, bright violet pink, abundantly produced.

Ramsey Tinsel

(chance seedling of Chesapeake), 1972, Nearing.

Rangoon
Rating
Hardy to −15°F
Semi-dwarf
April

(Fanfare x Gertrude Schäle), 1973, Leach. Lvs 3¾″ x 1½″; fls 2″ wide, moderate to dark red, up to 8 per truss.

Ravels
Rating
Hardy to −10°F
Low
Late May

(Leah Yates x Pink Twins), 1977, Yates, intrd M. Yates. Lvs 5½″ x 1¾″; fls 3½″ wide, pink, darker veins, yellowish green blotch, up to 12 per truss.

Ray, PA 1956
Rating 3/3
Hardy to 0°F
Medium
Mid-May

(*fortunei* x Idealist), 1958, James. Lvs 5½″ x 2″; fls 4″ wide, pale yellow, up to 12 per lax truss.

Raydel
Rating
Hardy to −10°F
Medium
Mid-April

(Unique x Mrs. W.C. Slocock), 1979, James, intrd Hitchcock. Lvs 4″ x 1¾″; fls 2½″ wide, yellow, throat tinged chartreuse, lobe edges shaded pink, up to 14 per ball truss.

Red Cat
(*catawbiense* hybrid), 1958, Gable.

Red Cloud, PA 1953
Rating 3/3
Hardy to 5°F
Medium
Mid-May

(Tally Ho x Corona), 1958, R. Henny. Lvs 7½″ x 2½″; fls 3½″ wide, claret rose overlaid scarlet within, up to 18 per conical truss.

Red Head
(parentage unknown), 1965, R. Henny.

Red Hot
(Britannia x Elizabeth), 1962, R. Henny.

Red Imp
(selected seedling of *haematodes*), 1962, Bovee.

Red Lion
Rating
Hardy to −10°F
Medium
Early June

(Tally Ho x *catawbiense*-Gable's red selection), 1973, Nearing. Lvs 5″ x 2″; fls 2″ wide, red with few faint spots, up to 10 per truss.

Red Majesty

(*elliottii* x *strigillosum*), 1965, Larson. Lvs 8″ x 2″; fls 3″ wide, currant red heavily spotted.

Red Mill

(Fusilier x Ruddy), 1972, Lyons.

Red Olympia
Rating
Hardy to 10°F
Tall
Mid-May

(Anna x Fusilier), 1975, Lem, dscrbd Pierce. Lvs 7¼″ x 2″; fls 4¼″ wide, cup-shaped, light red spotted black, reverse with darker stripes, up to 16 per truss.

Red Paint
Rating
Hardy to 0°F
Medium
Early April

(((Fabia x *haematodes*) x Earl of Athlone) x Jean Marie Montague), 1974, Goheen, intrd McNew. Lvs 5″ x 1½″; fls 3″ wide, clear bright red, few small spots, up to 14 per ball truss.

Red Pantaloons
Rating
Hardy to 15°F
Dwarf
Mid-April

(Wilbar x *chamaethomsonii* var. *chamaethauma*), 1977, Heller. Lvs 2½″ x 1¼″; fls 2½″ wide, hose-in-hose, red, up to 4 per lax truss.

Red Puff
Rating
Hardy to −15°F
Dwarf
Late May

(Golden Horn x Catanea), 1973, Nearing. Lvs 4″ x 1½″; fls 2″ wide, red speckled deeper, up to 16 per truss. Plant decumbent.

Red Snapper

(Azor x *griersonianum*), 1958, R. Henny.

Red Tape

(Earl of Athlone x Fabia), 1958, R. Henny.

Red Velvet

(Fusilier x *williamsianum*), 1964, Larson.

Red Wax, PA 1958
Rating 3/4
Hardy to 5°F
Semi-dwarf
Mid-May

(*haematodes* x May Day), 1962, R. Henny. Lvs 3″ x 1¼″, heavy indumentum; fls 2¼″ wide, orient red, unspotted, up to 15 per loose truss.

Redberth
Rating   (Mars x *yakushimanum* Koichiro Wada), 1976,
Hardy to −5°F   Reese. Lvs 6″ x 2¼″, variable; fls 3″ wide, red, slight
Semi-dwarf   spotting, up to 20 per truss.
Late May

Redder Yet
Rating   (parentage unknown), 1979, Leach, intrd Pride. Lvs
Hardy to −25°F 4″ x 1¾″; fls 2½″ wide, red with minor brown spot-
Medium   ting, up to 18 per ball truss.
Late May

Reine Long
                 (*taronense* x Else Frye), 1964, Bowman, intrd Long.

Renaissance
                 (Loderi King George x Peter Koster), 1958, Barto,
                 intrd Fogg.

Renhaven, PA 1955
Rating 4/3   (*elliottii* x Umpqua Chief), 1958, James. Lvs 4″ x
Hardy to 0°F   1½″; fls 3″ wide, dark red with slight speckling,
Low   calyx ⅔ length of corolla, truss flat.
Early May

Return to Paradise
Rating   (Sappho x unknown), 1978, Frederick, Jr. Lvs 6″
Hardy to −10°F x 1¾″; fls 3½″ wide, white with much golden tan
Medium   dorsal spotting, up to 16 per truss.
Mid-May

Reve Rose   also grex
Rating 3/3   (Bow Bells x *forrestii* var. *repens*), 1958, Brandt.
Hardy to 0°F   Lvs 1½″ x 1″; fls 1¾″ wide, neyron rose, up to 5
Semi-dwarf   per loose truss. More than one form in cultivation.
April

Rhodoland's Silver Mist
Rating   (selected seedling of *yakushimanum,* wild collected
Hardy to −20°F seed), 1978, Childers. Lvs 4″ x 1¼″; fls 2″ wide,
Semi-dwarf   white with green dorsal spotting, up to 13 per flat
Mid-May   truss.

Riplet, PA 1961 also grex
Rating 4/4   (*forrestii* var. *repens* x Letty Edwards), 1963,
Hardy to 0°F   Lem. Lvs 2½″ x 1½″; fls 4″ wide, crimson fading
Semi-dwarf   to salmon pink, up to 7 per truss. More than one
Mid-May   form in cultivation. Name was meant to be Replet,
                 but Riplet it is, by error. Anna's Riplet very fine.

Robert Allison   synonym Gable's Pink #2
Rating 4/3   (Caroline x *discolor*), 1958, Gable. Lvs large; fls 3½"
Hardy to −10°F wide, scented, pink with golden throat, truss flat.
Medium
Late May

Robert Forsythe
                     (*catawbiense* var. *compactum* x Mars), 1972, Bal-
                     danza.

Robert Huber
Rating   (Everchoice, open pollinated), 1979, Herbert. Lvs
Hardy to −5°F 4½" x 1¾"; fls 2¾" wide, 7 lobes, fragrant, pink with
Medium   darker edging and orange dorsal spotting, up to 14
Mid-May   per truss.

Robert Louis Stevenson
                     (May Day x Jester), 1967, Seabrook.

Robin Leach
                     (*catawbiense* var. *album* x (Adrain Koster x *wil-
                     liamsianum*)), 1972, Leach.

Rochelle
Rating 4/4   (Dorothea x Kettledrum), 1970, Nearing, intrd
Hardy to −10°F Baldsiefen. Lvs 7" x 3"; fls 4" wide, slightly fra-
Low   grant, rose with strawberry blotch, truss perfect.
Late May

Rocket
Rating 3/4   (Cunningham's White x red *catawbiense*), 1958,
Hardy to −15°F Shammarello. Lvs 4" x 1½"; fls 2½" wide, ruffled,
Medium   vivid pink with scarlet blotch, truss conical.
Late May

Rocketfire
                     (Dr. Stocker x Hawk), 1965, R. Henny, intrd L.
                     Henny.

Rococo
Rating 3/4   (Boule de Neige x *fortunei*), 1965, Gable, intrd
Hardy to −25°F Leach. Lvs 4¾" x 1½"; fls 2¼" wide, waved and flut-
Medium   ed, orchid pink edged darker, greenish yellow dorsal
Late April   rays, up to 12 per truss.

Rom
                     (Moser's Maroon x *griersonianum*), 1958, Lancas-
                     ter.

Roma Sun

Rating	(Loderi King George x Ostbo Y3), 1975, Bovee,
Hardy to 0°F	intrd Sorensen and Watson. Lvs 8½" x 3"; fls 4½"
Tall	wide, frilled and fragrant, yellowish pink, lobes
May	edged deep pink, reverse similar but darker, up to
	10 per truss.

Romeo

Rating 3/3	(red *catawbiense* seedling x America), 1972, Sham-
Hardy to −20°F	marello. Lvs 4" x 2"; fls 2½" wide, blood red with
Tall	darker blotch, truss globular.
Late May	

Ronkonkoma

Rating	(Blue Peter x Purple Splendour), 1977, Raustein.
Hardy to −10°F	Lvs 7" x 3" wide, violet with darker edging, dorsal
Semi-dwarf	flare and reverse, up to 22 per ball truss.
Late May	

Rose Elf, PA 1954

Rating 3/4	(*racemosum* x *pemakoense*), 1958, Lancaster. Lvs
Hardy to 0°F	¾" x ½"; fls 1" wide, white flushed bluish pink, in
Dwarf	profusion.
Late April	

Rose Haines

Rating	(*fortunei* hybrid), 1977, English, Jr., intrd Burlin-
Hardy to 0°F	game. Lvs 4½" x 2½"; fls 3" wide, orchid, throat
Medium	flushed sap green, up to 11 per flat truss.
Early May	

Rose Lancaster

Rating	(Tally Ho x *yakushimanum*), 1978, Lancaster,
Hardy to 5°F	rgstrd Goheen. Lvs 5" x 1¾"; fls 3" wide, pink, up
Low	to 30 per ball truss.
Late May	

Rose of China

Rating 3/3	(Tally Ho x *discolor*), 1958, Lem, intrd Lancaster.
Hardy to 0°F	Lvs 7" x 2"; fls 4" wide, clear china rose, up to
Low	12 per truss.
Early June	

Rose Pageant

Rating	(*discolor* x Corona), 1965, R. Henny, intrd L.
Hardy to	Henry. Lvs 9" long, fls 3½" wide, ruffled, neyron
Tall	rose, throat white, up to 12 per truss.
Late June	

Rose Pantaloons
Rating   (Wilbar x *chanaethomsonii* var. *chamaethauma*),
Hardy to 15°F   1977, Heller. Lvs 2″ x 1¼″; fls 2½″ wide, hose-in-
Dwarf   hose, rose, up to 5 per lax truss.
Mid-April

Rose Scott
Rating   (Else Frye x (*johnstoneanum* x *cubittii*)), 1977,
Hardy to   Scott. Lvs 3½″ x 1¼″; fls 4½″ wide, heavy sub-
Low   stance, fragrant, white with patches and flare of
Mid-March   fuchsine pink, up to 7 per flat truss.

Rose Splendour
Rating 4/3   (*griersonianum* x Purple Splendour), 1958, Lancas-
Hardy to 0°F   ter. Lvs. 5″ x 2″; fls 4″ wide, magenta rose with
Low   geranium lake eye, up to 12 per truss.
Late May

Roseann, PA 1956   synonym Tatoosh
Rating 4/4   (Britannia x Loderi Venus), 1958, R. Henny. Lvs
Hardy to 0°F   8½″ x 2½″; fls 4½″ wide, pink spotted crimson on
Tall   upper lobe, frosty appearance, up to 17 per truss.
Mid-May   Tatoosh, a sibling, also registered then apparently
                          abandoned in favor of Roseann.

Rosebud   see Jane Henny

Rosey Ball
Rating   (selected seedling of *rubiginosum*), 1974, Phette-
Hardy to −5°F   place. Lvs typical of species; fls 1½″ wide, deep pur-
Tall   plish pink with dark red spots, inflorescence a ball
Mid-April   up to 30 fls, composed of several trusses each with
                          up to 8 fls.

Roslyn, AE 1973
Rating 4/3   (Purpureum Elegans x Everestianum), 1972, Voss-
Hardy to −10°F   berg. Lvs 5″ x 2¾″; fls 2¼″ wide, frilled, violet pur-
Medium   ple shading to paler center, up to 12 per truss.
Late May

Ross Bigler
Rating   (advanced generation hybrid including *cataw-
Hardy to −15°F   *biense* and *maximum*), 1979, W. Smith. Lvs 4½″
Tall   x 2½″; fls 2½″ wide, deep pink with deeper blotch
May   and edging, up to 19 per ball truss.

Rowland P. Cary

Rating	(*brachycarpum* x Van der Hoop), 1974, Cary. Lvs
Hardy to −20°F	4½″ x 2″; fls 2½″ wide, blush pink with light tan
Tall	blotch of spots, up to 20 per ball truss.
Late May	

Roy Hudson

Rating	(*burmanicum* x *nuttallii*), 1978, Kerrigan. Lvs 3″
Hardy to	x 1½″; fls 3½″ wide, very fragrant, white with yel-
Medium	low throat, terminal inflorescence has multiple
Early April	buds, each up to 8 fls.

Royal Anne

(Azor x (Nereid x *discolor*)), 1962, Greig.

Ruby F. Bowman, PA 1951

Rating 4/4	(*fortunei* x Lady Bligh), 1958, Bowman, intrd
Hardy to −5°F	Druecker. Lvs 7″ x 2″; fls 4½″ wide, tyrian rose
Tall	with ruby red throat, up to 15 per truss.
Early May	

Ruby Hart

Rating	((Carmen x Elizabeth) x *elliottii*), 1976, Whitney,
Hardy to 0°F	intrd Sather. Lvs 2½″ x 1¼″; fls 1½″ wide, red, no
Semi-dwarf	markings, up to 7 per lax truss.
Early May	

Rudolph Friml

(Little Red Riding Hood x unknown), 1965, Seabrook.

Rudolph's Orange

Rating	(Fabia x Temple Belle), 1977, R. Henny, intrd
Hardy to 0°F	Caperci. Lvs 2¾″ x 1″; fls 2″ wide, pale orange with
Low	pink shading inside and outside, up to 6 per lax
Mid-May	truss.

Rudy-Leona

Rating	(Quinella selfed), 1970, R. Henny, intrd L. Henny.
Hardy to	Lvs 6″ x 2¾″; fls 3″ wide, currant red with few
Semi-dwarf	spots, semi-double to double, up to 10 per truss.
May	

Rudy's Candy

Rating 3/3	(Azor x Corona), 1970, R. Henny, intrd L. Henny.
Hardy to 0°F	Lvs 5½″ x 2″; fls 3″ wide, two-tone, deep pink out-
Low	side, up to 17 per truss.
Late May	

Rudy's Fairytale
(Loderi x *arboreum* var. *roseum*), 1972, L. Henny.

Ruth A. Weber
Rating
Hardy to −5°F
Medium
Late May

(Marchioness of Lansdowne x Old Port), 1974, Weber. Lvs 5½" x 1¾"; fls 3¾" wide, violet with light purple spotting, up to 17 per ball truss.

Ruth Davis
Rating
Hardy to −10°F
Semi-dwarf
Early May

(*yakushimanum* x *metternichii*), 1979, Gable, intrd Davis. Lvs 5" x 2"; fls 2¼" wide, white with minor chartreuse blotch, up to 17 per ball truss.

Ruth Hansen
Rating 4/3
Hardy to 0°F
Medium
Late May

(Idealist x China), 1969, Phetteplace. Lvs 6" x 2¾"; fls 4¼" wide, primrose yellow shading lighter outward, up to 13 per truss.

Ruth Lyons, PA 1961
Rating 4/3
Hardy to 0°F
Medium
Early May

(selected seedling of *davidsonianum*), 1962, Barto, intrd Lyons. Lvs typical of species, folded upward sharply from midrib in a V; fls 1¼" wide, very pure bright pink, unmarked, up to 7 per truss.

'Swansdown'   *Photo by Ted VanVeen*

Saint Mary's

Rating	((*brachycarpum* x *catawbiense*) x unnamed *fortun-*
Hardy to 0°F	*ei* hybrid), 1979, Skinner. Lvs 5″ x 2″; fls 3″ wide,
Tall	pale violet becoming pure white, basal flare varying
Early May	from fl to fl, up to 13 per truss.

Sally Fuller

Rating	(Helen Everitt x Dexter's Honeydew), 1978, Fuller.
Hardy to −15°F	Lvs 4½″ x 2¼″; fls 4″ wide, 7 lobes, fragrant, white
Tall	with hint of rose and yellow, up to 7 per truss.
Mid-May	

Samurai

(*occidentale* x Fusilier), 1969, Brandt. Azaleodendron.

Samuel B. Parsons

(*catawbiense* hybrid), 1958, Parsons. Unknown now.

Satin

(Boule de Neige x red *catawbiense* seedling), 1958, Shammarello.

Satin Bouquet

(Ray x Dot), 1972, Childers.

Sausalito, PA 1967

Rating	(*calophytum* x Loderi Venus), 1968, J. Henny, intrd
Hardy to −5°F	Bovee. Lvs 8″ x 2½″; fls 4″ wide, bright pink with
Tall	bright red blotch on upper lobe, up to 14 per truss.
Early April	

Scarlet Blast

(Mars x (Mars x *catawbiense* var. *rubrum*)), 1972, Leach.

Scarlet Glow

Rating 3/2	(red *catawbiense* seedling x red *catawbiense* seed-
Hardy to −15°F	ling), 1972, Shammarello. Lvs 3½″ x 1¾″; fls 2″
Medium	wide, brick red with no trace of magenta, truss con-
Late May	ical.

Scarlet Nymph

(*neriiflorum* x *strigillosum*), 1965, Larson.

Schamenek's Glow

Rating   (*yakushimanum* x *smirnowii*), 1976, Schamenek,
Hardy to −10°F intrd Tietjens. Lvs 5¼″ x 2″; fls 3½″ wide, faint
Semi-dwarf   pink to white, chartreuse blotch, up to 12 per ball
Late May   truss.

Schuylkill

Rating   (probably natural hybrid of *catawbiense* x *de-*
Hardy to −5°F *corum*), 1978, Herbert. Lvs 5¾″ x 2¼″ fls 3¼″ wide,
Semi-dwarf   pink fading to creamy white, deeper pink spotting
Late April   and center stripes, up to 18 per ball truss.

Scintillation, AE 1973

Rating 4/4   (parentage unknown, 1973, Dexter, intrd Vossberg.
Hardy to −10°F Lvs 6″ x 2″; fls 2½″ wide, fragrant, pink shading
Medium   lighter to center, bronze marking in throat, up to
Mid-May   15 per truss.

Sea-Tac

Rating   (Moser's Maroon x *williamsianum*), 1977, Larson.
Hardy to 0°F   Lvs 2½″ x 1¾″; fls 2½″ wide, dark red, up to 7 per
Semi-dwarf   truss.
Early April

Seattle Gold

                       (Diva x Lady Bessborough), 1958, Lem, intrd Mc-
                       Clure.

Seattle Queen

                       ((*lacteum* x Lodauric) x *campylocarpum*), 1958,
                       Lem, intrd McClure.

Seattle Springtime

Rating 3/2   (*leucaspis* x *mucronulatum*), 1958, Mulligan. Lvs
Hardy to 5°F   1¾″ x ¾″; fls 1¼″ wide, white flushed amaranth
Semi-dwarf   rose.
Early April

Senator Charles Sumner

                       (*catawbiense* hybrid), 1958, Parsons, Unknown now.

Senorita

Rating   (Loderi King George x Ostbo Y3), 1962, Bovee. Lvs
Hardy to −5°F 6″ x 2″; fls 4″ wide, ruffled, lavender pink, throat
Medium   yellowish pink spotted yellowish brown, edging red-
Mid-May   dish purple, up to 14 per truss.

Serenata

Rating 4/4	(Russell Harmon x (*dichroanthum* x (*discolor* x
Hardy to	*campylocarpum*))), 1965, Leach. Lvs held obliquely
Medium	at 45° angle; fls 2½″ wide, heavy substance, pale
Late May	orange yellow with strong orange spotted dorsal
	blotch, up to 17 per truss.

Serendipity

(*yakushimanum* x *chrysanthum*), 1972, Potter.

Shaazam

Rating	(Pink Twins x Leah Yates), 1977, Yates, intrd M.
Hardy to −10°F	Yates. Lvs 4½″ x 2″; fls 3¾″ wide, 7 lobes, neyron
Low	rose shading lighter to edges, yellow blotch, up to
Late May	10 per ball truss.

Shah Jehan

(Day Dream x Margaret Dunn), 1966, Brandt.

Shalimar

Rating	(Dexter hybrids, open pollinated), 1974, Vossberg,
Hardy to −5°F	intrd Schlaikjer. Lvs 7½″ x 3″; fls 4½″ wide, 7 lobes,
Medium	slight fragrance, pale orchid pink, up to 12 per ball
Late May	truss.

Shalom, CA 1973

Rating	(Anna x Antoon van Welie), 1974, Lem, intrd Hess.
Hardy to −5°F	Lvs 4¾″ x 1½″; fls 3½″ wide, white shaded rose with
Medium	darker flare, up to 16 per flat truss.
Mid-May	

Shamrock

Rating	(*keiskei*-dwarf form x *hanceanum nanum*), 1978,
Hardy to 5°F	Ticknor. Lvs 1¾″ x ¾″; fls 1½″ wide, pale green,
Dwarf	up to 9 per truss.
Mid-March	

Sham's Candy

Rating	(Pinnacle x Pink Cameo), 1975, Shammarello. Lvs
Hardy to −20°F	4½″ x 1¾″; fls 2¾″ wide, dark pink with yellowish
Medium	green blotch, truss conical.
Late May	

Sham's Juliet

Rating 3/3	(Boule de Neige x red *catawbiense* seedling), 1973,
Hardy to −20°F	Shammarello. Lvs 3½″ x 1¾″; fls 2½″ wide, apple-
Low	blossom pink with brown blotch, truss conical.
Late May	

Sham's Pink
Rating 3/2   (Boule de Neige x red *catawbiense* seedling), 1972,
Hardy to −20°F Shammarello. Lvs 3½″ x 2″, pea-green; fls 2½″ wide,
Low   rose pink, darker at edges, light red blotch, truss
Late May   a ball.

Sham's Ruby
Rating 2/2   (Kettledrum x America), 1958, Shammarello. Lvs
Hardy to −20°F 4½″ x 2¼″; fls 2¼″ wide, blood red, dark red blotch,
Medium   truss conical.
Late May

Shanghai
Rating   ((Mrs. Furnival x *catawbiense* var. *album*) x un-
Hardy to −10°F named seedling), 1973, Leach. Lvs 4¼″ x 1¾″; fls
Tall   3¾″ wide, pale pink, darker margins, bold spotting
Late May   of orange yellow to greenish yellow on dorsal lobe,
                    up to 18 per ball truss.

Sharon, PA 1955
                    (*souliei* x Loderi King George), 1958, James.

Sheila Ann
Rating 3/3   (parentage unknown), 1970, Caperci. Lvs 3″ x 1¼″;
Hardy to 5°F   fls 2″ wide, blackish crimson spotted black on upper
Dwarf   lobe, up to 10 per lax truss.
Late May

Shirley Rose Lent
Rating   (*strigillosum* x *praevernum*), 1977, Nelson, intrd
Hardy to 10°F Heller. Lvs 6″ x 1½″; fls 2¼″ wide, very dark pink
Low   with darker spotting on upper lobe, up to 13 per
Early March   ball truss.

'Lem's Cameo'
Photo by
Cecil Smith

Show Boat

Rating   (*yakushimanum* Exbury x Tumalo), 1975, Phette-
Hardy to —5°F   place. Lvs 4″ x 1¾″; fls 2¾″ wide, white with small
Medium   yellowish green throat blotch, up to 13 per truss.
Early May

Show-Off

(Moonstone x Carolyn Grace), 1964, Wright, Sr.
and Jr. Extinct.

Sierra Sunrise

(Mrs. Horace Fogg x Point Defiance), 1975, Lofthouse.

Sigmund Romberg

(Jasper x May Day), 1965, Seabrook.

Signal

(Moser's Maroon x Tally Ho), 1958, Lancaster.

Signal Horn

Rating   (Atrosanguineum x Goldsworth Yellow), 1973,
Hardy to —15°F   Nearing. Lvs 7″ x 2″; fls 2″ wide, rose pink with
Medium   darker edge, conspicuous spotted red blotch, up to
Mid-May   8 per lax truss.

Sigrid

Rating   (Marinus Koster x Pilgrim), 1977, Laxdall. Lvs 4½″
Hardy to 5°F   x 1½″; fls 3″ wide, pink fading lighter, reverse and
Low   edging deeper, up to 12 per truss.
Early June

Silver Bells

(*caucasicum* x *williamsianum*), 1967, Lancaster.
Lvs 2½″ x 1½″; fls 2½″ wide, bell-shaped, ruffled,
silvery white, up to 7 per truss.

Singapore

Rating   (Fanfare x Gertrude Schäle), 1973, Leach. Lvs 3¾″
Hardy to —15°F   x 1½″; fls 2¼″ wide, red with pearly overlay, up
Semi-dwarf   to 13 per truss.
Early May

Sir Arthur Conan Doyle

(*scyphocalyx* x Jasper), 1967, Seabrook.

Sir James

(probably Dexter hybrid), 1958, Dexter, intrd Gable.

Skipper
Rating 5/3
Hardy to 0°F
Medium
Early May

(Fawn x Indian Penny), 1972, James, intrd Thompson. Lvs 6″ x 2″; fls 5″ wide, empire yellow shading darker to throat, up to 14 per truss.

Skokomish

(*fortunei* x Dr. Dresselhuys), 1958, Parker.

Skyglow
Rating 3/2
Hardy to −5°F
Medium
Early June

synonym Dexter #9
(parentage unknown-Veitch to Farquhar to Dexter), 1978, rgstrd Heritage Plantation. Lvs 4½″ x 2½″; fls 3″ wide, 6 lobes, fragrant, peach with pink edging, pale greenish yellow blotch, up to 12 per flat truss.

Small Wonder
Rating 4/4
Hardy to −15°F
Dwarf
Late April

(Fanfare x (*Prometheus* x *forrestii* var. *repens*)), 1973, Leach. Lvs 3″ x 1¼″; fls 2″ wide, red with small light centers, up to 7 per globular truss.

Snow Bells

(Loder's White x *williamsianum*), 1968, Lancaster.

Snow Bird   see White Bird

Snow Cap
Rating
Hardy to −5°F
Semi-dwarf
Mid-April

(*souliei* x (Loderi White Diamond x *williamsianum*)), 1976, Whitney, intrd Sather. Lvs 3″ x 1¾″; fls 3¼″ wide, 7 lobes, white, no markings, up to 7 per truss.

Snow Crest
Rating
Hardy to −10°F
Tall
Mid-May

(Fawn x Crest), 1978, Childers. Lvs 4¼″ x 1¾″; fls 4″ wide, white slightly tinted rose, small maroon spot, up to 11 per truss.

Snow Lady, PA 1955
Rating 4/4
Hardy to 0°F
Semi-dwarf
March

(*ciliatum* x *leucaspis*), 1958, Lancaster. Lvs 3″ x 1″; fls 2″ wide, white with dark anthers, fragrant, truss lax.

Snow Sprite

(Snow Lady x *moupinense*), 1969, Lancaster.

Snowstorm

(*yakushimanum* x Cary Ann), 1973, Lofthouse.

Sofus Eckrem
Rating
Hardy to 10°F
Medium
Early June

(Marinus Koster x Pilgrim), 1979, Laxdall. Lvs 8" x 2¾"; fls 4½" wide, pink with deeper border, some spotting, up to 11 per truss.

Solitude

(Britannia x Fusilier), 1958, R. Henny.

Spanish Glory

(*elliottii* x Fabia), 1972, Sumner.

Sparkle Plenty

(Pilgrim x Redcap), 1964, R. Henny, intrd L. Henny.

Spatter Paint
Rating
Hardy to 5°F
Tall
Mid-March

(selected seedling of *irroratum*-Rock seed), 1979, C. Smith, rgstrd Kraxberger. Lvs 5½" x 1¾"; fls 2" wide, pale pink with heavy red spotting over entire corolla, up to 13 per flat truss.

Spectra

(*discolor* hybrid), 1962, Ostbo.

Spellbinder
Rating
Hardy to −15°F
Tall
Early April

(Russel Harmon x (*calophytum* x *sutchuenense*)), 1975, Leach. Lvs 9½" x 3"; fls 3½" wide, light lavender pink with red dorsal spotting, darker reverse, up to 16 per ball truss.

Sphinx
Rating 4/3
Hardy to 0°F
Tall
Late May

(parentage unknown), 1965, Luenenschloss. Lvs large; fls 4" wide, deep pink with large dark red blotch on upper lobe, up to 16 per truss.

Spring Dance

(*triflorum* hybrid), 1962, Barto, intrd Bovee.

Spring Frolic

Rating 4/5   (*catawbiense* var. *album* x *yakushimanum* Koi-
Hardy to −25°F   chiro Wada), 1972, Leach. Lvs 4½″ x 2″; fls and
Semi-dwarf   truss as *yakushimanum* but buds deep pink.
Early May

Spring Glory

Rating 4/2   (Cunningham's White x red *catawbiense* seedling),
Hardy to −10°F   1958, Shammarello. Lvs lustrous green; fls rosy
Medium   pink with large crimson blotch.
Early May

Spring Parade

Rating 3/2   (red *catawbiense* seedling x Cunningham's White),
Hardy to −20°F   1962, Shammarello. Lvs 4″ x 1¼″, recurved; fls 2½″
Medium   wide, clear scarlet red, truss globular.
Mid-May

'Dexter's Springtime'   *Photo by Heritage Plantation*

Spring Snow

Rating   (*chrysanthum* x *metternichii* var. *pentamerum*),
Hardy to −5°F   1978, University of Washington Arboretum, intrd
Semi-dwarf   Mulligan. Lvs 2½″ x 1″; fls 2″ wide, white with lilac
Late March   pink on reverse, up to 10 per truss.

Spring Song

                ((*racemosum* x *keiskei*) x *keiskei*), 1958, Hardgrove.

Springfield

Rating 4/3	(Umpqua Chief x Fawn), 1979, James, intrd Greer.
Hardy to 5°F	Lvs 4" x 1¼"; fls 4" wide, orange pink with slight
Medium	vivid red dorsal spotting and ring of red at base
Early May	of throat, up to 11 per flat truss.

Stacia

Rating	(*fortunei* x Everestianum), 1976, Druecker. Lvs 5¾"
Hardy to 15°F	x 2½"; fls 3¼" wide, 6 lobes, fragrant, cobalt violet
Medium	fading toward throat, faint uranium green blotch,
Late May	up to 12 per truss.

Star of Spring

Rating	(parentage unknown), 1979, Hardgrove, intrd
Hardy to −5°F	Royce. Lvs 5" x 2"; fls 3½" wide, 6 lobes, pink fading
Medium	to white, red spotting, up to 13 per truss.
Mid-April	

Star Trek

Rating	(*davidsonianum* Exbury x *davidsonianum* Ruth
Hardy to −15°F	Lyons), 1977, Childers. Lvs typical of species; fls
Medium	orchid with blotch of red spots on dorsal lobe, ter-
Late April	minal inflorescence of 5 buds, each with 4 fls.

Starlet, PA 1963

Rating 4/4	(Diva x *williamsianum*), 1964, Lem, intrd Fawcett.
Hardy to 5°F	Lvs 3" x 1½"; fls 4" wide, rose madder, up to 6 per
Semi-dwarf	loose truss.
Early May	

Starlight

(*carolinianum* x *leucaspis*), 1958, Hardgrove.

Starry Eyed

((*catawbiense* var. *rubrum* x *discolor*) x Azor), 1958, Hardgrove.

Stephanie

Rating	(parentage unknown), 1976, Whitney, intrd Sather.
Hardy to 0°F	Lvs 3" x 1½"; fls 2¾" wide, light red with no blotch
Low	or spotting, up to 9 per truss.
Early May	

Steven Foster

(May Day x *haematodes*), 1967, Seabrook.

Stewart Manville

Rating

Hardy to −15°F

Tall

Mid-May

(advanced generation hybrid including *cataw-biense* and *maximum*), 1979, W. Smith. Lvs 4″ x 1¾″; fls 3″ wide, pink with deep greenish yellow spotting, up to 14 per ball truss.

Stockholm

Rating

Hardy to −20°F

Low

Early May

(Catagla x *decorum*), 1974, seed Hobbie (Germany), intrd Leach. Lvs 3¾″ x 1½″; fls 2¼″ wide, white with 2 small rays of greenish yellow spots on dorsal lobe, up to 14 per ball truss.

Stoplight, PA 1951

Rating 4/2

Hardy to 10°F

Tall

Mid-April

(*griersonianum* x Cornubia), 1958, R. Henny. Lvs 6½″ x 1¾″; fls 3½″ wide, geranium lake faintly blotched, up to 13 per truss.

Sue

Rating 4/4

Hardy to 0°F

Tall

Early May

(Loderi King George selfed), 1958, James. Lvs 7″ x 2½″; fls 5½″ wide, fragrant, unfading deep pink, up to 12 per tall narrow truss.

Sugar Pink

Rating 3/3

Hardy to −5°F

Tall

Early May

(Trude Webster x (Fawn x Queen o' the May)), 1979, Greer. Lvs 7½″ x 3″; fls 5″ wide, cotton candy pink with light brown spotting, up to 12 per high truss.

Sugar Plum

Rating 3/3

Hardy to 0°F

Semi-dwarf

Mid-April

(Moonstone x Carolyn Grace), 1964, Wright, Sr. and Jr. Lvs 2½″ long; fls 3″ wide, deep pink, up to 8 per lax truss.

Summer Rose

Rating

Hardy to −10°F

Medium

Mid-June

(*maximum* x Romany Chai), 1979, Ticknor, intrd Weston Nurseries. Lvs 5″ x 1¾″; fls 2½″ wide, dark rose with dark red dorsal spotting, up to 12 per ball truss.

Summer Scandal

Rating

Hardy to −5°F

Medium

Late May

(parentage unknown), 1977, Kersey, intrd Fred-erick, Jr. Lvs 5½″ x 3¼″; fls 4″ wide, 7 lobes, fra-grant, pink shading darker at edges, throat green-ish, up to 12 per ball truss.

Summer Snow

Rating 4/2 (maximum x (*ungernii* x *auriculatum*))F$_2$, 1 9 7 0 ,
Hardy to Leach. Lvs 9½" x 2¾"; fls 3¾" wide, 6 lobes, white
Medium with small greenish yellow dorsal blotch, up to 11
Late June per truss.

Sun Flame

Rating (King of Jordan x unnamed Whitney hybrid), 1977,
Hardy to −5°F Jordan. Lvs 5½" x 1½"; fls 3½" wide, fragrant, yel-
Semi-dwarf low shading to peach at edges, reverse darker, up
Late May to 13 per open truss.

Sundari

Rating (*augustinii* Tower Court x *tricanthum* Tower
Hardy to −5°F Court), 1977, Short. Lvs 3¼" x 2"; fls 2¼" wide,
Medium violet shading lighter to center, yellowish green
Mid-April throat spotting, up to 12 per ball truss.

Sunset

(Earl of Athlone x Fabia), 1958, R. Henny.

Sunset Yates

Rating (Pink Twins x Leah Yates), 1977, Yates, intrd M.
Hardy to −10°F Yates. Lvs 5¼" x 1¾"; fls 3¼" wide, shades of
Low neyron rose with large red blotch, up to 15 per ball
Late May truss.

Sunspray

Rating (Alice Franklin x Crest), 1979, Swenson, intrd
Hardy to −5°F Greer. Lvs 6" x 2½"; fls 5" wide, 6 lobes, yellow
Tall shading deeper to throat, up to 10 per flat truss.
Late April

Super Jay

Rating (Else Frye x *johnstoneanum*), 1979, Anderson, intrd
Hardy to 15°F Braafladt. Lvs 3½" x 1¾"; fls 3½" wide, white with
Semi-dwarf orange dorsal blotch, up to 5 per truss.
Late March

Swansdown

Rating (Belle Heller x *catawbiense* var. *album*), 1966,
Hardy to Leach. Lvs 5" x 2"; fls 3" wide, white varying occa-
Medium sionally to very pale pink, bold dorsal blotch of
Late May strong yellow spots, up to 20 per pyramidal truss.

Sweet Sixteen

Rating
Hardy to −5°F
Tall
Mid-May

(parentage unknown), 1976, Whitney, intrd Sather. Lvs 6″ x 2¼″; fls 4¾″ wide, orchid pink, darker edging, few spots, up to 12 per ball truss.

Sweetie Pie

(Cowslip x *forrestii* var. *repens*), 1962, James.

Swen

Rating
Hardy to −10°F
Semi-dwarf
Mid-May

(*yakushimanum* x Mars), 1978, Swenson, intrd Childers. Lvs 4½″ x 2″; fls 2¾″ wide, red with white flare, fading but retaining edging, up to 15 per truss.

'Trude Webster'
Photo by
Harold Greer

Sylvia V. Knight

Rating
Hardy to 10°F
Medium
Late April

(J. H. Van Nes x Bow Bells), 1979, Briggs, intrd Knight. Lvs 4¾″ x 2″; fls 3¾″ wide, pink with white flares on each lobe, up to 10 per truss.

Tacoma Maiden
(*ciliatum* x *ciliicalyx*), 1960, Brandt, intrd Fawcett.

Tahiti
Rating
Hardy to
Low
Late May

((*maximum* x *catawbiense*) x (*dichroanthum* x (*discolor* x *campylocarpum*))), 1960, Leach. Lvs 4½" x 2"; fls 3" wide, ivory edged salmon orange, russet blotch on upper lobe, conspicuous calyx.

Taiping
(selected seedling of *triflorum*), 1965, Barto, intrd Hansen.

Talisman
Margaret Dunn grex
(*discolor* x Fabia), 1958, J. Henny.

Tan
(*fortunei* hybrid), 1958, Dexter.

Tanana
Rating
Hardy to −10°F
Semi-dwarf
Mid-March

(*decorum* x *yakushimanum* Exbury), 1978, Childers. Lvs 4" x 1½"; fls 3" wide, 7 lobes, white with yellowish green dorsal spotting, up to 15 per truss.

Tatoosh
see Roseann

Taurus, CA 1979
Rating 4/4
Hardy to −5°F
Medium
Early May

(Jean Marie Montague x *strigillosum*), 1972, Mossman. Lvs 7" x 2¾"; fls 3½" wide, very red with black speckling on upper lobe, up to 16 per truss.

Tecumseh
(*catawbiense* hybrid), 1958, Parsons. Unknown now.

Ted Greig
(*griersonianum* x (*campylocarpum* x *discolor*)), 1965, Greig.

Tell Taylor
(Jean Marie Montague x Carita), 1965, Seabrook.

Tempest
(Fabia x Mars), 1963, Wright, Sr. and Jr.

158

Variety Description and Rating

Terry Herbert
Rating
Hardy to −5°F
Low
Late April

(*carolinianum* x *augustinii*), 1978, Herbert. Lvs 2¾"
x 1¼"; fls 2" wide, orchid, no markings, terminal
inflorescence up to 5 buds, each up to 12 fls.

Tessa Bianca
Rating 4/4
Hardy to −5°F
Semi-dwarf
Early April

(Praecox x *moupinense*), 1965, Brandt. Lvs 1¾" x
1"; fls white flushed pink, yellow in throat, up to
3 per truss.

Thalia

(*ciliatum* x *ciliicalyx*), 1958, Brandt.

The Cardinal   see Kentucky Cardinal

The Chief   synonym Nez Perce Chief
Rating   (Romany Chal x *elliottii*), 1971, Childers. Lvs 8½"
Hardy to 0°F   x 3¼"; fls 3½" wide, oxblood red, up to 16 per truss.
Tall
Late May

The General
Rating 3/4   (red *catawbiense* seedling x red *catawbiense* seed-
Hardy to −20°F   ling), 1958, Shammarello. Lvs dark green, fls crim-
Medium   son with dark red blotch, truss upright.
Late May

Thelma, PA 1958

(*griersonianum* x Armistice Day), 1962, Lem.

Thomas Church

(*forrestii* var. *repens* x *Moonstone*), 1965, Brandt.

Thor   also grex
(Felis x *haematodes*), 1963, Brandt.

Three Star

(parentage unknown), 1958, Gable.

Thumbelina

(May Day selfed), 1965, McMurry.

Tiara

(Golden Jubilee x Loderi King George), 1965, Love.

Tick-Tock

(Jean Marie Montague x *williamsianum*), 1963, Greer.

Tidbit, PA 1957

Rating 3/3
Hardy to 5°F
Low
Early May

(*dichroanthum* x *wardii*), 1958, R. Henny. Lvs 3¼" x 1¼"; fls 2" wide, fleshy, straw yellow with orange red basal blotch, color intensifying, calyx prominent, up to 6 per truss.

Tiffany

Rating
Hardy to −5°F
Semi-dwarf
Early April

(Anna Baldsiefen x *keiskei*), 1972, Baldsiefen. Lvs small; fls small, rosebud like, shrimp pink, heavy bloom.

Tinker Hill

Rating
Hardy to −5°F
Medium
Early May

(*catawbiense* − red selection x Lavender Charm), ARS seed, 1978, Herbert. Lvs 4¼" x 1¾", fls 4" wide, 7 lobes, fragrant, rose with red blotch, up to 13 per ball truss.

Tinkerbell

(May Day selfed), 1965, McMurry.

Tioga

Rating
Hardy to 5°F
Medium
Mid-May

(Jalisco Elect x (Fawn x Sarita Loder)), 1974, James, intrd Joslin. Lvs 4" x 1½"; fls 4" wide, 7 lobes, primrose yellow with few reddish brown spots, up to 8 per lax truss.

Tish

Rating
Hardy to −5°F
Low
Late May

(Beckyann x (*fortunei* − Gable's cream form x Gable's *vernicosum* #1)), 1977, Yates, intrd M. Yates. Lvs 5¾" x 2¾"; fls 3¼" wide, 6 lobes, fragrant, yellow, slightly deeper in throat, no markings, up to 10 per truss.

Toandos Rose   see Double Date

Tod B. Galloway

(Fusilier x Jasper), 1965, Seabrook.

Tokatee, CA 1977

Rating
Hardy to 0°F
Semi-dwarf
Mid-April

(Mars x *williamsianum*), 1975, Lancaster, intrd Grothaus. Lvs 2¼" x 1½"; fls 2¾" wide, dark pink shading lighter in throat, few spots, up to 7 per lax truss.

C.I.S.
Photo by
Cecil Smith

Tolo

(Sarita Loder x (*lacteum* x Mary Swaythling)),
1958, James.

Tom Ethrington

Rating
Hardy to 10°F
Medium
Early April

((Virginia Scott x Alice Franklin) x *yakushimanum*), 1979, Larson. Lvs 5″ x 2″; fls 3¾″ wide, 8 lobes, fragrant, yellow, no spotting or blotch, up to 12 per truss.

Tom Koenig

Rating 3/3
Hardy to
Semi-dwarf
Late April

(*racemosum* x *keiskei*), 1970, Nearing, intrd Koenig. Lvs 2″ x ¾″; fls as *racemosum* but larger, pale pink.

Tomeka

Rating
Hardy to 10°F
Tall
May

((*dichroanthum* x *griersonianum*) x *decorum*), 1979, James, rgstrd Osborn. Lvs 6″ x 1¾″; fls 2¾″ wide, vermillion with orange glow, nectaries, dorsal spotting and veins red, up to 9 per lax truss.

Tony

Rating 3/3
Hardy to −20°F
Medium
Late May

(Boule de Neige x red *catawbiense* seedling), 1958, Shammarello. Lvs 4″ x 1¾″, slightly crinkled; fls 2½″ wide, cherry red, truss conical.

Topaz

Rating	(Loderi King George x Faggetter's Favourite), 1963,
Hardy to	R. Henny. Lvs 7″ x 2½″; fls 3½″ wide, phlox pink
Tall	outside, white inside, up to 10 per truss.
Mid-April	

Touch of Gold

Rating	(parentage unknown), 1978, Frederick, Jr. Lvs 8″
Hardy to −5°F	x 2¾″; fls 4″ wide, fragrant, pale peach with golden
Medium	chartreuse blotch, up to 7 per ball truss.
Mid-May	

Tow Head

Rating 3/5	(*carolinianum* var. *album* x *ludlowi*), 1969, Leach.
Hardy to −15°F	Lvs 1¾″ x 1¼″, scaly on both surfaces; fls 1¼″ wide,
Dwarf	brilliant greenish yellow dotted orange on dorsal
Early May	lobe, up to 5 per truss.

Towhee, PA 1956

Rating 3/3	(C.P. Rafill x (Red Cap x Tally Ho)), 1958, James.
Hardy to 5°F	Lvs 4½″ x 1½″; fls 3″ wide, bright red, up to 10
Low	per truss.
Late May	

Traci Suzanne

Rating	(Blue Peter x Loderi King George), 1977, Kaiser,
Hardy to 5°F	rgstrd Granston. Lvs 6″ x 1¾″; fls 3½″ wide, fra-
Tall	grant, pale orchid with green spotting covering
Early June	most of dorsal lobe, up to 12 per ball truss.

Trail Blazer

Rating	(Mrs. Furnival x Sappho), 1979, Wright, Sr. and Jr.
Hardy to −5°F	Lvs 4½″ x 1¾″; fls 3″ wide, orchid pink shading
Medium	lighter to throat, red dorsal blotch, up to 19 per
Late April	truss.

Tranquility

(Corona x Vulcan), 1958, Wright, Sr. and Jr.

Tressa McMurry

Rating	(*occidentale* x *ponticum*), 1978, McMurry. Azaleo-
Hardy to 15°F	dendron. Lvs 3″ x ½″; fls 1½″ wide, pink with blotch
Semi-dwarf	of sienna spots, up to 18 per truss.
Mid-May	

Trinity

Rating	(Powell Glass selfed x *yakushimanum*), 1979, Pride.
Hardy to −25°F	Lvs 4½″ x 1¾″; fls 2¾″ wide, white with faint green
Semi-dwarf	dorsal spotting, pink on edges, up to 14 per truss.
Late May	

Trude Webster, SPA 1971

Rating 5/4
Hardy to −5°F
Tall
Early May

(Countess of Derby x unknown), 1961, Greer. Lvs 7″ x 3″; fls 5″ wide, rich pink with dark spots on upper lobe, up to 14 per truss.

Trula

Rating
Hardy to 10°F
Medium
Mid-May

(Belvedere x Jasper), 1979, Larson. Lvs 4½″ x 1½″; fls 3″ wide, yellow, green spotting on dorsal lobe, edging and reverse reddish orange, up to 10 per truss.

Trumpeter

Rating 3/3
Hardy to −10°F
Medium
Late May

((red *catawbiense* hybrid x (*griersonianum* x Romany Chai)) x (Mars x *catawbiense* var. *rubrum*)), 1973, Leach. Lvs 4¼″ x 1¾″; fls 2½″ wide, heavy substance, strong red with darker dorsal spotting, up to 15 per truss.

Tumalo, PA 1955

Rating 4/3
Hardy to 0°F
Medium
Early May

(*decorum* x Loderi King George), 1958, James. Lvs 6½″ x 2½″; fls 5″ wide, white suffused green at base, pale chartreuse bud, fragrant, truss loose.

Tutu

Rating
Hardy to
Low
Late May

(Mrs. Lindsay Smith x C.I.S.), 1971, Parker. Lvs 7″ x 3″; fls 4″ wide, buff shading to empire yellow, up to 9 per loose truss.

Twinkles

Rating 3/2
Hardy to 0°F
Low
Mid-April

(*racemosum* x *spiciferum*), 1958, Wright, Sr. and Jr. Lvs small; fls small along stem, light pink, very profuse.

Twins Candy

Rating
Hardy to −5°F
Medium
Early May

(Pink Twins x Cotton Candy), 1978, Herbert. Lvs 5″ x 2½″; fls 4″ wide, 7 lobes, dark pink shading lighter to center, red spotting on upper 2 lobes, up to 18 per ball truss.

Tyee, AE 1960

Rating
Hardy to
Medium
Late May

(Esquire x Idealist), 1962, James. Lvs 4″ x 1½″; fls 4″ wide, primrose, uranium green throat, up to 11 per lax truss.

Umpqua Chief

(Fabia x Azor), 1958, James.

Vallerie Kay

Rating   (*yakushimanum* x Leo), 1974, Freimann. Lvs 5½″
Hardy to 0°F   x 2″; fls 3″ wide, carmine fading lighter, up to 20
Semi-dwarf   per ball truss.
Mid-May

Valley Creek

Rating   (Essex Scarlet x *fortunei*), 1976, Gable, intrd Her-
Hardy to −5°F   bert. Lvs 6¾″ x 2½″; fls 3½″ wide, 7 lobes, slightly
Tall   scented, deep rose pink, scarlet blotch in throat,
Mid-May   up to 10 per truss.

Valley Forge

Rating   (Atrosanguineum x (*fortunei* x *williamsianum*)),
Hardy to −5°F   1976, Herbert. Lvs 5″ x 2″; fls 2½″ wide, deep rose,
Tall   dark blotch in throat, up to 18 per truss.
Late May

Vampire, PA 1951

(Britannia x Fabia), 1958, Wright, Sr. and Jr. Extinct.

Van

Rating 3/3   (*griersonianum* x Countess of Derby), 1979, Van
Hardy to −5°F   Veen, Sr., rgstrd Greer. Lvs 4″ x 1¾″; fls 4½″ wide,
Medium   deep rose with red spotting on dorsal lobe, up to
Late May   15 per truss.

Van Veen

Rating 3/2   (*griersonianum* x Pygmalion), 1956, Van Veen, Sr.
Hardy to −5°F   Lvs 5″ x 2″; fls 3″ wide, dark red, up to 7 per round-
Tall   ed truss.
Late May

Veesprite

Rating   (*impeditum* x *racemosum*), 1968, Forster. Lvs ¾″
Hardy to −10°F x ½″; fls ¾″ wide, persian rose, terminal clusters
Dwarf   of 5 fls.
Late April

Velma Rozetta

((Azor x *griersonianum*) x Pink Beauty), 1958,
Whitney.

Vera Elliott

Rating
Hardy to 0°F
Tall
Mid-May

(Virginia Richards x *fortunei*), 1977, W. Elliott. Lvs 6″ x 2½″; fls 4½″ wide, 7 lobes, rose with slight orange red spotting on upper 3 lobes, up to 10 per lax truss.

Vera Hawkins

Rating
Hardy to
Tall
Mid-May

(Albatross x Fabia), 1964, Larson. Lvs 6″ x 2″; fls 4″ wide, porcelain rose veined and netted a deeper shade, dotted with deep orange, thin overlay or pale yellow, up to 12 per truss.

Verna Carter

Rating
Hardy to 0°F
Semi-dwarf
Mid-May

(*yakushimanum* x Leo), 1974, Freimann. Lvs 4″ x 1½″; fls 2″ wide, frilled and fragrant, pink buds opening to white, up to 12 per ball truss.

Verna Phetteplace

Rating
Hardy to −5°F
Medium
Mid-May

(Lady Bessborough x *yakushimanum* Exbury), 1975, Phetteplace. Lvs 5¼″ x 2″; fls 3½″ wide, ivory with pink shading, pink reverse diffusing through, small vivid red blotch, up to 15 per ball truss.

Vernus

Rating 3/3
Hardy to −25°F
Medium
March

(Cunningham's White x red *catawbiense* hybrid), 1962, Shammarello, intrd Leach. Lvs 5″ x 1¾″; fls 2″ wide, pale pink, follows *mucronulatum* quickly.

Veronica Milner

(*campylocarpum* x Little Ben), 1962, Greig.

Vesper Bells

(*williamsianum* x *albertsenianum*), 1967, Lancaster.

Vestale

(*catawbiense* var. *album* hybrid), 1958, Leach.

Vicki Reine, CA 1971

Rating
Hardy to
Medium
Mid-May

(parentage unknown), 1963, Clark. Lvs 7½″ x 2″; fls 4½″ wide, deep rose red at edges shading to white throat, up to 12 per truss.

Victor Frederick

Rating
Hardy to 5°F
Tall
May

(parentage unknown), 1974, Lem, intrd Sinclair. Lvs 8″ x 4″; fls 5″ wide, bright red with dark red blotch all around throat, up to 17 per truss.

Victor Herbert

(Mrs. Horace Fogg x *strigillosum*), 1965, Seabrook.

Vida

Rating 3/3   (probably *decorum* hybrid), 1965, Steinmetz, intrd
Hardy to 0°F   Childers. Lvs 6″ x 2½″; fls 4½″ wide, orange yellow
Low   in bud opening deep yellow, unmarked, up to 10
Early May   per loose truss.

Viking Lady

(parentage unknown), 1971, Loeb.

Vinestar

Rating   (*keiskei* x *racemosum*), 1978, Forster. Lvs 2¼″ x
Hardy to −5°F   1¾″; lfs 1¾″ wide, canary yellow with brownish
Semi-dwarf   orange flecking in throat, terminal inflorescence of
Early May   2 buds, each up to 4 fls.

Violet Gose

(*ponticum* x *sutchuenense* var. *giraldii*), 1965, Love.

Virgin

(*catawbiense* var. *album* x *fargesii*), 1958, Abbot.

Virginia Anderson

Rating   (*yakushimanum* Koichiro Wada x Bow Bells), 1975,
Hardy to 0°F   Bovee, intrd Sorensen and Watson. Lvs 3½″ x 1½″;
Semi-dwarf   fls 3″ wide, deep pink fading to white, reverse with
Late May   red striping, up to 20 per truss.

Virginia Leach

Rating   (((*maximum* x *catawbiense*) x (*dichroanthum* x
Hardy to −15°F   (*discolor* x *campylocarpum*))) x (*catawbiense* var.
Semi-dwarf   *album* x *griersonianum*)), 1972, Leach. Lvs 4½″ x
Late May   1¾″; fls 3″ wide, brilliant greenish yellow, rimmed
strong pink, faint blotch of brownish orange spots,
up to 18 per pyramidal truss.

Virginia Richards   also grex

Rating 4/4   ((*wardii* x F.C. Puddle) x Mrs. Betty Robertson),
Hardy to −5°F   1966, Whitney. Lvs 4¼″ x 2¼″; fls 4½″ wide, opening
Tall   pale yellow suffused pink, turning darker, crimson
Early May   blotch, up to 12 per truss. More than one form in
cultivation.

Virginia Scott

(possibly *souliei* hybrid), 1958, Larson.

Virginia Stewart

Rating (Countess of Haddington x *nuttallii*), 1975, Kerri-
Hardy to 25°F gan, intrd Stewart. Lvs 4″ x 2″; fls 3½″ wide, very
Medium fragrant, white, yellow blotch, up to 7 per flat truss.
Late April

Vivacious

Rating (America x Dr. Ross), 1976, Forster, intrd Horticul-
Hardy to −5°F tural Research Institute of Ontario. Lvs 5¾″ x 1¾″;
Semi-dwarf fls 2½″ wide, shaded red, up to 10 per ball truss.
Late May

Voodoo, PA 1952

Rating (Britannia x May Day), 1958, R. Henny. Lvs 4½″
Hardy to x 1½″, margins recurved; fls 2½″ wide, cardinal red,
Medium up to 9 per loose truss.
Mid-May

Vulcan's Bells

(Vulcan's Flame x *williamsianum*), 1967, Lancaster.

Vulcan's Flame

Rating 3/4 (*griersonianum* x Mars), 1958, Lancaster. Lvs 8″
Hardy to −20°F x 2″; fls 3″ wide, cardinal red, up to 15 per truss.
Medium
Early May

Walluski Chief

(*griersonianum* x *macrophyllum*), 1965, Baker. Lvs
7″ x 2″; fls 3″ wide, soft rose red, darker dorsal
spots, up to 15 per truss.

Wally Zeglat

(*fortunei* LuShan x unknown), 1973, Zeglat.

Walter Curtis

Rating (advanced generation hybrid including *maximum*
Hardy to −15°F and *catawbiense*), 1979, W. Smith. Lvs 4½″ x 2½″;
Tall fls 3″ wide, pink with brilliant yellow green spot-
May ting, up to 18 per ball truss.

War Dance

Rating (Mars x Pygmalion), 1979, Hall, intrd Brown. Lvs
Hardy to −10°F 5¼″ x 2″; fls 3¾″ wide, red with black dorsal blotch
Medium and spotting, up to 21 per ball truss.
Mid-May

Warlock

Rating	(Romany Chal x Purple Splendour), 1975, Bledsoe.
Hardy to 0°F	Lvs 5½" x 2¼"; fls 3¾" wide, dark reddish purple
Tall	with heavily embossed black dorsal blotch and
Early June	spotting, up to 14 per flat truss.

Warm Glow

Rating	(*dichroanthum* hybrid x Vida), 1979, Greer. Lvs
Hardy to 0°F	4½" x 1½"; fls 2½" wide, pale orange, throat darker,
Semi-dwarf	slight dark red spotting, reddish orange reverse, up
Mid-May	to 12 per lax truss.

Warm Spring

(Dido x Fawn), 1962, James.

Warpaint, PA 1956

(selected seedling of *elliottii*), 1958, James.

Washington

(no record of this plant), 1958, Lancaster.

Wayne Pink

Rating	(parentage unknown), 1966, Dexter, intrd Knippen-
Hardy to	berg. Lvs 7" x 2½"; fls 3½" wide, spiraea red, up
Tall	to 22 per truss.
Late May	

Weber's Pride

Rating	(Lady Clementine Mitford x Kate Waterer), 1974,
Hardy to −5°F	Weber. Lvs 8" x 2¼"; fls 3¼" wide, rhodamine pur-
Tall	ple with orange blotches on upper 3 lobes, up to
May	17 per truss.

Welshpool

Rating	(*decorum* x *yakushimanum* Koichiro Wada), 1977,
Hardy to −5°F	Reese. Lvs 3¼" x 2½"; fls 2" wide, 6 lobes, fragrant,
Low	white with faint yellow dorsal blotch, up to 10 per
Mid-May	ball truss.

Wendy

(Cornish Cross x *williamsianum*), 1962, Brandt.

Westhaven, CA 1978

Rating	(selected seedling of *aberconwayi*), 1972, McGuire.
Hardy to −5°F	Lvs typical of species; fls 3¼" wide, flat, saucer-
Low	shaped with wavy margins, white with few maroon
Early May	spots on upper lobe, up to 15 per truss.

Weston

Rating   (parentage unknown), 1979, Dexter, selected and
Hardy to −10°F   rgstrd Mezitt. Lvs 4½″ x 1½″; fls 2″ wide, rose with
Medium   golden spotting on dorsal lobe, reverse darker, up
Late May   to 10 per truss.

Wheatley, AE 1973   synonym H. Phipps #2

Rating 4/3   (Westbury x Meadowbrook), 1973, Phipps, intrd
Hardy to −10°F   Voss berg. Lvs 7″ x 3″; fls 3¼″ wide, 6-7 lobes, frilled
Medium   and fragrant, delicate silvery pink shaded deeper
Mid-May   to edge, yellow green rays in throat, up to 16 per
                    ball truss.

Whimsey

Rating 3/3   (*souliei* x Bow Bells), 1958, R. Henny. Lvs 2½″ x
Hardy to 0°F   2″; fls 2¼″ wide, rose shaded to buff, unspotted,
Semi-dwarf   truss lax.
Late April

White Bird   synonym Snow Bird

Rating   (King Tut x *yakushimanum* Koichiro Wada), 1979,
Hardy to −25°F   Pride. Lvs 3¾″ x 1¾″; fls 2¼″ wide, white with faint
Semi-dwarf   green spots, up to 14 per ball truss.
Late May

White Gold

Rating 3/3   (Mrs. J.G. Millais x unknown), 1979, Greer. Lvs 3½″
Hardy to −5°F   x 1½″; fls 3½″ wide, 6 lobes, white with large yellow
Medium   dorsal flare, up to 10 per truss.
Early May

White Gull

Rating   (*yakushimanum* open pollinated, a hybrid), 1979,
Hardy to −5°F   Herbert. Lvs 5″ x 2″; fls 2¾″ wide, white, char-
Semi-dwarf   treuse dorsal spotting, up to 20 per truss.
Mid-May

White Mustang   synonym Debutante

Rating   (*calophytum* x Goldsworth Yellow), 1965, R.
Hardy to   Henny, intrd L. Henny. Lvs 10″ x 3½″; fls 3½″ wide,
Tall   white with dawn pink blotch.
March

White Olympic Lady, PA 1960   see Olympic Lady

White Queen

Rating   (*discolor* x *campylocarpum*), 1967, Herbert. Lvs
Hardy to   6½″ x 3″; fls 4″ wide, heavy substance, 7 lobes,
Medium   white, upper lobes spotted deep chocolate, up to
Late May   10 per truss.

White Rose

(Dr. Stocker x Fabia), 1965, R. Henny, intrd L. Henny. Lvs 7" x 2½"; fls 3" wide, pale yellow bud opening white.

White Velvet

Rating
Hardy to −5°F
Dwarf
Mid-May

(selected seedling of *yakushimanum*-Japanese seed), 1974, Greer, intrd Ward. Lvs 3" x 1½"; fls 2" wide, light pink fading white, tan spots on upper lobe, up to 16 per truss.

White Wedding

Rating
Hardy to
Dwarf
May

(*yakushimanum* Exbury x *makinoi*), 1971, Lofthouse. Lvs heavily indumented; fls 2½" wide, pink fading to white, up to 15 per truss, 3 trusses per terminal.

Whitney's Double Pink   see Double Date

Whitney's Orange

Rating
Hardy to 0°F
Low
Early May

(parentage unknown), 1976, Whitney, intrd Sather. Lvs 5" x 1½" fls 2" wide, pale orange, darker blotch, spotting and edging of red, up to 15 per ball truss.

Willamette

(no details for this plant), 1960, James.

William R. Coe

(fortunei hybrid), 1958, Dexter.

William Montgomery Atrier grex

(Atrosanguineum x *griersonianum*), 1958, Gable.

Win Paul

Rating
Hardy to 0°F
Low
Early May

(*souliei* x Diva), 1971, Larson. Lvs 5" x 2"; fls 3½" wide, pink, lighter center, ball truss.

Windbeam, AE 1972

Rating 4/4
Hardy to −25°F
Low
Late April

(Conestoga hybrid), 1958, Nearing. Lvs 2¾" x 1"; fls 1" wide, apricot, fading to light salmon, very profuse.

Winifred Kenna

(parentage unknown), 1965, Loeb.

Wink, PA 1960

(Loderi x Mrs. Mary Ashley), 1962, R. Henny.

Winterset, CA 1975

Rating   (*mucronulatum* selfed), 1976, Grothaus, selected
Hardy to 10°F   and intrd. Brockenbrough. Lvs typical of species;
Tall   fls 2″ wide, pink with undertone of flesh, up to 5
Late February   per truss.

Witch Doctor

Rating   ((Doncaster x Nereid) x Vulcan), 1974, Lem, intrd
Hardy to 0°F   J. Elliott. Lvs 5″ x 2″; fls 3″ wide, cardinal red heav-
Low   ily spotted dark red on all lobes, up to 6 per flat
Mid-May   truss.

Wizard, AE 1959

Rating 3/2   (*catawbiense* var. *album* x Fabia), 1962, Lem. Lvs
Hardy to −10°F   5″ long; fls 2″ wide, apricot buff, old rose at mar-
Medium   gins, up to 20 per truss.
May

Wyanokie

Rating 3/4   (Conestoga hybrid), 1958, Nearing. Lvs 3″ x ¾″; fls
Hardy to −25°F   small, white, 2″ ball truss, very floriferous.
Low
Early May

Yaku Angel, CA 1975

Rating   (selected seedling of *yakushimanum*), 1976, Allen,
Hardy to −15°F   intrd Greer. Lvs 4″ x ¾″; fls 2″ wide, white with
Semi-dwarf   faint brown dorsal spotting, up to 17 per ball truss.
Early May

Yaku Cream

Rating   (Lackamas Cream x *yakushimanum* Koichiro
Hardy to −10°F   Wada), 1965, Lancaster. Lvs 4″ x 1½″; fls 2″ wide,
Dwarf   mimosa yellow fading to primrose, up to 12 per
Early May   truss.

Yaku Duchess

Rating   (King Tut x *yakushimanum* Koichiro Wada), 1977,
Hardy to −10°F   Shammarello. Lvs 4½″ x 2″; fls 2¼″ wide, deep pink
Semi-dwarf   with light pink blotch, fading lighter, up to 15 per
Late May   ball truss.

Yaku Duke

Rating

Hardy to −10°F

Semi-dwarf

Late May

(King Tut x *yakushimanum* Koichiro Wada), 1977, Shammarello. Lvs 5″ x 1½″; fls 2¼″ wide, deep pink with light pink throat, fading lighter, up to 14 per ball truss.

Yaku Frills

Rating

Hardy to −10°F

Semi-dwarf

Mid-May

(*smirnowii* x *yakushimanum* Koichiro Wada), 1969, Lancaster. Lvs 4½″ x 1¼″; fls 2½″ wide, pink buds opening white, frilled, up to 14 per truss.

Yaku King

Rating

Hardy to −10°F

Semi-dwarf

Late May

(King Tut x *yakushimanum* Koichiro Wada), 1977, Shammarello. Lvs 4½″ x 2″; fls 2¼″ wide, deep pink, light pink blotch, reverse deeper, fading lighter, up to 18 per ball truss.

Yaku Picotee

Rating 4/3

Hardy to −10°F

Semi-dwarf

Mid-May

(Moser's Maroon x *yakushimanum* Koichiro Wada), 1969, Lancaster. Lvs 5″ x 1¾″; fls 2¾″ wide, rose bengal shading to white center, up to 15 per truss.

Yaku Prince

Rating

Hardy to −10°F

Semi-dwarf

Mid-May

(King Tut x *yakushimanum* Koichiro Wada), 1977, Shammarello. Lvs 5″ x 2″; fls 2¼″ wide, pink, lighter blotch, reddish orange spotting, fading lighter, up to 14 per ball truss.

Yaku Princess

Rating

Hardy to −10°F

Semi-dwarf

Mid-May

(King Tut x *yakushimanum* Koichiro Wada), 1977, Shammarello. Lvs 3¾″ x 1½″; fls 2½″ wide, apple-blossom pink with blush blotch and greenish spots, fading lighter, up to 15 per ball truss.

Yaku Queen

Rating

Hardy to −10°F

Semi-dwarf

Late May

(King Tut x *yakushimanum* Koichiro Wada), 1977, Shammarello. Lvs 4½″ x 1½″; fls 2½″ wide, pale pink with faint yellow blotch, reverse strong pink, fading white, up to 16 per ball truss.

Yaku Splendour

Rating

Hardy to −10°F

Dwarf

Mid-May

(Rose Splendour x *yakushimanum* Koichiro Wada), 1968, Lancaster. Lvs 5″ x 1½″; fls 2¾″ wide, phlox pink outside, paler pink inside, up to 18 per truss.

Yaku Sunrise

Rating
Hardy to −10°F
Semi-dwarf
Early May

(Vulcan's Flame x *yakushimanum* Koichiro Wada), 1967, Lancaster. Lvs 3″ x 1½″; fls 2¾″ wide, rose madder, deeper at margins and reverse, up to 10 per truss.

Yaku Warrior

Rating
Hardy to −10°F
Semi-dwarf
Mid-May

(Mars x *yakushimanum* Koichiro Wada), 1967, Lancaster. Lvs 4½″ x 1¾″; fls 2″ wide, tyrian rose shading lighter to throat, up to 18 per truss.

Yates' Albino

Rating
Hardy to −10°F
Semi-dwarf
Late May

(*catawbiense*-red selection x Mars), 1977, Yates, intrd M. Yates. Lvs 5¼″ x 2¼″; fls 2¾″ wide, white with few greenish yellow spots, no pink in bud, up to 11 per lax truss.

Yates' Best

Rating
Hardy to −15°F
Semi-dwarf
Late May

(Mrs. H.R. Yates x *yakushimanum* Koichiro Wada), 1977, Yates, intrd M. Yates. Lvs 4″ x 1¾″; fls 1¾″ wide, pink fading to white with minor yellow spotting, up to 12 per ball truss.

Yates' Hazel

Rating
Hardy to −20°F
Medium
Late May

(Mrs. C.S. Sargent x *vernicosum* #1), 1978, Yates, intrd M. Yates. Lvs 5½″ x 2¾″; fls 3″ wide, 6 lobes, pink with pale yellow throat and greenish yellow spotting, up to 12 per ball truss.

Yates' Purple

Rating
Hardy to −5°F
Semi-dwarf
Late May

(*catawbiense grandiflorum* x Purple Splendour), 1979, Yates, intrd M. Yates. Lvs 5¾″ x 1¾″; fls 2½″ wide, purple with darker blotch and spotting to top of dorsal lobe, up to 13 per truss.

Yates' Red

Rating
Hardy to −5°F
Low
Late May

(Leah Yates x Pink Twins), 1977, Yates, intrd M. Yates. Lvs 5″ x 1½″; fls 3″ wide, cardinal red shading to magenta throat, darker blotch, up to 15 per truss.

Yates' Second Best

Rating
Hardy to −15°F
Semi-dwarf
Mid-May

(Mrs. H.R. Yates x *yakushimanum* Koichiro Wada), 1977, Yates, intrd M. Yates. Lvs 4¾″ x 1¾″; fls 2½″ wide, pink becoming white, yellow dorsal spotting, up to 10 per ball truss.

Yellow Bells

Rating 2/2   (Cunningham's Sulphur x Moonstone), 1967, New-
Hardy to 0°F   kirk, intrd Lancaster. Lvs 2½" x 1½"; fls 1½" wide,
Semi-dwarf   ruffled, chrome yellow, up to 12 per truss.
Late April

Yellow Creek, PA 1958

Rating 4/2   (Idealist x Sarita Loder), 1962, James. Lvs 6" x 1¾";
Hardy to 5°F   fls 4" wide, flat and flaring, primrose yellow, up to
Medium   10 per truss.
Early May

Yellow Jacket

(*croceum* x Fabia), 1958, R. Henny

Yellow Spring

Rating   (*keiskei* x *racemosum*), 1976, Herbert. Lvs 2" x 1";
Hardy to −5°F   fls 1" wide, pink shading to yellowish throat, yellow
Dwarf   green spots, terminal inflorescence of 10 buds, each
Mid-April   up to 5 fls.

Yellow Wolf

(*scyphocalyx* x (*chrysanthum* x (Rubina x Fabia))),
1966, Witt.

Yo-Yo

Rating   (parentage unknown), 1976, Whitney, intrd Sather.
Hardy to −5°F   Lvs 2½" x 1¼"; fls 1¼" wide, red with dull purple
Dwarf   spots on upper lobe, up to 8 per flat truss.
Mid-April

UNREGISTERED AMERICAN HYBRIDS

An * before a name indicates registration is completed, but not yet published in the Quarterly Bulletin of the ARS, or is in the process of completion as of January 1, 1980. Only plants with clonal names are listed, no group of siblings identified only by parentage, such as *impeditum* x *sinogrande*. The list is keyed simply to availability and recognition. In no way is this list offered as complete. Some are in the trade, some soon will be, some will go no further than this list. An NC after the listing denotes the name has been registered for another plant, name is too close to a name already in use, or conflicts with "The international Code of Nomenclature of Cultivated Plants", 1969. Others of these names, even though not so noted, may present problems for registration. Comments, corrections, deletions and additions are solicited by the Registrar, Edwin Parker, American Rhododendron Society, Rt. 5, Box 35, Astoria, Oregon 97103.

*Acclaim, Dexter hybrid
*Accomac, Dexter hybrid
Accomplishment, Dexter hybrid
*Adele's Yellow, Fetterhoff
Adelphia, Dexter hybrid
Agatha, Dexter hybrid synonym Abington
Alandale, Nearing, Gable
*Alice in Wonderland, Dexter hybrid
Alice Poore, Dexter hybrid
Alice Swift, Yavorsky
Alpine Snow, Richards, Spini
Alumni Day, Nearing, Gable
Always Admired, Swarthmore-Tyler
Amber, Knippenberg
*Ambie, Fetterhoff
Anna Caroline Gable, Gable
Anna Lise, Prycl
Anne Glass, Gable synonym which has replaced the registered, but
    erroneous, name 'Mrs. Powell Glass'.
Anne Glass, Wheeldon (NC)
Anne's Pet, Whitney, Sather
Anton Rubinstein, Seabrook
Apple Blossom, Dexter hybrid (NC) (1)
*Aravir, Moynier
*Aromimink, Dexter hybrid
Athens, Leach (NC)

Atkar, Gable grex (NC)
Autumn Splendor, Newberry
*Avondale, Dexter hybrid
Baccalaureate, Gable
Balakyn, Swarthmore
Bali, Leach
Ballet, Pride
Bamboo, Gable synonym Salmon Bamboo (NC)
Barbara Hardgrove, Hardgrove
*Barefield's Best Girl, Barefield
*Barefield's Bridget, Barefield
*Barefield's Granddaughter, Barefield
*Barefield's Liza, Barefield
*Barefield's P. Lee, Barefield
Barnstable, Dexter hybrid
Bass River, Dexter hybrid
Bayberry, Knippenberg (NC)
Beauty of Halesite, Dexter hybrid, Schlaikjer
Bengal, Leach (NC)
Ben Moseley, Dexter hybrid
Bergie, Larson, *ciliatum* selection
Bermuda, Leach
Better Half, Whitney, Sather
Big Red, Stokes (NC)
Biggie, Wildfong (NC)
Bill, Fetterhoff, Pride
*Billy Bear, Fetterhoff
Bittersweet, Knippenberg (NC)
Black Sport, Nelson
Blazen Sun, Leach, Pride synonym Sunburst
Blondie, Leach, Pride
Blueblood, Knippenberg
Blushing Bride, Herbert
Bobbie's Butter, Murcott
Bonita, Whitney, Sather
Bonnie, Gable
Bosutch, Gable
Bosutch, Pink, Gable
Brachdis, Gable grex (NC)
Bramax, Gable grex (NC)
Brenda Yates, Yates
Brewster, Dexter hybrid
Bridal Bouquet, Whitney, Sather (NC)
Bridgeport, Larson
Bright Prospect, Swarthmore-Tyler
Bronze Wings, Stokes
Brookville, Vossberg

Bryantville, Dexter hybrid
Burnaby Sunset, Brandt
Buttercup, Knippenberg (NC)
Butterscotch, Knippenberg (NC)
Cabaret, Whitney, Sather
*Calavar, Moynier
Camay, G. Clarke
Candleglow, Knippenberg (NC)
Candlelight, Knippenberg (NC)
Candy Stripe, Whitney, Sather
Capri, Leach (NC)
*Cardiff, Reese
Carolina Rose, Knippenberg Azaleodendron
Carol's Super White, Gable
Carrie Jacobs Bond, Seabrook
Carved Ivory, Knippenberg
*Cary's Cream, Cary
*Cary's Yellow, Cary
Cathy Jo, Disney
C.E. Moyer, Moyer Azaleodendron (NC)
Ceylon, Leach
Cha-Cha-Cha, Whitney, Sather
Chalfont, Dexter hybrid
Chappeau, Disney
Charles Robinson, Pride
Chatham, Dexter hybrid
Cherry Red, Dexter hybrid
Chief's Daughter, Stokes
China Moon, Eichelser
Christina, Delp (NC)
*Circus, Grothaus
Clearbrook, Dexter hybrid
*Clipsie, Moynier
Cloud Twelve, Pride
Clover Coe, Dexter hybrid
Comet, Skonieczny
Congo, Leach
Consolini's Pink Fortunei, a hybrid, Consolini (NC)
Constance, Knippenberg
Constellation, G. Clarke (NC)
Copper Cream, Hardgrove
Copper Sun, G. Clarke
Copperside, Knippenberg
Coral, Knippenberg (NC)
Corky, G. Clarke
Count Vitetti, Dexter hybrid
County Fair, Lem

County of York, Gable AE, 1960 synonym which has replaced the
   registered name 'Catalode'.
Courage, Whitney, Sather
Cranberry, Knippenberg (NC)
Cream Puff, Whitney, Sather (NC)
Cream Trumpet, Herbert
Crepe Myrtle, Knippenberg (NC)
Crete, Leach
Cricket, J. Elliott
Crimson Glory, Cottage Gardens (NC)
Crossroads, Larson
Crowning Touch, Swarthmore
Crushed Velvet, Wildfong
*Crystal Springs, Crystal Springs Garden, Kraxberger
Cup o' Gold, Whitney, Philp
Cutalosa, Dexter hybrid
Cyprus, Leach
Dainty Cloud, Swarthmore
Dainty Sue, Wildfong
Dandy, Whitney, Sather
Dark Eyes, Whitney, Sather (NC)
Dark Red #1, Robinson (NC)
Dark Shadows, G. Clarke
*Dean Hall, Hall
Debra Lynn, Tuomala
Decatros, Gable grex (NC)
Delayed Event, Swarthmore
Delayed Surprise, Swarthmore
Delicate Splendor, Dexter hybrid
Delkyn, Swarthmore-Tyler
DeWilde's Yellow, Gable
Dexter's Amethyst, Dexter hybrid
Dexter's Champagne, Dexter hybrid
Dexter's Harlequin, Dexter hybrid synonym Arlequin
Dexter's Honeydew, Dexter hybrid
Dexter's Orchid, Dexter hybrid
Dexter's Pink, Dexter hybrid (NC) (2)
Dexter's Pink Satin, Dexter hybrid
Dexter's Purple, Dexter hybrid
Dexter's Ramona, Dexter hybrid
Dexter's Red, Dexter hybrid
Dexter's Red Velvet, Dexter hybrid
Dexter's Ruby Heart, Dexter hybrid, Knippenberg
Dexter's Salmon, Dexter hybrid
Dexter's Zanzibar, Dexter hybrid
Dilemma, Consolini
Diploma, Gable

Doc Tolstead, Prycl (NC)
Doctor Bruce Bradley, Pride
Doctor Joseph Rock, Gable
Doctor Lewis Santini, Pride
Doctor Richard Meriam, Pride
Doctor William Fleming, Pride
Don Pablo, Wildfong
Don Perigon, Heyderhoff grex (NC)
Dorothy Macklin, Hancock
Dorothy Russell, Dexter hybrid, Schwoebel
Dot's Cherry Jubilee, Dexter hybrid
Dr. Bess, Gable (NC)
Double Dip, Gable
Double Winner, Larson
DuPont's Apricot, Gable
Dutch Master, Newberry
Early Accent, Consolini
Eastham, Dexter hybrid
Edgemont, Dexter hybrid
Eighteenth of May, G. Clarke
*Eileen Hall, Hall
Elegance, Sumner
Eliza Ann, Yates
Elizabeth Poore, Dexter hybrid
Eminent, Swarthmore-Tyler (NC)
Emissary, Dexter hybrid
Enchantment, Whitney, Sather
Enigma, Consolini
Esther Wood, Whitney, Sather
Eugene, Greer
Evening Sky, Hancock
Everitt's Coral Bell, Everitt synonym Evcore
Everitt Miller, Dexter hybrid
Fabulous, Whitney, Sather
Fairhaven, Dexter hybrid
Fairmont Lodge, Swarthmore
Fairmont Pride, Swarthmore
Falcon, G. Clarke
Falling Snow, Pride
Fascination, Whitney, Sather
Felix Mendelsohn, Seabrook
*Festive Feast, Dexter hybrid
Fiji, Leach
Firepink, Knippenberg
*Flamenco, Leach
Flaming Snow, Dexter hybrid
*Flicker, James

*Flirt, J. Elliott
Folcroft, Swarthmore
Fordham, Dexter hybrid
Forest Border, Swarthmore
Forestdale, Dexter hybrid
Fort Bragg Fire Bell, Tuomala
Fort Bragg Glow, Druecker
Fort Nisqually, R. Clark grex (NC)
Fort Stevens, Parker
Foxfire, Foster
Frazzles, Gable
Freckles, Gable
Freckles, Whitney
Friday Surprise, G. Clarke
Fritz, Pride
Frontier, Swarthmore (NC)
Gable's Blackie, Gable
Gable's Blue Jay, Gable
Gable's Flamingo, Gable
Gable's Pioneer, Gable
Gable's Red Head, Gable synonym Atrier #10
Gable's Rennaissance, Gable
Gable's Tom Thumb, Gable
Gable's White Lily, Gable
Gay Nineties, Whitney, Sather
Gaywink, Winkler
George Fraser, Gable
George Watling, Greig
Georgeanne, Whitney, Sather
Giant Jack, Pride
Gibbon, Reese
Glenda Farrell, Dexter hybrid
Glenolden, Dexter hybrid
Glorious Lady, Lem
Glory Be, R. Clark
Glowlight, Hardgrove
Gogetter, Lem
Golfer, Caperci
Golden Boy, Wildfong
Golden Crest, Whitney
Golden Glow, Wildfong (NC)
Good Hope, Leach
Gorgeous, Whitney, Sather
Grand Teton, G. Clarke
Great Day, Pride
Great Eastern, Dexter hybrid
Gretsel, Lem

Haag's Choice, Gable
Haag's Yellow Fortunei, a hybrid, Haag (NC)
Halesite, Dexter hybrid
Half and Half, Whitney, Sather
Halolight, Hardgrove
Hansel, Lem
Hardy Splendor, Shapiro
Harrisville, Delp grex (NC)
Harry Madison, Nelson CA 1975
Harwich, Dexter hybrid
Hatchville, Dexter hybrid
Heart of Gold, G. Clarke
Heatherwood, Swarthmore
Heavenly Scent, Whitney, Sather
Heidi, James
Helen Louise, P. Saunders CA 1972
Helen Mangan, Whitney
Henry Coe, Dexter hybrid
*Henry's Red, Mezitt
Herbert's Find, Gable
Herbert's Fortunei, a hybrid, Herbert (NC)
Hereford, Reese
Hiawatha, Stokes (NC)
High Esteem, Swarthmore-Tyler
High Gold, Eichelser
High Hope, Swarthmore
High Regard, Swarthmore
High Tower, Newberry
Hi-Ho, G. Clarke
Hillcrest, Briggs
H.M.S. Pinafore, G. Clarke
Ho Kusi, G. Clarke
Holy Moses, Lem
Hong Kong, Leach
Hopewell, Gable
Horizon, R. Henny
Humbug, Wildfong
Hunting Hill, Dexter hybrid
Huntington, Dexter hybrid
Hyak, Whitney
Imperial, Greer
Imperial Yellow, Whitney
Irresistible, Swarthmore-Tyler
Irving Berlin, Seabrok
Isabel Gable, Gable
Ivory Cloud, Knippenberg
Jackpot, Knippenberg

Java, Leach
Jawane, Newberry
Jean Baptiste Reboul, Hardgrove
Jenny, Delp
*Jenny Lind, Seabrook, Jarvis
Joe Brooks, Yelton
*John C. White, Ring, Goodrich
John McLaren, Walther
John Q., G. Clarke (NC)
*Johnny Bender, Seabrook, Eichelser
*Josephine V. Cary, Cary
Josie Nelson, Nelson
Joyous, Swarthmore-Tyler
*Judy Spillane, Swarthmore-Tyler, Wister
July Appreciation, Swarthmore-Tyler
July Delight, Swarthmore-Tyler
July Expectation, Swarthmore
July Holiday, Swarthmore
July Hope, Swarthmore-Tyler
July Morn, Swarthmore-Tyler
July Possibility, Swarthmore-Tyler
July Reward, Swarthmore-Tyler
*Junco, James
June Achievement, Swarthmore
June Champion, Swarthmore
June Day, Swarthmore
June Fire, Wister
June Magic, Swarthmore
June Maid, Swarthmore
June Melody, Swarthmore
June Miss, Swarthmore
June Rhapsody, Hardgrove
June Rose, Knippenberg
Karol, G. Clarke
Katherine Slater, Dexter hybrid, Mezitt
Kay Kay, Swarthmore-Tyler
Kelley, Dexter hybrid
Kenya Queen, G. Clarke
*King's Dome, Lem, Barefield
Kingswood, Dexter hybrid
Kirklyn, Swarthmore
Knee High, Knippenberg
KSW, Lem (NC)
Lady Decora, Dexter hybrid
Lady Laura, James
Lady of Belfield, Dexter hybrid
*Lady of June, Dexter hybrid

Lady of Vernon, Dexter hybrid
Lady of Wakefield, Dexter hybrid
Lahaska, Dexter hybrid
Late Arrival, Swarthmore
Late Beginning, Swarthmore
Late Discovery, Swarthmore
*Laurie, Mezitt
Lavender Lace, Hardgrove
Lavender Queen, Shammarello (NC)
Leeanne Hardgrove, Hardgrove, PA 1962
Lemon Chiffon, Hardgrove
Lemon Custard, J. Elliott
Lemon Ice, Bosley
Lemon Pie, G. Clarke
Lemon Tart, G. Clarke
Lemonade, Eichelser
Lem's Monarch, Lem
Lem's Salmon, Lem
Leschi, R. Clark (NC)
Little Beaver, G. Clarke
Little Beth, G. Clarke
Little Bonnie, Gable
Little Boy Blue, Hancock
Little Flame, Hardgrove
Little Princess, Baldsiefen
Liz Ann, Caperci
*Liza's Yellow, Barefield
Llenroc, Mezitt
*Lois, Greer
Lois K., G. Clarke (NC)
Lola, Skonieczny
Lord Fauntleroy, Brandt, Pierce PA 1967
Lyta Way, Tuomala
Mac Kantrus, Gable
Madah Jean, Newberry
Madison Hill, Dexter hybrid
Malta, Leach
*Mammoth Pink, Barefield
Marcat, Gable grex (NC)
Mariposa, Knippenberg
Marshfield, Dexter hybrid
*Martin's Pride, Wappler, Loucks
Mary Garrison, Gable
Mary K., Gable (NC)
*Mary Kittel, Mezitt
Matilda, Yavorsky (NC)
Maxfield Parrish, Seabrook

Maxhaem Red, Gable
Maxhaem Salmon, Gable
Maxhaem Yellow, Gable
May Moonlight, Dexter hybrid
May White, Hardgrove
Maybell, Knippenberg
Maywood, Knippenberg
Megansett, Dexter hybrid
Melba Elizabeth, G. Clarke
Memories, R. Henny (NC)
Merley Cream, Dexter hybrid
Mighty Mite, G. Clarke
Midway, G. Clarke
Millstream Maiden, Foster
Millstream Red, Foster
Milo, Gable
Minnetonka, Motzkau
Minuet, Baldsiefen
*Mist Maiden, Leach
M.L. Webb, Becales (NC)
Monte Carlo, Leach
Mood Indigo, Brandt
Moon Shot, Gable
Moondrop, Knippenberg
Moonflower, Knippenberg (NC)
Moonlight Bay, Dexter hybrid
Moonlight Serenade, Whitney, Sather
Moonmist, Leach (NC)
*Moonwood, Moynier
Morning Star, Hardgrove
Morocco, Leach (NC)
Mother Greer, Greer
Mount Constance, Whitney, Sather
Mount Joy, Herbert
Mount Misery, Herbert
Mr. Dee, Newberry (NC)
Mr. W.R. Coe, Dexter hybrid (NC) (3)
Mrs. Ensor, Gable, (NC)
Mrs. H.R. Yates, Gable   synonym Caroline Cream
My Choice, R. Henny
Nassau Red, Vossberg
Nearing Pink, Gable
*Nelle Barefield, Barefield
Nelson's Choice, Nelson
Nepal, Leach
Newburyport Beauty, Dexter hybrid
Newburyport Belle, Dexter hybrid

Newburyport Charm, Dexter hybrid
New Hope, Knippenberg (NC)
Nodding Bells, Amateis
Noni C., R. Clark (NC)
*Norlen, Hall
Norma Cleary, Newberry
Northern Lights, Lewis
Nugget, G. Clarke
Oh Johnny, Whitney, Sather
Oh Joy, Dexter hybrid
*Olga, Mezitt
Olive Egan, Egan
O My, R. Henny synonym Pink Jewel
Opal, Stokes
Orange Honey, Pride
Oritani,
Our Choice, Knippenberg
*Oz, Lem, Barefield
Pagoda, Whitney, Sather
Painted Star, Hardgrove
Pam, James
Panama, Leach
Party Dress, G. Clarke
*Patricia Lee, Phetteplace, Sparks
Patty Corbin, Corbin
*Pauline Bralit, Mezitt
Peach Brandy, Swarthmore
Peach Parasol, R. Henny
*Peach Parfait, Leach
Peaches, Gable
Peaches and Cream, Leach, Pride
Peaches and Cream, Yates (NC)
Pearce's American Beauty, Pearce
Pearce's Golden Jubilee, Pearce
Peekaboo, Whitney
Peg Coe, Dexter hybrid
Peppermint Frills, Skonieczny
Perfume, Whitney, Sather
Periwinkle, Stokes (NC)
Persia, Leach
Persimmon, Knippenberg (NC)
Phyllis, Shanklin
Pink Beauty, Herbert
Pink Bonnet, Pride
Pink Delight, Swarthmore
Pink Dove, R. Henny
Pink Floss, Larson

*Pink Fluff, Greer
Pink Fondant, Gable, Pride
Pink Icing, Pride
Pink Mango, Leach, Pride
Pink Pompon, Hancock
Pink Promise, Swarthmore
Pink Queen, Herbert
Pink Sparkler, Dexter hybrid
Pink Symphony, Hardgrove
Pink Tipp, Pride
Pink Touch, Pride
Pink Twins, Gable   synonym Cathaem #4
Pink Walloper, Lem
Pioneer Silvery Pink, Hoogendoorn Nursery (NC)
P.J.M., Mezitt grex (NC)
P.J. Mezitt   This clone of above grex grown and named by
     Windsor Great Park (England) received AM from RHS in 1972.
Plain Pink, Gable
Platinum, Knippenberg
Polar Cap, Winkler (NC)
Potlatch, R. Clark
Powder Puff, Dexter hybrid
Powder Puff, G. Clarke (NC)
Prince Charming, Stokes, (NC)
Prodigal's Return, Nelson
Purest, Mezitt
Pygmey, Skonieczny
Queen of Sheba, Lem
Quiet Quality, Dexter hybrid
Radiant Star, Hardgrove
Radnor, Reese
*Rae's Delight, Berry, Crystal Springs Garden, *degronianum*
     selection
*Raspberry Sherbet, Blyskal
Raspberry Sundae, Yates
Red Brave, Pride
Red Cracker, Pride
Red Eye, Swenson, Greer
Red Flag, Knippenberg
*Red Frilled, Mezitt
Red House, Dexter hybrid, Schwoebel
Red Loderi, Lem (NC)
Red Sox, Gable
Red Velour, Whitney, Sather
Red Walloper, Lem
Red Yard, Dexter hybrid, Schwoebel
Reflection, R. Henny (NC)

Rik, Yavorsky
Ripe Peach, Knippenberg
Robby, Delp
Robert Coe, Dexter hybrid
*Robert Verne, Laxdall
Rocky White, Herbert
Rocklyn, Swarthmore
Roman Candle, Pride
Rona Pink, Dexter hybrid
Rose Pink, Robinson
Rose Point, Lem
Rose Trumpet, Herbert
Rose Walloper, Lem
Rosina, R. Clark
Rosy Dawn, Whitney
Roxanne Hardgrove, Hardgrove
Royal Silk, G. Clarke
Royal Star, Hardgrove
Royalty, Whitney (NC)
Royston Red, Greig
Rudy's Witchery, R. Henny
Running Deer, Gable, Yates
*Russell Harmon, LaBar
Sagamore Bayside, Dexter hybrid
*Sagamore Bridge, Dexter hybrid
Sahara, Leach (NC)
Salmon Beauty, Hardgrove
Salmon Glow, Hardgrove
Sam Baldanza, Pride
*Sasha, Raustein
Scintillation #1, Reiley (NC)
*Scott Hall, Hall
Seamist, R. Henny (NC)
Second Honeymoon, Whitney
Seventy-fifth Avenue, R. Henny
Seville, Leach (NC)
Shady Lady, Hardgrove
Shannon White, Larson
*Shasta, Moynier
Shawme Lake, Dexter hybrid
Sheer Delight, Swarthmore
*Sherill, James
Shooting Star, Hardgrove
Show Time, G. Clarke
Siam, Leach
Silver Ray, Hardgrove
Silver Sheen, Larson
Silverside, Knippenberg

Sir Lancelot, Amateis, Baldsiefen
Skerryvore Monarch, Dexter hybrid
Skylark, Baldsiefen, Gable
Slippery Rock, Delp grex (NC)
Smirhaem, Gable grex (NC)
Smokey Joe, Wildfong
Smokey #9, Lem (NC)
Snow Bunting, Knippenberg (NC)
Snow Shimmer, Swarthmore
Sparkler, Shapiro (NC)
Sparkling Jewel, Swarthmore
Spider, Lem
Splash, Knippenberg
Spring Fire, Wildfong
Spring Song, Hardgrove (NC)
Springfield, Knippenberg (NC)
Springwood Pink, Knippenberg
Springwood White, Knippenberg
Stan Kubas.
Star Sapphire, Hardgrove
Starlight, Hardgrove
Sterling, Knippenberg (NC)
Stony Acres, Herbert
Stony Acres Discolor, a hybrid, Herbert (NC)
Straw Hat, Gable, Yates
*Strawberries and Cream, Cary
Strawberry, Whitney, Sather (NC)
Strawberry Swirl, Gable   synonym Jacksonii #5
Sudan, Leach
Sumatra, Leach
Summer Jewel, Swarthmore
Sun Sheen, Swarthmore
Sunburst, Eichelser (NC)
Sundance, Eichelser (NC)
Sunlit Snow, Swarthmore
Sunset Glow, Whitney
Super Star, Greer (NC)
*Susan Hall, Hall
Sutter's Gold, G. Clarke
*Suzy Bell, Gable, Yates   synonym Tinkerbell
Swamp Beauty, J. Elliott
Sweet Leilani, Brandt
Taffy, Wildfong (NC)
Taku, G. Clarke
Tanniyak, G. Clarke
Teaticket, Dexter hybrid
Temptation, Eichelser (NC)
Terrific, Leach, Pride

Tiger Lily Whitney, Sather (NC)
Timmy Foster, Foster
Tinicum, Dexter hybrid
Toastmaster, Dexter hybrid
Todmorden, Dexter hybrid
Tohicon, Dexter hybrid
Tom Everitt, Dexter hybrid
Tommy, Gable, Yates grex (NC)
Top Dollar, Whitney
Top Hat, Whitney, Sather
Topaz, Knippenberg (NC)
Topps, Knippenberg
Totenham, Mezitt Azaleodendron
Tribute, Pride
Tripoli, Dexter hybrid
Tripoli, Leach (NC)
Tropicana, Whitney, Sather (NC)
Troutrun, Herbert
Truce, Larson (NC)
True Treasure, Dexter hybrid
Tuaq, Wildfong
Tulpehocken, Dexter hybrid
Turkish Delight,
Twilight Time, Whitney, Sather
Unimak, Lem PA 1962
Up Front, Dexter hybrid
Uranus, M. Lyons
Vallya, Mezitt synonym Wally
Virginia Delito, Yavorksy
Virginia Hall, Hardgrove
Walloper, Lem grex (NC)
*Walter Hunnewell, Mezitt
Waltham,Ticknor, Mezitt
Waltz Time, G. Clarke (NC)
Wardian Cream, Nelson CA 1971
*Wareham, Dexter hybrid
Warren, Cribbs
Warwick, Dexter hybrid
Watchung,
Wax Red, Skonieczny (NC)
Waxwing, Lem
Wedding Bouquet, Anderson
Wedding Cake, Shapiro
Weezie, Winkler
Wellfleet, Dexter hybrid
Wendy Lyn, Delp
Westbury, Dexter hybrid
Westdale, Dexter hybrid   synonym Frontier

*Weston's Pink Diamond, Mezitt
*Weston's P.J.M. var. Elite, Mezitt
*Weston's P.J.M. var. Regal, Mezitt
*Weston's P.J.M. var. Victor, Mezitt
Whipped Cream, Leach, Pride
*White Angel, Mezitt
White Cap, Lem PA 1961
White Gem,
White Lily, Ostbo PA 1952
Whiteland, Herbert
Whitney's Snow Goose, Whitney
*Whittenton, Dexter hybrid
*Wianno, Dexter hybrid
*Willard, Dexter hybrid
William Fetterhoff, Fetterhoff, Pride
*William P. Cary, Cary
Willis Diekma, Seabrook
*Winneconnet, Dexter hybrid
Wisp of Glory, G. Clarke
Wissahickon, Dexter hybrid
Wisteria, Knippenberg (NC)
Wonderful One, Whitney, Sather
Woodlawn, Mezitt
Woodscolt, Newberry
Wyandanch Pink, Dexter hybrid
Xerox, Dexter hybrid
Yakudedi, G. Clarke
Yatton, Reese
*Years of Peace, Mezitt
Yellow Bud, Whitney
Yellow Discolor, a hybrid, Case (NC)
Yellow Jack, Knippenberg
Yellow Rolls Royce, G. Clarke
Yellow Sunbeam, Yates
Yellow Wing, Whitney
Yellowthroat, Gable
Yelton's Choice, Gable   synonym Dr. Yelton
Yukon, Leach
Zest, Dexter hybrid

(1) This clone may not be registered because of prior use of the name and is a different clone from the registered 'Dexter's Appleblossom'. As it is widely distributed the name may not be changed for registration.

(2) There is also a Dexter azalea by this name registered in "The International Rhododendron Register", 1958.

(3) This is a different plant from the registered 'William R. Coe'; the name may not be registered because it contradicts the Code.

AMERICAN HYBRIDIZERS

* before the name indicates a hybridizer who does not appear in
the list of Registered Hybrids.

Abbot, Frank L.; Saxton's River, Vermont
Allen, Ernest; Eugene, Oregon
Amateis, Edmond; Brewster, New York
*Anderson, E.T.; Longview, Washington
Anderson, M.D., Richard; Eureka, California
Bacher, John; Portland, Oregon (deceased)
Bagoly, Lewis; Strafford, Pennsylvania
Baker, George; Astoria, Oregon (deceased)
Baldanza, Samuel; Benton Harbor, Michigan (deceased)
Baldsiefen, Warren; Bellvale, New York (deceased)
Barefield, Grady E.; Seattle, Washington (deceased)
Barto, James; Eugene, Oregon (deceased)
Becales, Joseph; Glen Mills, Pennsylvania
Beck, Mrs. Howard; Edmunds, Washington
Berg, Warren; Kent, Washington
Berry, Mrs. A.C.U.; Portland, Oregon (deceased)
Beury, James; Margate, New Jersey
Bledsoe, M.D., D.; Snohomish, Washington (deceased)
*Blyskal, Walter J.; Spring Valley, New York
Bosley, Paul; Mentor, Ohio
Bovee, Robert; Portland, Oregon (deceased)
Bowers, Clement Gray; Binghampton, New York (deceased)
Bowman, Paul; Fort Bragg, California
Braafladt, M.D., J.H.; Eureka, California
Brandt, Lester; Tacoma, Washington (deceased)
Briggs, Bruce; Olympia, Washington
Brockenbrough, M.D., Edwin C.; Bellevue, Washington
Brydon, Jock; Salem, Oregon
Caperci, James; Seattle, Washington
*Case, L.C.; Winchester, Massachusetts
Childers, Arthur; Vida, Oregon
Clark, Roy W.; Olympia, Washington
*Clarke, George; Portland, Oregon
Consolini, Anthony; Sandwich, Massachusetts (deceased)
Coplen, M.G.; Rockville, Maryland (deceased)
Corbin, William; Portland, Oregon
Core, William; Silvercreek, Washington
Cottage Gardens, Eureka, California (out of business)
Cribbs, M.D., Dalmas; Butler, Pennsylvania

*Delp, Weldon; Harrisville, Pennsylvania
Dexter, Charles, Sandwich, Massachusetts (deceased)
*Disney, John; Tacoma, Washington
Dobbs, Olin O.; Eugene, Oregon
Dosser, Lillie; Centralia, Washington
Druecker, John S.; Fort Bragg, California
Drewry, James; Fort Bragg, California (deceased)
Egan, Ernest K., New Haven, Connecticut
*Eichelser, John; Olympia, Washington
Elliott, James A.; Astoria, Oregon
Elliott, Walter; Shelton, Washington
English, Jr., Carl; Seattle, Washington
Esch, Bernard; Portland, Oregon
Everitt, Samuel; Huntington, L.I., New York
Farquhar Nursery; Barstable, Massachusetts (out of business)
Fawcett, Carl; Tacoma, Washington
Fennichia, Richard A.; Rochester, New York
*Fetterhoff, William; Gibsonia, Pennsylvania
*Foster, Lincoln; Falls Village, Connecticut
Forster, R. Ray; Ontario, Canada
Fraser, George; Vancouver, B.C., Canada (deceased)
Frederick, Jr., Mrs. Halsey; Bryn Mawr, Pennsylvania
Freimann, LaVern; Bellingham, Washington
Frye, Else; Seattle, Washington (deceased)
Fuller, Henry; Easton, Connecticut
Gable, Joseph; Stewartstown, Pennsylvania (deceased)
Gatke, M.D., R.M.; Salem, Oregon (deceased)
Goheen, David; Camas, Washington
Golden, Albert; San Francisco, California
Grace, George; Portland, Oregon (deceased)
Graves, Wilbur; Tacoma, Washington
Greer, Edgar; Eugene, Oregon (deceased) and
Greer, Harold; Eugene, Oregon
Greig, E.J.; Vancouver Island, B.C., Canada (deceased) and
Greig, Mary; Vancouver Island, B.C., Canada
Grothaus, Mrs. Louis; Lake Oswego, Oregon
Guttormsen, W.L.; Canby, Oregon
*Haag, Charles; Brevard, North Carolina and
*Haag, Velma; Brevard, North Carolina
Hall, Maurice E.; Bridgewater, Maine
Hancock, M.L.; Mississauga, Ontario, Canada (deceased)
Hansen, Ruth; Portland, Oregon
Hardgrove, Donald L.; Merrick, L.I., New York (deceased)
Heineman, A.R.; Milton, Washington
Heller, Carl G.; Poulsbo, Washington
Henny, John; Brooks, Oregon
Henny, Rudolph; Brooks, Oregon (deceased) and

Henny, Leona; Brooks, Oregon
Herbert, Charles; Phoenixville, Pennsylvania (deceased)
Hess, Nathaniel; Sands Point, L.I., New York
*Heyderhoff, Henry; Bloomingdale, New Jersey
Hindla, Louis A.; Bohemia, New York
Holden, A. John; Shelton, Washington
Hughes, J. Hollis; Warrior, Alabama
Ihrig, Herbert; Seattle, Washington (deceased)
Irvine, Stanley; Vancouver, B.C., Canada (deceased)
Janeck, Kenneth; Tacoma, Washington
James, Del; Eugene, Oregon (deceased) and
James, Ray; Eugene, Oregon
Jordan, Bernice I.; Tumwater, Washington
Joslin, W.V.; Coos Bay, Oregon
Kaiser, E.L.; Seattle, Washington
Kehr, August E.; Hendersonville, North Carolina
Kerrigan, Howard; Hayward, California
Kersey, Roy J.; Devon, Pennsylvania
Klupenger, Joseph; Aurora, Oregon
Knippenberg, Mrs. John; Wayne, New Jersey
Kordus, Theodore; Jamesburg, New Jersey
Krug, Harold; Portland, Oregon
Kruschke, Franz; Clackamas, Oregon (deceased)
Kruse, Ray; Newport, L.I.; New York
LaBar's Nursery, Stroudsburg, Pennsylvania
Lancaster, Benjamin; Camas, Washington (deceased)
Larson, Hjalmer, Tacoma, Washington
Lawton, Lloyd H.; Tiverton, Rhode Island
Laxdall, Sigrid; Bellingham, Washington
Leach, David; North Madison, Ohio
Lem, Halfdan; Seattle, Washington (deceased)
*Lewis, G. David; Colt's Neck, New Jersey
Loeb, Clarence; Puyallup, Washington
Lofthouse, John; Vancouver, B.C., Canada
Love, Melvin V.; Bellevue, Washington
Luenenschloss, Carl; Fair Haven, New Jersey
Lyons, Marshall; Eugene, Oregon (deceased)
Maloney, Francis; Seattle, Washington
Mauritsen, Richard; Kent, Washington
McGuire, Thomas J.; Portland, Oregon
McMurry, Tressa; Bellingham, Washington
McNew, Charles; Kelso, Washington
Mezitt, Edmund V.; Hopkinton, Maine
Mossman, M.D., Frank D.; Vancouver, Washington
*Motzkau, Henry W.; Whitewater, Wisconsin
Moynier, William; Los Angeles, California
Mulligan, Brian O.; Kirkland, Washington

*Murcott, Richard; East Norwich, New York
Nearing, Guy; Ramsey, New Jersey
Nelson, Benjamin; Suquamish, Washington (deceased)
Nelson, Milton R.; Vancouver, Washington
*Newberry, Pauline; Fort Bragg, California, (deceased)
Newkirk, Donald; Camas, Washington
Ostbo, Endre; Seattle, Washington (deceased)
Parker, Edwin; Astoria, Oregon
Parsons, Samuel; Long Island, New York (deceased)
Phetteplace, M.D., Carl; Leaburg, Oregon
Phipps, Howard; Westbury, L.I., New York
Pike, R.B.; Lubec, Maine
Pot, Julian; Chesterfield, Ohio (deceased)
Potter, B.C.; Port Ewen, New York
Pride, Orlando S.; Butler, Pennsylvania
*Prycl, Otto; New Stanton, Pennsylvania
Raustein, Alfred A.; Holbrook, New York
Reese, M.D., W.A.; Pennsburg, Pennsylvania
*Reiley, Harold; Woodsboro, Maryland
*Richards, Charles; Fort Bragg, California
*Ring, George W. III; Fairfax, Virginia
*Robinson, N.W.; Alfred, New York
Schamanek, John; Philadelphia, Pennsylvania (deceased)
Schlaikjer, Mrs. Hugo C.; Halesite, L.I., New York
Schumacher, F.W.; Sandwich, Massachusetts
Scott, Robert; Kensington, California
Seabrook, Cecil S.; Tacoma, Washington
Senko, Joseph; Cornelius, Oregon
Shammarello, A.M.; South Euclid, Ohio
*Shanklin, Robert; Old Lyme, Connecticut
*Shapiro, Benjamin; East Brunswick, New Jersey
Short, Howard A.; Bainbridge Island, Washington
Sifferman, Karl; Seattle, Washington
Skinner, Henry T.; Hendersonville, North Carolina
*Skonieczny, Eugene; Kensington, Connecticut
Slonecker, Howard; Milwaukie, Oregon
Smith, Cecil C.; Aurora, Oregon
Smith, W. David; Spring Grove, Pennsylvania
Stanton, Ernest N.; Grosse Ile, Michigan
Steinmetz, Joseph; Springfield, Oregon
Stephens, J. Freeman; Bellingham, Washington
Stokes, Warren C.; Butler, Pennsylvania (deceased)
Sumner, Maurice H.; San Francisco, California
Swain, George S.; Nova Scotia, Canada
Swenson, Willard; Eugene, Oregon
Thompson, Charles D.; Eugene, Oregon
Ticknor, Robert L.; Canby, Oregon
Tuomala, Carl; Fort Bragg, California

Van Veen, Allen; Portland, Oregon
Van Veen, Sr., Theodore; Portland, Oregon (deceased) and
Van Veen, Jr., Theodore; Portland, Oregon
Vernimb, Bryan; Glen Rock, New Jersey
Vossberg, Paul; Westbury, L.I., New York (deceased)
*Walther, Eric; San Francisco, California (deceased)
*Wappler, Martin; Portland, Oregon
Weber, Edwin O.; Seattle, Washington
Wheeldon, Thomas; Richmond, Virginia (deceased)
Whitney, William E.; Brinnon, Washington
*Wildfong, M.; Mission, B.C., Canada
*Winkler, Walter; Brunswick, Maine
Wister, John C.; Swarthmore, Pennsylvania
Witt, Joseph; Seattle, Washington
Wright, Sr., Arthur; Milwaukie, Oregon (deceased) and
Wright, Jr., Arthur; Canby, Oregon
Wyatt, Vernon; Union, Washington
Wyman, Richard M.; Framingham, Massachusetts
Wyrens, M.D., Rollin G.; Everett, Washington
Wytovich, Edward; Port Carbon, Pennsylvania
Yates, Henry T.; Frostburg, Maryland (deceased)
*Yavorsky, Leon; Freehold, New Jersey
*Yelton, M.D., Ernest; Rutherfordton, North Carolina
Zeglat, W.; British Columbia, Canada

HOW TO SUCCEED IN PRODUCING RHODODENDRON SEED

by Weldon E. Delp
Harrisville, Pennsylvania

All too frequently, during the past 30 years, seed production from rhododendron pollinations made outdoors during the cool spring and early summer weather of Western Pennsylvania has been either poor (few seeds) or non-existent. More recently, on plants pollinated in the greenhouse under high heat and humidity conditions, seed production is much improved. This phenomenon of improved seed production with high temperatures and humidity has been utilized to produce viable seed from hitherto "impossible" crosses, including a number of cold-climate rhododendrons with Malaysians. The more difficult crosses can be made with the use of a special high temperature and humidity cabinet described later in this article.

For a number of years now I have been letting my plants go dormant outside and then bringing them into my cold house in January where hybridizing can be performed under controlled conditions. The temperature is 40°F at the time of entry and each week I raise it by 10° until a 65°F. night temperature is reached. During the daytime hours the temperature reaches a 90°F. high when the sun is shining. The warm temperatures plus supplementary light to lengthen "daylight" hours are ideal to make the buds swell and blooming soon begins. This gives me the advantage of early crossing, while avoiding contamination from outdoor sources since there are no insects present nor any severe wind activity. Air circulation in the cool house is minimal and the chances of accidental pollination are quite low. The controlled temperature and high humidity give ideal conditions for hybridizing and I have been very successful in obtaining large seed capsules containing excellent viable seed. Another advantage of this procedure is that this hybridizing can be done when snow is still on the ground and there is more time available.

The good seed production obtained by following this procedure has also inspired me to experiment further with using heat in hybridizing. After exchanging ideas on this subject with the late Dr. E. A. Hollowell, an excellent authority on heat in hybridizing, and with other breeders who think along these lines, I began 17 years ago to try other crosses and temperature conditions. I want to mention here that I also read all available material on the subject, and a few of the important facts dug up during this research are as follows: When hybridizing Lilium, Dr. S. Emsweller heated the pistil to 120°F. in water — dried it and pollinated.[1] Dr. W. Ackerman made crosses on Camellia, but when he dropped the temperature more than 8°F the same crosses failed to set seed. In 1932, L. F. Randolph used high temperature on polyploidy and other variations in maize (as printed in American Society Agronomy Journal, 28:990-996).

I began my serious experimental work by constructing a growth-temperature chamber of 3/4-inch plywood, painted white inside to provide supplemental light and to protect the wood from moisture. The top is plate glass, with fluorescent fixtures on the outside. There are six fluorescent tubes to enable me to give red light, white light, or a full spectrum of light to the plants. The cabinet has a glass front to allow observation of plants. On each end there is a small fan, and on the one end there is a hot plate installed above the fan. The combination of fan and heater supplies heated air throughout the chamber. On the inside at the bottom is another hot plate on which I can place a pan of water to produce steam and raise the humidity (at will). The heat and humidity systems are personally monitored for a 2-hour period, making adjustments as necessary to keep the temperature in the effective ranges. The aim is to have as much heat and humidity as possible without dehydrating the foliage on the plants. This is the principle I use when hybridizing plants that have proven difficult or impossible to produce seed by more conventional techniques. I have found that the temperature range which plants will withstand is 110 to 114°F (for a maximum of about 3 hours) with the humidity as close to 100 percent as possible. At this temperature I found the plants remained in good active condition with no wilting or other detrimental effects on them. Van Hoff's rule states: "For every ten degrees rise in temperature, the speed of chemical reaction is doubled."[1] With this in mind, I decided that if I could hold this temperature for around 2 hours, without any ill effects, it would be the same as having the pollen on the plant for a period of 32 hours, which should be sufficient time for the pollen to act. As a matter of fact, I am sure the pollen reacted in a much shorter period of time and was more effective with the increased heat and humidity. A comparison of the amount and size of seed of selfed *R. yakushimanum* produced by this method to that by pollination in the greenhouse reveals three times more seed and larger seeds. Relative size of the capsules is more than double.

In 1974, I crossed 'County of York' with *R. laetum* and successfully produced hybrid seed. Thirty-six plants have been grown from this cross. These were kept inside the cold house year round. Some bloomed in 1977, others in 1978, and a few in 1979. Some of the blooms resembled those of *R. spinuliferum* (never fully opened — the pistil protruded), some opened halfway, but there was no pollen. I had no success whatsoever in making further crosses with these using *R. laetum, macgregori, aurigerianum,* and *zollerii* as the pollen parents. The pistils seemed to be active and I kept trying with the conventional method (no excess heat and humidity) but no seeds were produced. I felt the problem might be related to the fact that they had been kept indoors, so this year, after they budded, I put them outdoors. If there are any survivors I will test further with them.

Another cross I am closely watching is [((Mrs. Yates x *R. yakushimanum*) x Maletta)) x *R.* macgregoriae]. There are nine plants from this cross. Two budded and bloomed in 1979 inside the cold house. The florets were fully opened, but the stamens did not develop pollen. When these bloomed, I crossed them again (no excess heat or humidity) with the same set of Malasians I used on the 'County of York' cross. None made any effort to develop a seed capsule.

My greatest success in the heat chamber came within the lepidotes. I had been trying for years to cross my good, extremely hardy, pink *carolinianum* with 'P.J.M.,' which some have reported as pollen sterile. My purpose was to get a later blooming plant and still capture the good traits of 'P.J.M.,' or even an improved combination of the two. My pink *carolinianum* blooms late in May or early in June. I used the heat treatment and put 'P.J.M.' pollen on my pink *carolinianum* and now have many seedlings as a result of this cross. I know definitely that the cross is true, for when I make a cutting or snap a leaf of the seedlings, there is the same odor that is present in 'P.J.M.' This odor does not exist in my pink *carolinianum*. To date I have selected and numbered nine of these seedlings that I like best. The number nine I selfed last year under normal conditions in the greenhouse and it set good seed. These plants are now growing and the results are awaited with much interest. When dormant, as they now are, the foliage has a bronze/red rather than a dark red/purple fall color, as does 'P.J.M.'

Using the heat treatment I also put 'P.J.M.' pollen on 'Pioneer' and definitely realized hybrids since these plants haven't the characteristics of either plant in foliage. Some are deciduous, being completely defoliated outside at present after several hard freezes.

Based on my experience, rhododendron crosses made under controlled conditions of high temperatures and humidity produce larger and more seeds than those made at cooler temperatures. In certain instances the use of high temperatures and humidity produces seed from wide crosses where normal techniques have been unsuccessful. This new technique seems to have potential for combining the drought resistance and brilliant colors of Malaysian rhododendrons with the cold resistance of hardy hybrids and species.

[1] Proceedings of Breeders Roundtable, 1973, American Rhododendron Society.

RHODODENDRONS IN LANDSCAPE DESIGN

S.E. and C.H. Sanders
Bethesda, Maryland

The genus rhododendron has so much variety of size, form, texture of foliage, color and season of bloom that it can fill many needs of landscape design. Although the generally known varieties are shrubs of medium to large size, with broad, rather leathery, evergreen leaves, there are many other forms, ranging from dwarf and prostrate varieties suitable for rock gardens and edgings, to others which are tree-like and may reach a height of twenty-five feet or more. Azaleas are a part of the genus Rhododendron and include evergreen and deciduous species of varying height, form and blooming period. With such a range of plant types to draw upon, it is possible to plan many landscape designs using mainly rhododendrons and azaleas.

While perhaps the most common use of rhododendrons is in residential plantings, there are other types of development where they are suitable. They may be used to advantage in public parks, around public buildings, and at corporate headquarters in garden areas or as a screen for parking. In sections of the country where rhododendrons and azaleas are common in the wild, they have been effectively used along parkways, such as the ocean highways of the Northwest and the Blue Ridge Parkway in North Carolina.

Design applications include the division of spaces of different uses and of varying heights and widths within a garden; group masses; background planting; screens for privacy and to block undesirable views; woodland naturalized planting that blends into or supplements existing natural planting; foundation planting; edgings along paths, lawns and paved areas; accents of form or color in a formal garden; and hedges. Rhododendrons do not like wind, so should not be planted as a windbreak, but should be protected from prevailing winds by other plants, ground forms or structures.

Many varieties of rhododendrons and azaleas may be grown in containers, as demonstrated by the outstanding display at the ARS annual convention in Vancouver, B.C., in 1979. These pot grown plants would have many uses for indoor display and on patios and terraces where planting space is limited. Because they may be moved around with relative ease, advantage may be taken of shifting light and shade and of other climatic conditions. Small leaved rhododendrons and azaleas are also suitable subjects for bonsai.

A few landscape principles should be kept in mind when planning a garden. Points to consider are compatibility of leaf texture; masses of large leaved plants should be arranged with smaller rhododendrons or azaleas with the larger masses and textures in the background, and the smaller forms in front. Another point to consider is the color combinations of the flowers and the season of bloom. The distribution of strong colors such as red and purple should be used as accents, with a predominance of white or pale shades of pink and yellow. As a rule of thumb, use twice as many white and pastel flowered plants as those with strong colors.

The evergreen leaves of rhododendrons give these plants great winter value in any landscape. When evergreen and deciduous plants are used together, it is generally more effective to place those that will lose their leaves in winter in the background, or at least where some evergreen foliage will partially obscure the bare branches. An exception is when it is desired to have the stems form a pattern against a contrasting background. Some azaleas, both deciduous and semi-evergreen, display considerable attractive fall color, and may be planted with this effect in mind, to give interest at that season when there is not much in bloom.

Companion plants can be used to protect rhododendrons from wind and too much sun. Varieties of hemlocks in masses are very useful as a windbreak in wooded areas, since they do well under those conditions. Pines and other coniferous evergreens may be planted to provide shelter and background in open areas. Tall and high branching deciduous trees give desired shade and interesting patterns of light and shadow. These should be of types that do not have heavy masses of roots near the ground surface to interfere with the roots of the rhododendrons. Small trees such as dogwood, holly and magnolia may be planted among rhododendrons to give added interest. In many cases they should be stemmed-up in order not to cast too dense shade.

Nearly all ericaseous plants are suitable to use with rhododendrons, either as background, interplanted, or as foreground and ground cover. Native ferns and wild flowers are charming when carpeting the ground among rhododendrons, and some bulbs and perennials are also satisfactory.

—————

The word "blotch" as applied to rhododendron flowers is the marking in the throat of the corolla. There are other words which would more properly and pleasantly describe this signal patch, such as fan, eye, rays, and thumbprint.

————

The rhododendron trusses most familiar to gardeners to this day are the ball-like clusters of flowers. So long as the effect is pleasant, loose trusses and flat-topped trusses are not a sign of inferiority. It is difficult to imagine a hybrid as 'Lady Chamberlain' with a ball truss.

RHODODENDRON HYBRIDS

Kendall W. Gambrill
Sumner, Washington

This list of rhododendron hybrids grouped by height, color and season of bloom is intended as a guide for those who may be unfamiliar with the many rhododendrons available, but need a plant whose growth habit will fit an available site, or whose color will suit a planting scheme or simple preference, or whose blooming will be at a desired period. In order to keep its scope and length manageable, the list includes only the more available and typical hybrids; it does not include azaleas or species — equally worthy landscape plants of the genus Rhododendron.

The primary groups of this list are based upon the height of ten-year old plants. The categories are those recognized in the trade and refer to average conditions. Fertility and shade may increase upward growth, while exposure, rabbits, and children may yield a more compact habit.

Color is the secondary division of this chart. Since the color range of rhododendrons is very broad, any division limited to five major groups, as here, is inevitably arbitrary and crude. In this chart the lilac tones of such cultivars as 'Everestianum', 'P.J.M' and 'Pink Drift', have been placed with the lavender-blue grouping; they are as easily categorized as pink. The deep rose and carmine shades, such as 'Cynthia' and 'Wilsoni', have been placed in the pinks; they are often listed as red. The creamy color of 'Harvest Moon' and 'Letty Edwards' — white if they were marigolds — have been placed in yellows, following the prevailing custom with rhododendrons.

The blooming periods are average for the Pacific Northwest growing area centered around Portland. The length of season will depend mainly on the proximity to coasts and degree of maritime influence, with progressively shorter seasons toward the center of the continent. The timing of mid-season primarily will be determined by latitude, later seasons with more northerly locations. And, of course, each year will have its own peculiar variations of timing, especially with earlier blooming cultivars.

Finally, this chart should serve only as the point of beginning in choosing cultivars for a specific purpose. It offers suggestions — ones which you should then evaluate further with the aid of descriptions of individual clones, the advice of gardeners in your area, and, if possible, your observation of the plants in bloom and in growing sites before purchase.

There are of course many different methods of planting a plot of ground; it is always a personal choice. Some plan for a long extended season of bloom covering the many differing forms of rhododendron stature, foliage and inflorescene, even one of a kind — a collector's garden. Some desire a grand splash of color achieved by planting a number of plants of a favorite variety in one area — as a ribbon of 'Jean Marie Montague'. Others enjoy blending with their rhododendrons different species of plants, a truly fascinating pursuit with the ending never quite in sight. *Pieris japonica* blooms in April, *Kalmia latifolia* in June, *Eucryphia nymansay* in August. A cornel can provide just the necessary shade on its northeast flank for a 'Crest'. The brilliant reds and dark hues are most effective in daytime; they are gorgeous with the light shining through the blooms. The pale shades and white are the first to become visible in the early morning and the last to fade into the darkness of night. Such arrangements can make a difference in the view from a certain point.

For hybridizers, this list can have a different use. The sparse areas, such as later blooming dwarf and semi-dwarf reds, and later May dwarf to low pinks, lavenders, and whites should suggest goals for breeding programs. There may be many hybrids, but we are far from having a plant for every purpose.

SIZE AT 10 YEARS, COLOR AND BLOOMING SEQUENCE OF SELECTED RHODODENDRONS

Kendall W. Gambrill

RED includes crimson and orange red
PINK includes deep rose and salmon
BLUE includes lilac, lavender and purple
YELLOW includes orange and apricot

*DWARF (Less than 1½ feet)
SEMI-DWARF (Less than 3 feet)

Bloom Period	Red	Pink	White	Blue	Yellow
March		Cilpinense Pink Snowflakes	Bric-a-Brac Lucy Lou *Ptarmigan		Lemon Mist *Shamrock Valaspis
Early April	*Creeping Jenny Jaipur	Conchita Racil Riplet Thomwilliams	Snow Lady	Bluebird Blue Tit *Purple Gem *Ramapo Sapphire	Ann Carey *Chikor Moonstone *Patty Bee Quaver
Late April	Baden-Baden Blood Ruby *Carmen Elisabeth Hobbie	Candi Hardijzer Beauty Lori Eichelser Molly Ann	Dainty Jean Dora Amateis	Bluette Morheim Oceanlake *Pink Drift *Prostigiatum	*Curlew *Honey Mary Fleming *Princess Anne

Early May	*Ethel, Humming Bird, Ostfriesland, Peekaboo, Scarlet Wonder, Willbrit, Fayetta, *Little Gem, Ruby Hart	Pink Fluff, *Rose Elf, Tiffany, *Treasure, Windbeam, Arthur J. Ivens, Gipsy Queen, Ken Janeck	*Maricee	*Cutie, *Watchung	Devonshire, Cream, Doubloons, Goldbug, Jingle Bells
Mid May		*Kim, Mardi Gras		*Mother Greer	
Late May	*Othello				Nereid
June		Myrtifolium, Wilsoni			

LOW (Less than 4½ feet)

Bloom Period	Red	Pink	White	Blue	Yellow
March	Maxine Childers	Christmas Cheer Conemaugh Rosy Bell Seta	Tessa Bianca	Praecox Tessa	Bo-peep
Early April	#Elizabeth Leaburg	Anna Baldsiefen Cheer Conewago Reve Rose Rosamundi Temple Belle Twinkles Wilbar	Miss Prim Snow Cap	Augfast	Cream Crest Show Off Unique

Late April	Chevalier Felix
	  de Sauvage
	Fireman Jeff
	Gipsy King
	May Day
	Nodding Bells
		Alison Johnstone
		Bow Bells
		Brocade
		Jock
		Karin
		Kimberly
		Mission Bells
		President
		  Roosevelt
		Sham's Juliet
			White Olympic
			  Lady
				Barto Alpine
				Blue Diamond
				Crater Lake
					Canary
					Goldstrike
					Hello Dolly
					Honeymoon
					Medusa
					Souvenir of
					  W. C. Slocock

Early May	Cary Ann
	Jean Marie
	  Montague
	Wilgen's Ruby
		Brickdust
		Coral Velvet
		Flora Markeeta
		King Tut
		Royal Pink
		Winsome
			Boule de Neige
			Chionoides
			Helene Schiffner
			Nestucca
					Carolyn Grace
					Hotei
					Mrs. Betty
					  Robertson
					Odee Wright
					Tidbit

Mid May	Blitz #Elizabeth Mars Max Sye #Thor Tony	Sham's Pink	Anna H. Hall Mist Maiden Peeping Tom	Humboldt	China Moon Dido Fabia Whitney's Orange
Late May	Grosclaude Kluis Sensation	Betty Arrington County Fair Sham's Candy	Cunningham's White	Daphnoides Minnetonka Olin O. Dobbs	Broughtonii Aureum Fred Hamilton Golden Belle Jade Wizard
June	Arthur Osborn				

Different clones under group name.

MEDIUM (Less than 6 feet)

Bloom Period	Red	Pink	White	Blue	Yellow
March	Lee's Scarlet	Else Frye Nobleanum Venustum Pioneer		Olive	August Moon
Early April	Grace Seabrook Ibex Spring Glory Unknown Warrior	Jacksonii Vernus	Dr. Stocker	P.J.M.	Yellow Hammer
Late April	Burgundy Earl of Athlone Etta Burrows Holden Queen of Hearts	Boule de Rose Cosmopolitan Mrs. C. B. van Nes Pink Cameo Rocket Todmorden	Loder's White	Blue River Ilam Violet Russautinii	Carita Fred Rose Idealist

Early May	Blaze
	Goldsworth
	   Crimson
	Halfdan Lem
	Hallelujah
	Harold Amateis
	J. H. van Nes
		Alice
		Annie Dalton
		Betty Wormald
		Cotton Candy
		David Gable
		Elizabeth
		   Titcomb
			Beaufort
			Belle Heller
			Ice Cube
			Lodestar
			Tumalo
				Blue Peter
				Lavender Queen
				Van Nes
				   Sensation
					Brinny
					Butterfly
					Harvest Moon
					Mary Belle
					Virginia
					   Richards

Mid May	Lamplighter Markeeta's Prize Nova Zembla Noyo Chief	Hurricane Janet Blair Oregon Queen Pink Petticoats Pink Twins Pinnacle Queen Mary Wheatley	Besse Howells Dr. H. C. Dresselhuys General Eisenhower Gi Gi Hamma Hamma Radium #Thor	Dawn's Delight Lem's Cameo Mrs. Bernice Baker Mrs. Furnival Mrs. Horace Fogg Parker's Pink President Lincoln Rainbow Scintillation Sweet Sixteen	Helen Everett Mother of Pearl Mrs. A. T. de la Mare Mrs. Lindsay Smith The Bride	Aunt Martha Ben Mosely Blue Ensign Lavender Girl Purple Splendour Royal Purple Royal Star	Barbara Hardgrove C.I.S. Golden Star Lem's Goal Old Copper

MEDIUM (Less than 6 feet)

Bloom Period	Red	Pink	White	Blue	Yellow
Late May	America	Annie E. Endtz	Catawbiense	Blue Pacific	Autumn Gold
	Bonfire	Atroflo	Album	Dorothy Amateis	Bacher's Gold
	Britannia	Clementine	Ermine	Purple Lace	Day Dream
	Cavalier	Lemaire	Lodestar	Purpureum	Evening Glow
	Crimson Glory	Countess of	Martha Isaacson	Grandiflorum	Gold Mohur
	Dr. A. W. Endtz	Derby	Madame Masson		Goldsworth
	Kubla Khan	Henrietta	White Gold		Orange
	Lady Bligh	Sargent			Goldsworth
	Leo	Ignatius			Yellow
	Lord Roberts	Sargent			King of Shrubs
	Madame de Bruin	Lady C. Mitford			Phyllis Ballard
	Moser's Maroon	Maryke			
	Paricutin	N. N. Sherwood			
	Red Head (Gable)	Parson's Gloriosum			
	Trilby	Prof. Amateis			
	Van Veen	Ruby Bowman			
	Vulcan	Vanessa Pastel			
	Vulcan's Flame				
June	Bagshot Ruby	Azor	Candidissimum	Anah Kruschke	Edward Dunn
	Caractacus	Helen Johnson	Mrs. J. C.	Blue Jay	Margaret Dunn
	Good News	Lucky Strike	Williams	Marchioness of	Talisman
	Independence Day	Midsummer	Mrs. P. D.	Lansdowne	Polynesian
	Michael Waterer	Robert Allison	Williams		Sunset

Viking Prince

Mrs. T. H.
Lowinsky

Romany Chal
Tally Ho

TALL (More than 6 feet)

Bloom Period	Red	Pink	White	Blue	Yellow
March	Cornubia Taurus		Babylon		
Early April		Dame Nellie Melba Sausalito			
Late April	Bibiani	Faggetter's Favourite Lady Roseberry Mrs. G. W. Leak Spring Dawn	Sir Charles Lemon	Susan	Diane
Early May	David Exotic Giganteum	Fawn Furnival's Daughter Jan Dekens Loderi Venus Mrs. E. C. Stirling Naomi Glow Pink Dawn Puget Sound Trude Webster	Beauty of Littleworth Hyperion Loderi King George White Swan	Old Port	Crest Royal Flush

Mid May	Anne Hardgrove Red Olympia Wissahickon	Anna Antoon van Welie Cynthia Dr. A. Blok Isabel Pierce Lem's Monarch Marinus Koster Mrs. Charles E. Pearson Pink Pearl Point Defiance Sugar Pink	County of York Sappho White Pearl	Caroline Dexter's Orchid	China Goldfort Ole Olson
Late May	Damozel Red Cloud	Anna Rose Whitney Cadis English Roseum Jean Kate Waterer Meadowbrook Mrs. W. R. Coe Roseum Elegans	Album Elegans Mrs. J. G. Millais	A. Bedford Catawbiense Grandiflorum Everestianum Fastuosum Plenum Lee's Dark Purple Purpureum Elegans	
June	Captain Jack Princess Elizabeth	Aladdin Mrs. Phillip Martineau Springfield	Albatross Disca Lodauric Polar Bear	Lady Decies	

RHODODENDRONS
WHICH HAVE RECEIVED AWARDS

For information on the Awards Program see the Quarterly Bulletin of the American Rhododendron Society, Volume 31, Spring, 1977, page 105.

SUPERIOR PLANT AWARD S.P.A.

'Lem's Cameo'. S.P.A. 1971 . . . . Lem
'Trude Webster', S.P.A. 1971 . . . . Greer

AWARD OF EXCELLENCE A.E.

'Annie Dalton', A.E. 1960. . . . . Gable
'Atroflo', A.E. 1959 . . . . Gable
'Beechwood Pink', A.E. 1960 . . . . Gable
'Blue River', A.E. 1961. . . . . Lyons
'Cadis', A.E. 1959. . . . . Gable
'Carolyn Grace', A.E. 1960. . . . . Grace
'Catalode', A.E. 1960 synonym 'County of York'. . . . . Gable
'Cutie', A.E. 1962. . . . . Larson
'David Gable', A.E. 1960 . . . . Gable
degronianum, 'Rae's Delight', A.E. 1956. . . . Crystal Springs Garden
Dora Amateis, A.E. 19? . . . . Amateis
'GiGi', A.E. 1973 . . . . Dexter
'Ken Janeck', A.E. 1969. . . . . Janeck
'Kim', A.E. 1973 . . . . Caperci
'Lemon Mist', A.E. 1969. . . . . Scott
'Maricee', A.E. 1959. . . . . Caperci
'Mary Fleming', A.E. 1973 . . . . Nearing
'Mary Harmon', A.E. 1958. . . . . Ostbo
'Meadowbrook', A.E. 1973 . . . . Vossberg
'Mrs. A.F. McEwan', A.E. 1956. . . . . Ihrig
'Mrs. Donald Graham', A.E. 1958. Ostbo
'Opal Fawcett', A.E. 1958. . . . . Ostbo
'Parker's Pink', A.E. 1973. . . . . Dexter
'Roslyn', A.E. 1973. . . . . Vossberg
'Scintillation', A.E. 1973. . . . . Dexter
'Tyee', A.E. 1962 . . . . James
'Wheatley' A.E. 1973 . . . . Phipps
'Windbeam', A.E. 1973. . . . . Nearing
'Wizard', A.E. 1959 . . . . Lem

CONDITIONAL AWARDS C.A.

'Mi Amor', C.A. 1969 A.M. R.H.S. 1975. . . . . .Sumner
'Lem's Monarch', C.A. 1971 . . . . Lem, Fisher and Bailey
'Noyo Chief', C.A. 1971 . . . . .Bowman
'Pink Petticoats', C.A. 1971 . . . . .Lofthouse
'Vicki Reine', C.A. 1971 . . . . R. Clark
'Wardian Cream', C.A. 1971. . . . . Nelson
'Helen Louise', C.A. 1972 . . . . P. Saunders
'Lydia', C.A. 1972. . . . . Greer
'Ananouri', C.A. 1973. . . . . Phipps
'Shalom', C.A. 1973 . . . . .Lem, Hess
'Award', C.A. 1974 . . . . .James, Ward
'Peppermint Stick', C.A. 1974. . . . . Lancaster, McGuire
'Crater Lake', C.A. 1975. .Phetteplace
'Guardian Fir', C.A. 1975 . . . . Lem, Butler
'Hallelujah', C.A. 1975. . . . . Greer
'Harry Madison', C.A. 1975 . . . . Nelson, Short
'Winterset', C.A. 1975 . . . . Grothaus, Brockenbrough
'Yaku Angel', C.A. 1975 . . . . Greer
'Julia Grothaus', C.A. 1976. . . . . Grothaus
'Amigo', C.A. 1977 . . . . .Goheen
'Tokatee', C.A. 1977. . . . . Grothaus
'Westhaven', C.A. 1978. . . . . C. Smith, McGuire
'Taurus', C.A. 1979 . . . . Mossman

PRELIMINARY AWARD P.A.

'Alice Franklin', P.A. 1960 . . . . Lem
'Alley Cat', P.A. 1960. . . . . .Ostbo
'Anna', P.A. 1952. . . . . Lem
'Anna Rose Whitney', P.A. 1954. . . . . .Whitney
'Ann Carey', P.A. 1966. . . . . Anderson
'Bacher's Gold', P.A. 1955 . . . . Bacher
'Bern', P.A. 1955 . . . . Bacher
'Captain Jack', P.A. 1956. . . . . R. Henny
'Captain Kidd', P.A. 1960. . . . . R. Henny
'Carol Jean', P.A. 1957. .Klupenger
'Cary Ann', P.A. 1961 . . . . Wright
'Chief Paulina', P.A. 1954. . . . . .James
'C.I.S.', P.A. 1952. . . . . R. Henny
'Confection', P.A. 1956. . . . . R. Henny

'Coral', P.A. 1956. . . . . Ostbo
'Darlene', P.A. 1952 . . . . Lem
'Diane Titcomb', P.A. 1958. . . . . Larson
'Doris Caroline', P.A. 1960 . . . . R. Henny
'Edna McCarty', P.A. 1959. . . . . Ostbo
'Edward Dunn', P.A. 1958 . . . . Ostbo
'Elizabeth Titcomb', P.A. 1958. . . . . Larson
'Endre Ostbo', P.A. 1954 . . . . Ostbo
'Eulalie Wagner', P.A. 1963 . . . . Lem
'Exotic', P.A. 1961 . . . . Bovee
'Fair Lady', P.A. 1959 . . . . R. Henny
'Fawn', P.A. 1959. . . . . .James
'Flatterer', P.A. 1957 . . . . R. Henny
'Flora Markeeta', P.A. 1967 . . . . .Beck
'Full Moon', P.A. 1955. . . . . J. Henny
'Geneva', P.A. 1955 . . . . Bacher
'George Grace', P.A. 1952. . . . . R. Henny
'Gladys Johnson', P.A. 1958 . . . . Johnson
'Gold Mohur', P.A. 1955. . . . . Brandt
'Golden Witt', P.A. 1967 . . . . Michaud
'Great Lakes', P.A. 1960. . . . . Leach
'Helen Johnson', P.A. 1956. . . . . Ostbo
'Hotei', P.A. 1964. . . . . Sifferman
'Idol', P.A. 1957. . . . . R. Henny
'Inca Gold', P.A. 1961 . . . . Lancaster
'James Barto', P.A. 1953 . . . . Barto
'Jan-di-lyn', P.A. 1961 . . . . .Wyrens
'Julie Titcomb', P.A. 1958 . . . . Larson
'Kimberly', P.A. 1963. . . . . Greer
'King of Shrubs', P.A. 1950 . . . . Ostbo
'Lackamas Blue', P.A. 1963 . . . . Lancaster
'Lackamas Cream', P.A. 1962 . . . . Lancaster
'Lackamas Gold', P.A. 1962 . . . . Lancaster
'Lackamas Spice', P.A. 1962. . . . . Lancaster
'Lake Labish', P.A. 1955. . . . . R. Henny
'Last Chance', P.A. 1957 . . . . R. Henny
'Leaburg', P.A. 1956. . . . . .Phetteplace
'Leeanne Hardgrove', P.A. 1962 . . . . .Hardgrove
'Lem's Goal', P.A. 1952 . . . . Lem
'Lisa', P.A. 1962. . . . . Gable
'Little Gem', P.A. 1962. . . . . Whitney
'Little Lou', P.A. 1963 . . . . .Sumner
'Little Pudding', P.A. 1953 . . . . R. Henny
'Little Sheba', P.A. 1954. . . . . R. Henny
'Lord Fauntleroy', P.A. 1967 . . . . Pierce
'March Sun', P.A. 1963 . . . . Wyrens

'Marine', P.A. 1960 . . . . Bovee
'Martha Isaacson', P.A. 1956 . . . . Ostbo
'Mary Belle', P.A. 1962 . . . . Gable
'Mary Mayo', P.A. 1960 . . . . Bovee
'Merle Lee', P.A. 1954 . . . . Esch
'Mildred Fawcett', P.A. 1960 . . . . Fawcett
'Miss Olympia', P.A. 1960. . . . . Ostbo
'Moontide', P.A. 1955. . . . . R. Henny
'Mrs. Horace Fogg', P.A. 1963 . . . . Larson
'Nestucca', P.A. 1950 . . . . .C. Smith
'Odee Wright', P.A. 1966 . . . . Wright
'Ostbo's Low Yellow', P.A. 1960 . . . . Ostbo
'Phyllis Ballard', P.A. 1956. . . . . Ostbo
'Pink Mermaid', P.A. 1954 . . . . .Esch
'Pink Parfait', P.A. 1961. . . . . .Senko
'Ray', P.A. 1956. . . . . .James
'Red Cloud', P.A. 1953 . . . . R. Henny
'Redwax', P.A. 1958 . . . . R. Henny
'Renhaven', P.A. 1955 . . . . .James
'Riplet', P.A. 1961 . . . . Lem
'Roseann', P.A. 1956 . . . . R. Henny
'Rose Elf', P.A. 1954 . . . . Lancaster
'Ruby F. Bowman', P.A. 1951. .Bowman
'Ruth Lyons', P.A. 1961. . . . . .Lyons
'Sausalito', P.A. 1967 . . . . Bovee
'Sharon', P.A. 1955 . . . . .James
'Snow Lady', P.A. 1955 . . . . Lancaster
'Starlet', P.A. 1963. . . . . Lem
'Stoplight', P.A. 1951 . . . . R. Henny
'Thelma', P.A. 1958 . . . . Lem
'Thor', P.A. 1961 . . . . Brandt
'Tidbit', P.A. 1957 . . . . R. Henny
'Towhee', P.A. 1965 . . . . .James
'Tumalo', P.A. 1955 . . . . .James
'Unimak', P.A. 1962 . . . . Lem
'Vampire', P.A. 1951. . . . . Wright
'Virginia Richards', P.A. 1962. Whitney
'Voodoo', P.A. 1952 . . . . R. Henny
'Warpaint', P.A. 1956. . . . . .James
'White Cap', P.A. 1961. . . . . Lem
'White Lily', P.A. 1952. . . . . Ostbo
'White Olympic Lady', P.A. 1960 . . . . Clark
'Wink', P.A. 1960. . . . . R. Henny
'Yellow Creek', P.A. 1958 . . . . .James

All unnamed, or never named, P.A. seedlings previous to 1967 have
been omitted from this list.

GOOD-DOER RHODODENDRONS

George W. Ring III
Fairfax, Virginia

It has been noted that certain rhododendron varieties thrive and perform faithfully year after year with little care. The American Rhododendron Society, believing that new members would benefit from learning the names of some of these varieties, requested the local chapters to provide information on outstanding rhododendrons easy to grow in their areas. Twenty chapters provided data, mostly from experienced member growers, on large and small leaved rhododendrons, hybrids, deciduous and evergreen azaleas, and on rhododendron species. In addition, one chapter provided information on Malaysians noted as outstanding in their area.

The varieties recommended vary from chapter to chapter, and from region to region, depending on cultural conditions, grower experience, and the varieties that have been available in the past.

Climate and soil conditions, as furnished, are summarized for each chapter to provide the reader with an understanding of local growing conditions which are reflected in the recommended varieties.

To keep the data manageable and to provide continuity for the reader, it was sometimes necessary to provide only part of the furnished information for publication. In most instances, this reduction was accomplished by retaining only the most highly recommended varieties. For the most part, species and hybrids are combined in each of four categories. Those varieties included in the final recommended lists are likely to be available at nurseries who carry a good selection of rhododendrons and azaleas.

There is a considerable variation in the data supplied by the chapters. The column entitled "Votes" should be used as an indication of the popularity of the plant within a chapter. In some instances, it is the number of persons who recommended the plant. In other places it represents the number of partially reduced lists on which the plant was found.

New members will benefit greatly from discussing rhododendron and azalea plants and their culture with the more experienced growers. There is much local knowledge about culture, about the likes and dislikes of plants, and about the availability and sources for desirable plants.

The plant data was collated and assembled by Bruno Kaelin, Potomac Valley Chapter.

CONNECTICUT CHAPTER

Some members of the Connecticut Chapter who live near Long Island Sound benefit from its moderating effect, seldom experiencing 0°F. The lowest mean monthly temperature occurs in February with 8.9°F in Norfolk and 34.5°F in Danbury. Snowfall in the colder regions is heavier and longer lasting, protecting the plants which would otherwise be injured by wind and low temperature. Highest mean temperature is 78°F in the central valley and 72.5°F in Norfolk in the northwestern hills. Precipitation average is 44 to 48 inches with some areas receiving up to 58 inches.

ELEPIDOTES	Votes	Flower	Plant	Comments
Blue Peter	2	5	3	
Boule de Neige	7	3.4	3.4	
R. catawbiense	2	3	2	Rock hardy
R. catawbiense album	2	3.5	3	Always dependable
Chionoides	2	3	3.5	
County of York	2	4	2	
Everestianum	2	5	5	
R. fortunei	3	2	3	
Janet Blair	3	3	3.5	Fragrant, floriferous
Mars	3	4.5	3.5	Moderate shade
Mrs. C.S. Sargent	4	3.7	3	
Mrs. Furnival	2	5	4	A little finicky
Nova Zembla	2	3	2	
Roseum Elegans	2	4	4.3	
Russell Harmon	2	3	3	
Scintillation	8	3.7	4.2	A must
R. smirnowii	2			
Vulcan	2	4.5	3	Several clones
Westbury	3	3	3	
R. yakushimanum	5	4	4.3	Mist Maiden more floriferous

LEPIDOTES				
R. carolinianum	6	3.5	3	
R. dauricum	4	3	3	
Dora Amateis	5	3.3	4.3	Light shade
R. keiskei, dwarf form	7	3	3.6	Good substance
Mary Fleming	4	3.7	3.3	
R. minus compactum	3	3.5	3.5	Mezitt selection
R. mucronulatum	5	3.7	3	
Myrtifolium	3	2.7	3.7	
P.J.M.	6	3.3	4.1	Sun for dense growth
R. racemosum	3	3.5	4	Select good form
Ramapo	4	3	3.8	
Windbeam	6	3	2.9	Improves with age

EVERGREEN AZALEAS

Delaware Valley White	3	3	3	
Kaempo	4	3.7	3.3	Large flowers
R. kiusianum	4	3.5	3.5	White and Pink forms
R. nakaharai	4	2.7	3	Bovee's #3 best
Rosebud	3	4.5	4.5	
Stewartstonian	5	3.7	4	Fall color, long lasting flowers

DECIDUOUS AZALEAS

R. arborescens	3	2.5	2	Very fragrant
R. calendulaceum	3	3	2	
Gibraltar	3	3.5	3.5	Among best oranges
R. schlippenbachii	4	3.7	2.3	
R. vaseyi, White Find	3	3.5	3	

NEW YORK CHAPTER

All responses were from Long Island where the lowest recent temperature was −10°F and 100°F is reached but rarely in the summer. The soil on Long Island varies from sand near the shore to clay further inland. Drainage, however, is generally good. One respondent reported on plants at the home of a friend in Oneonta, NY, where the temperature fell to −20°F with high winds. These plants were P.J.M., *dauricum* and Dexter #109 (Great Eastern).

ELEPIDOTES	Votes	Flower	Plant	Comments
Ben Moseley	4	4.3	4.3	
Boule de Neige	6	3.2	4.4	Compact early white
Cadis	5	3.6	4	Superb late bloom
R. catawbiense album	4	3.5	4	Great hardy white
County of York	3	3.7	3	
R. degronianum	3	3.3	3.7	
R. fortunei	5	4.5	3.9	Minimum insect damage
GiGi	8	4	4	Good truss, compact
Golden Star	3	3.7	3.7	
Janet Blair	6	4	4.3	Excellent bloomer
Jean Marie Montague	5	4.6	3.2	Beautiful red
R. makinoi	3	3	4.3	Unusual foliage
R. metternichii	4	3.8	3.8	Great foliage
Parker's Pink	3	4.3	4	
Scintillation	14	4.1	4.2	Lustrous foliage
Vulcan	4	4.3	3.3	Consistent in shade
Wheatley	6	4.3	4.5	Dependable bloom

Wyandanch Pink	3	3.7	3.7	Vigorous
R. yakushimanum	9	4.3	4.9	
R. yakushimanum Mist				
Maiden	3	4.7	5	

LEPIDOTES

Anna Baldsiefen	4	4.5	3.8	Delightful pink
R. carolinianum	3	3.3	3.7	Drought resistant
R. dauricum	4	3.8	3.3	Rugged plant
Dora Amateis	8	3.9	4.5	
R. keiskei	5	3.4	3.6	
Mary Fleming	10	3.8	3.6	Sometimes frost nipped
R. mucronulatum	5	3.2	3	Early bloom
P.J.M.	7	3.7	4.3	
Windbeam	8	3.8	3.8	Dependable

EVERGREEN AZALEAS

Allure	3	4	2.7	Lovely shell pink
Dayspring	3	4.7	4	
Geisha	3	4	3	
Gumpo White	3	3.2	4	Dense grower
R. kiusianum	6	4	4.5	
Margaret Douglas	3	4.7	4	Bicolor
Nancy of Robin Hill	3	4.7	4.7	Pretty pink double
Palestrina	3	4	4	
Rose Greeley	5	4	3.5	Dependable white
Rosebud	3	3.7	3.2	
Stewartstonian	4	3.5	3.5	Good red, fall color

DECIDUOUS AZALEAS

R. calendulaceum	3	4	3.8	
Gibraltar	7	4.3	4	
Klondyke	4	4.3	3.5	Rich burnt yellow
Narcissiflora	3	4	3.7	
R. schlippenbachii	6	4.5	3.8	Early, shade
Strawberry Ice	3	4.7	3.7	Full truss
Toucan	3	3.7	3.3	Fragrant, tall
R. vaseyi	6	4	4.3	
R. viscosum	4	2.8	3	Delightful fragrance

PRINCETON CHAPTER

The Princeton Chapter is in central New Jersey. Its members live in an area that extends from "old mountains" to the seacoast. The temperatures were reported as 0°F to −15°F for the low and 85°F to 105°F for the high. Soil ranges from heavy clay to light sand, varying sharply between areas.

ELEPIDOTES
R. catawbiense album
R. fortunei
Janet Blair
Mrs. W.R. Coe
Scintillation
Tom Everitt
Wheatley
R. yakushimanum

LEPIDOTES
Anna Baldesiefen
R. carolinianum
R. dauricum
R. keiskei
R. mucronulatum
P.J.M.
R. racemosum
Windbeam

EVERGREEN AZALEAS
Delaware Valley White
Geisha
Hahn's Red
Hershey's Red
Hino-Crimson
R. kiusianum
Rose Greeley
Rosebud
Springtime
Stewartstonian
Vuyk's Rosy Red

DECIDUOUS AZALEAS
Balzac
Brazil
Cecile
Daviesii
Gibraltar
Golden Dream
Homebush
Hugh Wormald
Klondyke
Nancy Waterer
Primrose
R. schlippenbachii
Strawberry Ice
R. vaseyi, White Find

POTOMAC VALLEY CHAPTER

Northern Virginia, Maryland, southeastern Pennsylvania and Delaware are included in the Potomac Valley Chapter. The lowest temperature quoted was −6°F but sub-zero readings are unusual. Summer temperatures are generally in the 90°F range. Rainfall averages 36 to 40 inches distributed farily well over the year. Soil near the coast is sandy but clay is prevalent elsewhere. Drainage can be a problem.

ELEPIDOTES	Votes	Flower	Plant	Comments
Blue Peter	4	4	3.5	
Boule de Neige	6	3.6	4.3	
Cadis	8	4.1	4.5	
Caroline	9	3.7	3.7	
County of York	4	3.7	3.3	
Gomer Waterer	3	3.7	5	
Janet Blair	11	4	4.2	
R. maximum	4	2.4	4	
R. metternichii	3	3.3	4	
Nova Zembla	5	3.7	3.7	
Rochelle	3	3.3	3	
Roseum Elegans	10	2.9	4.2	
Scintillation	17	4.1	4.4	
Wheatley	5	4.5	3.8	
R. yakushimanum	7	4.3	4.8	

LEPIDOTES				
R. carolinianum	3	3	3.5	
Mary Fléming	4	4	3	
R. mucronulatum	4	4	2.5	
P.J.M.	10	3.2	3.9	
Windbeam	6	3.4	3.8	

EVERGREEN AZALEAS				
Delaware Valley White	4	4	3.5	
Dream	4	5	3.7	
Louise Gable	3	4	4	
Palestrina	3	3.5	3	
Polaris	4	4.7	4.3	
Rose Greeley	5	3.9	3.5	
Springtime	3	4	3.3	
Stewartstonian	4	3.8	3.7	

DECIDUOUS AZALEAS				
R. calendulaceum	3	3.5	3	
Gibraltar	3	4.5	3.5	
R. vaseyi	4	4	2.7	

MIDDLE ATLANTIC CHAPTER

The report of the Middle Atlantic Chapter includes the western mountains and central land of Virginia and the tidewater area, a wide variation in growing conditions. Normal winter lows may be 15°F at the shore and −5°F near the mountains, with a corresponding difference in summer highs. The soil is sandy near the coast to clay condition nearer the mountains and is generally moderately acid.

ELEPIDOTES	Votes	Flower	Plant	Comments
A. Bedford	2	4	3	
Anna Rose Whitney	2	4	4	
Cadis	2	4	4	
Caroline	3	3	4.5	
R. catawbiense	2	3	4	
R. catawbiense album	2	4	3	
R. catabiense Boursault	3	2.5	4	
County of York	2	4	3	
Dr. H.C. Dresselhuys	2	4	4	
English Roseum	3	3.5	4.5	
Gomer Waterer	2	4	4	
Janet Blair	2	4	4	
Jean Marie Montague	2	4	4	
R. makinoi	3	3.5	4.5	
R. metternichii	3	4	4.5	
Nova Zembla	2	4	3	
Roseum Elegans	2	3	5	
Scintillation	2	4	4	
R. yakushimanum	3	3.5	5	

LEPIDOTES				
R. carolinianum	3	3	3.5	
R. chapmanii	2	4	4	
Mary Fleming	2	4	3	
P.J.M.	2	4	5	

EVERGREEN AZALEAS				
Cavalier	1	3	5	Tidewater
Coral Bells	2	4	4.5	
Corsage	1	4	3	
Delaware Valley White	1	4	3	
Elsie Lee	2	4	3.5	
Flamingo (Pericat)	1	5	5	Tidewater
Glacier	2	4	5	
Hampton Beauty	1	4	3	Tidewater
Helen Curtis	1	3	4	Tidewater

Herbert	1	3	3
Hershey's Red	2	3	4
Hino-Crimson	2	3	4
KBA Gloria	1	4	3	Tidewater
Peggy Ann	1	5	5	Tidewater
Rosebud	1	4	4
Stewartstonian	1	4	3
White Rosebud	1	5	3	Tidewater

DECIDUOUS AZALEAS

R. atlanticum	1	4	3
R. bakeri	1	4	4
Brazil	1	4	5
Bullfinch	1	5	4
R. calendulaceum	1	4	4
Cecile	1	4	4
Gibraltar	2	4.5	3.5
Gold Crest	1	4	5
Golden Peace	1	5	5
Goldflake	1	4	4
Kilauea	1	4	4
Klondyke	2	4.5	3
R. nudiflorum	1	3	3
R. roseum	1	3	3
Roxanne Waterer	1	5	4
Toucan	2	4	4
R. vaseyi	1	4	3
R. viscosum	1	4	5

PIEDMONT CHAPTER

The Piedmont Chapter serves North Carolina, from the Smoky Mountains, past the piedmont and on toward the eastern shore. The temperature range quoted by members is 0°F in winter to 100°F in summer. The rainfall is from 35 inches to 46 inches per year. A sandy loam seems to be the general soil, but some report woods mold over clay.

ELEPIDOTES	Votes	Flower	Plant	Comments
Anna Rose Whitney	2			
Cadis	3			
R. catawbiense album	3			
Chionoides	2			
Cynthia	3			
Jean Marie Montague	3			
R. maximum	2			

Nova Zembla	3	Best in raised bed
Roseum Elegans	5	
Ruby F. Bowman	2	
Scintillation	3	
Vulcan	3	
R. yakushimanum	2	

LEPIDOTES

R. chapmanii	2
Dora Amateis	3
Mary Fleming	4
Windbeam	2

EVERGREEN AZALEAS
Chinsoy
Delaware Valley White
Gumpo
Guy Yerkes
R. macrantha
Modesty
Moonbeam
Pink Pearl
Vespers
Wakabisu

DECIDUOUS AZALEAS

R. atlanticum	2
R. calendulaceum	2
Exbury azaleas	2
R. nudiflorum	2

SOUTHEASTERN CHAPTER

The eastern part of South Carolina and the southern part of North Carolina are included in this Chapter. Temperatures range from a winter low of 0°F to a summer high of 100°F. Normal rainfall is 40 inches per year.

ELEPIDOTES	Votes	Flower	Plant	Comments
A. Bedford	15	3.3		
America	24	3.4		
Anah Kruschke	15	3.3		
Anna Rose Whitney	23	3.9		
Antoon van Welie	15	3.4		

Belle Heller	20	3.1
Besse Howells	20	3.6
Betty Wormald	15	3
Blue Ensign	20	3.6
Blue Peter	28	3
Boule de Neige	14	2.7
Cadis	14	3.3
Caroline	21	3.8
R. catawbiense album	17	3.6
Chionoides	23	3.2
County of York	18	3.4
Cynthia	23	4
Dr. Rutgers	15	2.6
English Roseum	27	4.2
R. fortunei	14	4.3
Gomer Waterer	25	3.7
Holden	17	3.6
Ignatius Sargent	17	2.6
Janet Blair	17	4.6
Jean Marie Montague	26	4.4
King Tut	15	2.2
Lee's Dark Purple	17	3
Mars	17	3.2
Mrs. Furnival	22	3.1
Nova Zembla	30	3.9
Pink Pearl	20	3.4
Sappho	17	2.4
Scintillation	29	4.8
Vulcan	20	3.5
R. yakushimanum	24	3.8

LEPIDOTES

Anna Baldsiefen	6	2.7
R. augustinii	4	3.5
R. carolinianum	18	3.7
R. carolinianum album	5	3.8
R. chapmanii	4	3.5
Conewago	8	2.8
Dora Amateis	20	3.2
R. keiskei	11	2.5
Pioneer	9	2.8
P.J.M.	16	3.3
R. racemosum	10	3.4
Ramapo	19	2.9
Wilsoni	7	3.3

WILLIAM BARTRAM CHAPTER

The area situated at the juncture of North Carolina, South Carolina and Georgia is the home of this Chapter, named in honor of the early plant explorer who botanized this land. Temperatures range from −5°F at the low to 100°F at the high. Annual rainfall is between 50 and 60 inches. Soil is predominantly clay loam.

ELEPIDOTES	Votes	Flower	Plant	Comments
A. Bedford	4	4	3	Big plant
America	4	4	3	
Anna Rose Whitney	6	5	4	Large
Brookville	3	3	5	Easy
Cabaret	6	5	5	Superb
Cadis	5	3	4	
Caroline	5	3	5	Root rot resistant
R. catawbiense album	3	4	3	
Champagne	3	4	4	Almost yellow
Chionoides	4	2	4	
Cynthia	7	5	3	
Daphnoides	3	2	5	
David Gable	5	4	4	
R. decorum	5	4	4	
R. discolor	4	3	3	
Dorothy Amateis	4	4	4	
Faggetter's Favourite	4	4	4	
R. fortunei	5	4	4	Easy, beautiful
GiGi	6	4	4	
Goldfort	7	4	4	Slow grower
Gomer Waterer	7	3	5	
Halfdan Lem	3	5	4	
R. hyperythrum	6	4	5	Lovely low grower
Jean Marie Montague	5	4	3	
Madame Guillemot	5	4	4	
Mary Belle	6	3	3	
R. maximum	4	2	3	Native to area
R. metternichii	5	3	5	Great
Mrs. T.H. Lowinsky	8	3	3	
Nova Zembla	6	4	4	
Rocket	5	3	4	
Roseum Elegans	9	3	5	Best all around
Ruby F. Bowman	4	5	4	Outstanding
Sappho	4	4	2	
Scintillation	8	5	5	Very fine
Todmorden	3	5	4	Beautiful bicolor
Tom Everitt	3	5	4	Slow growing
Trilby	6	4	4	

Trude Webster	10	5	4	Enormous pink truss
Van Nes Sensation	3	4	3	
Vulcan	5	3	3	
Wyandanch Pink	5	3	5	
R. yakushimanum	6	4	5	Beautiful form

LEPIDOTES

Anna Baldsiefen	4	3	3	
R. carolinianum	6	3	3	Native to area
Dora Amateis	5	3	3	
R. keiskei	5	3	3	Good yellow dwarf
Mary Fleming	6	4	5	
Windbeam	3	3	3	

EVERGREEN AZALEAS

Ambrosia	4	4	3	Color "one of a kind"
Apple Blossom	4	4	3	Forms vary
Ben Morrison	4	4	3	Striking bicolor
Buccaneer	4	3	4	
Coral Bells	7	3	3	
Daphne	4	5	4	Delicate appearance
Delaware Valley White	8	4	4	
Delos	4	4	3	Rosebud form
Fashion	8	3	3	
Fawn	4	4	4	
Flame Creeper	5	4	5	
George L. Tabor	6	3	3	
Gillie	4	5	5	
Gumpo	9	4	4	
Gyokushin	4	4	5	
Hershey's Red	8	4	4	
H.H. Hume	4	3	3	
Hino-Crimson	4	4	4	
Kehr's White Rosebud	4	5	5	Perfection in form
Marion Lee	4	5	5	
Martha Hitchcock	5	5	3	
Mildred Mae	6	5	3	
Nancy of Robin Hill	4	5	4	
Pink Pearl	5	3	3	
Rose Greeley	4	5	5	Fragrant
Rosebud	4	5	5	
St. James	4	5	5	Striking
Stewartstonian	6	4	4	Beautiful fall foliage

DECIDUOUS AZALEAS

| *R. alabamense* | 4 | 3 | 4 | Fragrant dwarf |

R. *bakeri*	5	5	5	Easy, beautiful
R. *calendulaceum*	4	5	5	Rated for best forms
R. *canescens*	5	4	4	Clear colors, great
Choptank River	5	5	5	Pink, fragrant, perfect
R. *nudiflorum*	4	3	3	Rated for best forms
R. *prunifolium*	5	5	5	Easy
Ralph Pennington	5	5	5	
R. *vaseyi*	4	5	4	

AZALEA CHAPTER

The Azalea Chapter is centered in Atlanta, Georgia, covering the piedmont and lower piedmont regions of Georgia. The general climate is that of dry summers and wet winters. Summer temperatures in the 90's are general and sometimes reach 105°F or more. In winter the temperature may go to 0°F briefly, but the soil does not freeze for very long. The soil is generally heavy and must be lightened and elevated for good long-term results.

ELEPIDOTES	Votes	Flower	Plant	Comments
A. Bedford	10	3.5	3.3	Full sun, large
Anna Rose Whitney	10	4.4	4.2	Good color
Blue Peter	11	3.2	3.4	Early, easy
R. *catawbiense*	9	3	3	Mediocre
R. *catawbiense album*	11	3.5	3.7	Good tall white
Cynthia	11	4.1	3.9	Lovely flowers
English Roseum	13	3.2	3.7	Easy to grow
Jean Marie Montague	13	3.8	3.8	Good red
R. *maximum*	14	2.4	3	Background, good
Mrs. T.H. Lowinsky	8	3.5	3.4	Unusual
Nova Zembla	13	3.3	3.3	Easy
Roseum Elegans	15	3.3	3.5	Easy
Sappho	8	3.2	2.2	Leggy
Scintillation	13	4	4.1	Reliable
Vulcan	13	3.5	3.2	Good red

LEPIDOTES				
R. *carolinianum*	12	2.8	3	
R. *chapmanii*	9	3.8	3.5	Easy, heavy bloom
R. *minus*	10	3.2	2.8	Open plant
Windbeam	8	3.1	3.1	Soft pink

EVERGREEN AZALEAS				
Christmas Cheer	12	3.2	3.2	Good winter foliage
Coral Bells	18	3.8	3.5	Good color

Fashion	13	3.7	3.3	Dependable
Festive	10	3.8	3.5	
Flame	10	3.5	3	
George L. Tabor	11	4.4	4	Hardy Indian
Glacier	8	4	4.4	Excellent foliage
Hino-Crimson	10	3.7	3.5	Bright red
Hinodigiri	11	2.8	2.4	Color not clear
Pink Pearl	13	3.8	3.2	Dependable
Pink Ruffles	12	3.8	3.5	Large flowers
Purple Splendor	8	3.2	3.5	Good color
Rosebud	8	4	4	Excellent
Sherwoodi	10	3.4	3.5	Fades in sun
Sweetheart Supreme	9	3.7	3.5	Good semi-double

DECIDUOUS AZALEAS

R. alabamense	15	3.2	3	Fragrant white
R. arborescens	7	3	3	Fragrant white
R. atlanticum	11	2.8	3.1	Fragrant, low
R. austrinum	12	3.7	3.5	Fragrant yellow
R. bakeri	10	4.1	3.5	Low, red to orange
R. calendulaceum	19	4.4	3.7	Red, yellow, orange
R. canescens	20	2.8	3	Tall, variable
Choptank River	4	3	3	
Gibraltar	4	5	4	
R. nudiflorum	10	2.7	3.4	Not always clear color
R. prunifolium	14	4.4	4	Excellent, light shade
R. speciosum	8	4	3	Excellent, low
R. vaseyi	5	3	4	"Different native"
R. viscosum	8	2	2	Fragrant, variable

GREAT LAKES CHAPTER

The Great Lakes Chapter encompasses the area near Cleveland, Ohio, and the southern and eastern shores of Lake Erie. Except near the lake, the summers are hot with temperatures in the 90's and the winters are cold, perhaps to −35°F on occasion. Soils are frequently clayey and not always sufficiently acid.

ELEPIDOTES	Flower	Plant	Comments
Albert Close	3	3	
America	3	2	Hardiest red
Besse Howells	3	4	
Boule de Neige	3	4	
R. brachycarpum	3	4	
Brown Eyes	4	3	
Caroline	3	3	Rcommended for beginners

R. catawbiense	3	2.5	Variable
Dexter's Pink	4	3	
English Roseum	3	4	Recommended for beginners
Ice Cube	3	3	
Janet Blair	4	4	
Lee's Dark Purple	3	3	Recommended for beginners
Nova Zembla	3	3	Not as hardy as America
Newburyport Belle (Fowle 19)	4	3	
Parker's Pink	4	3	
R. yakushimanum	4	5	

LEPIDOTES

R. carolinianum	4	4
R. dauricum	4	3
Dora Amateis	4	4
R. hippophaeoides	3	3
R. impeditum	4	5
Mucram	3	3
P.J.M.	3	4
Windbeam	3	3

EVERGREEN AZALEAS
Cascade
Corsage
Fedora
Geraldine (Pride)
Herbert

R. kiusianum	4	4

Marjorie (Pride)
Nadine (Pride)
Springtime

DECIDUOUS AZALEAS
R. arborescens
R. bakeri
R. calendulaceum
R. canadense
R. nudiflorum
R. vaseyi

INDIANA CHAPTER

In Indiana, the summer temperature averages 85°F or above. The winter brings temperatures of −25°F, or even lower. Rainfall averages 46 inches in the south to 34 inches in the north, with most falling in October to December and April and May. Summer is dry. Soil varies from clay to sandy loam to silt loam, slight acid to neutral in the north and moderate to strongly acid in the south.

ELEPIDOTES	Votes	Flower	Plant	Comments
Besse Howells	3	4	4	Buds easily
R. catawbiense album	2	4	4	
R. catawbiense				
Boursault	2	3	4	
County of York	2	5	4	Needs some shade
Francesca	2	5	4	
Ice Cube	3	4	4	Best white
Janet Blair	2	5	5	
Lemon Ice	3	3	3	
R. maximum roseum	2	3	4	
Paul R. Bosley	2	4	4	
Roseum Elegans	2	4	4	Old stand-by
Roseum Pink	2	4	4	
Scarlet Wonder	2	5	5	
Scintillation	4	5	5	Best of Dexters
Skyglow	2	4	4	
Spring Parade	3	4	5	
Tiffany	2	4	4	
Tony	3	4	4	Needs some shade
Vulcan	2	5	4	
Warwick	2	5	3	
Wheatley	2	4	4	
Wissahickon	2	5	5	
Yaku Prince	2	5	5	Best yakushimanum hybrid
Yaku Princess	2	5	5	
LEPIDOTES				
Anna Baldsiefen	2	3	4	
R. carolinianum album				
compactum	2	3	3	
Mary Fleming	2	4	5	Needs light shade
P.J.M.	3	5	5	Good for mid-west
Ramapo	2	4	5	
Windbeam	3	5	5	Excellent

EVERGREEN AZALEAS

	Votes	Flower	Plant	Comments
Boudoir	2	4	3	
Fedora	2	4	3	
Greeting	2	3	4	
Hahn's Red	2	4	4	Excellent plant
Helen Curtis	2	5	5	Excellent
Herbert	2	4	4	Hardiest
John Cairns	2	4	3	
Louise Gable	3	4	3	
Mildred Mae	3	4	3	Excellent grower
R. mucronatum	2	4	4	
R. poukhanense	2	4	3	
Rosebud	2	4	3	
Stewartstonian	2	5	4	

DECIDUOUS AZALEAS
None received 2 votes

SEATTLE CHAPTER

Seattle Chapter members live in many micro-climates in this area. On the west is Puget Sound, a large body of seawater which moderates temperatures near the shore. Moving east are two large lakes and, further east, are the foothills of the Cascade Mountains, with elevations up to 1500 feet. There is light rainfall over the entire year, with July and August the driest months, and little snow in winter. The temperature rarely goes below 10°F in winter or above 90°F in summer. Soil is naturally on the acid side.

ELEPIDOTES

	Votes	Flower	Plant	Comments
Bow Bells	8	3.5	4	Compact, good foliage
R. bureavii	15	3	5	Excellent foliage
Crest	18	5	3.5	Best yellow
Etta Burrows	7	5	4	
Faggetter's Favourite	7	4	4	Beautiful leaves
R. fictolacteum	7	3	5	Wind, sun protection
Hotei	10	4	4	Fertilizer sensitive
Jean Marie Montague	11	4	4	
Loderi King George	12	5	4.5	Large, some shade
Loderi Venus	10	5	4.5	Large, some shade
Mrs. A.T. de la Mare	7	4	4	Full exposure
Mrs. Furnival	7	4	4	
Odee Wright	7	4	4.5	Compact, good yellow
R. pseudochrysanthum	8	4	4	Compact
Sir Charles Lemon	8	3.5	5	Outstanding foliage

Unique	19	4	5	Compact, good foliage
Virginia Richards	9	5	4	Excellent
R. wardii	7	4	4	
R. williamsianum	10	3.5	4.5	Low, good foliage
R. yakushimanum	40	4	4	Hardy, excellent

LEPIDOTES
R. augustinii	18	4	4	
Cilpinense	7	4	4	Early bloom
Dora Amateis	7	4	4	Good, sun or shade
R. keiskei	9	3.5	4	

DECIDUOUS AZALEAS
R. schlippenbachii	11	4	4	Needs shade

SHELTON CHAPTER

Shelton is at the base of the Olympic Peninsula at the southern tip of Puget Sound. The temperature extremes are 0°F in winter and 75°F in summer. Rainfall totals 38 inches, chiefly during the winter months. Soil is for the most part sandy loam, but some areas report clay soil. A naturally acid condition prevails over the entire Northwest.

ELEPIDOTES	Votes	Flower	Plant	Comments
Anna Rose Whitney	4	4		
Bow Bells	4	4		
Britannia	5	4		Shade, scarlet
Cotton Candy	4	4		
Cynthia	4	4		
R. decorum	3	3		
R. discolor	3	3		Summer, fragrant
Elizabeth	4	4		April, red
R. fargesii	3	3		
Fastuosum Flore Pleno	4	4		June, lavender
R. fortunei	3	3		
Gomer Waterer	4	4		
Helene Schiffner	4	4		Slight shade
Jean Marie Montague	4	4		
Jock	3	4		
Loder's White	5	5		
Mary Briggs	4	4		
Mrs. Furnival	5	5		
Mrs. G.W. Leak	4	4		
R. orbiculare	4	5		Lovely foliage
R. oreodoxa	3	3		March, pink

Purple Splendour	4	3	June, purple
Ruby Hart	4.5	4.5	
R. sutchuenense var.			
giraldii	3	4	Large, blotched
Unique	4	4	
Van Nes Sensation	4	5	
Virginia Richards	5	4	
Vulcan	4	4	
R. yakushimanum	5	5	

LEPIDOTES

R. augustinii	3	3	Many clones, blue
Blue Diamond	5	4	
R. campylogynum var.			
cremastum	4	4.5	Dwarf, dusty pink bells
Dora Amateis	4	4	
R. impeditum	4	4	
R. oreotrephes	3	4	Orchid pink, bluish foliage
Snow Lady	4	4	

GRAYS HARBOR CHAPTER

Grays Harbor is at the base of the Olympic Peninsula on the Pacific Ocean. Soil in the area varies from deep silt loam to a clay loam with some gravel benches to a sandy loam near the beaches. In most years the temperature extremes range from a low of 15°F to a high of 85°F. Rarely do temperatures reach 0°F or 95°F. Rainfall varies from 70 to 120 inches per year.

ELEPIDOTES	Votes Flower	Plant	Comments
Autumn Gold	4	3	
Bow Bells	3	3	
Cary Ann	3	3	
Crest	5	3	Full sun
Elizabeth	4	4	
Faggetter's Favourite	5	4	Light shade
R. fargesii	4	3.5	
Helene Schiffner	4	3	
Hotei	4	4	Full sun to bloom
Ladybird	5	4	
Lady Bligh	4	3	Shade
Loder's White	5	3	
R. orbiculare	3	3.5	
Pilgrim	4	3	
Rosamundi	3	3	
Ruby F. Bowman	4	4	

Ruby Hart	4	5	
Susan	4	4	Light shade
Van Ness Sensation	4	4	Light shade
Virginia Richards	4	4	
R. williamsianum	3	4	
R. yakushimanum	3.5	4	

LEPIDOTES

R. augustinii	3	3
Blue Diamond	5	4
Chikor	4	4
R. davidsonianum	3	3.5
Dora Amateis	5	4
R. hemitrichotum	2	3
R. impeditum	3	4
R. keleticum	3	4
Mary Fleming	4	4
P.J.M.	3	4
R. rubiginosum	2	3
Seta	4	3

EVERGREEN AZALEAS

	Votes Flower	Plant	Comments
Atalanta	3	3	
Blaauw's Pink	4	3	
Everest	4	5	
Gaiety	4	4	
Gumpo	4	3	
Helena	4	4	
Hino-Crimson	4	4	
Pinky Pearce	4	4	
Rosebud	5	3	

DECIDUOUS AZALEAS

R. albrechtii	4.5	2
Ballerina	4	3
Bright Straw	4	2
Cecile	4	2
Homebush	4	2
Krakatoa	4	3
Narcissiflora	3	3
Orangeade	4	3
Princess Royal	3	3
R. schlippenbachii	4	3
Strawberry Ice	4	3
Sun Chariot	2	3

TUALATIN VALLEY CHAPTER

The Tualatin Valley is west of Portland, extending to the Coast Range. The temperatures here range from 10°F in winter to 100°F in summer, but do not persist at these extremes for long periods. Rainfall is plentiful, between 30 and 50 inches annually. Soils vary even in one garden from loam to clay, most have excellent drainage. Soil is naturally acid.

ELEPIDOTES	Votes	Flower	Plant	Comments
Carmen	4	4.3	4.8	
Cotton Candy	4	4.8	4	
Elizabeth	4	3.8	3.5	
Faggetter's Favourite	4	4.3	4.3	
Furnival's Daughter	4	4.8	3.8	
Hotei	4	4.5	4	
Hurricane	3	4.3	4	
Jean Marie Montague	4	4	3.3	
Kim	3	4.3	3.7	
Lem's Cameo	4	4.8	4	
Loderi Pink Diamond	3	5	4	
Moonstone	5	3.8	3.8	
Mrs. Furnival	5	4.6	3.8	
Noyo Chief	5	4	4.2	
Odee Wright	4	4.5	4.5	
Olympic Lady	5	4	4.4	
R. orbiculare	3	4.3	4.3	
R. pseudochrysanthum	4	4	4.5	
Purple Lace	3	4	4	
Red Olympia	4	4.8	3.8	
Ruby Hart	4	4.5	4.3	
Scintillation	4	4.3	4.3	
Shamrock	4	4	4.3	
Sir Charles Lemon	3	4	4.3	
Susan	5	4.4	4	
Taurus	5	4.6	3.8	
Unique	6	4	4.5	
Van Nes Sensation	5	4.2	3.8	
Virginia Richards	4	4.3	4.5	
Vulcan	3	4	4.3	
R. williamsianum	4	3.8	5	
R. yakushimanum	5	4.2	4.8	
LEPIDOTES				
Blue Diamond	3	4.3	3.7	
Chikor	3	4.3	4.3	

R. davidsonianum	4	4.5	3.8
R. glomerulatum	3	4.3	3.7
Goldstrike	6	4.3	3.7
R. hanceanum	5	4	4.6
R. keiskei	5	4	4
R. leucaspis	4	4.3	4
R. lutescens	3	4	3.3
R. oreotrephes	5	4.2	3.8
R. racemosum	5	3.8	3.2
R. russatum	4	4.5	4
Snow Lady	5	3.8	4

EVERGREEN AZALEAS

R. kiusianum	3	4.3	4.3

DECIDUOUS AZALEAS

Homebush	4	4.3	3.8
R. schlippenbachii	4	4.5	4

CALIFORNIA CHAPTER

The California Chapter is located in the San Francisco Bay area. Frost occurs seldom near the coast where Maddeniis and Malaysians may be grown outdoors. Intense summer heat is seldom experienced because of the proximity of the Pacific Ocean.

ELEPIDOTES	Votes	Flower	Plant	Comments
Anna Rose Whitney	4	4		
Antoon van Welie	4	3.8		
R. arboreum	4.8	4.8		
Bow Bells	4	4.3		
Captain Jack	5	4.5		
Cary Ann	3.8	3.5		
C.I.S.	3.8	3.5		
Cornubia	4	4		
Cotton Candy	4	3.8		
R. decorum	3.5	4		
R dichroanthum var. scyphocalyx (Golden Gate form)	3.5	4.8		
Elizabeth	4	3		
R. elliottii	4	3.5		
Fabia var. Tangerine	4	3.8		
R. fortunei	3.8	3.8		
Helene Schiffner	4.8	4		
Jean Marie Montague	4	4.3		

John Coutts	4.3	4
Loder's White	4.3	4
Loderi King George	4	3.8
Loderi Venus	4.3	3.8
Leo	4	3.8
Mrs. A.T. de la Mare	4	3.8
Noyo Chief	4	4.5
R. ponticum	3.3	4.3
Purple Lace	4	3
Purple Splendour	3.8	3
Rainbow	3.5	4
Unique	3.5	4.3
R. yakushimanum	4.3	4

LEPIDOTES

R. augustinii	4.5	4
Blue Diamond	4.8	4.3
R. burmanicum	3.8	4
R. carolinianum	4	4
Cilpinense	3.5	3.5
Countess of Sefton	4	4
Countess of Haddington	3.8	3.3
R. cubittii	4.5	4
Dora Amateis	4	3.3
Eldorado	3.5	3.8
Else Frye	4	3.5
Forsterianum	4	3.5
Fragrantissimum	4	3
R. glaucophyllum	4	4
Hardijzer's Beauty	4.5	4.5
R. hippophaeoides	4.8	4.8
Lady Alice Fitzwilliam	3.5	3.5
R. leucaspis	4.3	4.5
R. lutescens	3.5	3.5
R. maddenii	4.5	4.5
Mi Amor	4.5	3.8
R. mucronulatum	4	3.5
P.J.M.	4.3	4.3
R. racemosum	4.3	4.3
Ramapo	4	4
Saffron Queen	3.8	3.8
Seta	4	4
Snow Lady	4.3	3.5
Thalia	4	4.3
Windbeam	4	4

EVERGREEN AZALEAS

Coral Bells	4	4

Gumpo	3	4
Hino-Crimson	4.5	4.3
Honodigiri	4	4
Kintaiyo	4	3.5
R. kiusianum	3.8	3.8
Madonna	4	5
Pink Champagne	4	3.8
Sherwood Orchid	4.5	4
Sherwood Red	4.5	3.5
Stewartstonian	4.5	3.5
Ward's Ruby	5	4
White Grandeur	4	3.8

DECIDUOUS AZALEAS

Bright Sraw	4.8	4
Cecile	5	4
Gallipoli Red	4.8	4.5
Gibraltar	4.8	4.5
Homebush	4.3	3.8
Irene Koster	4.5	3.5
Old Gold	5	4.5
Pink Ruffles	4	4
Princess Royal	4.8	4
R. Schlippenbachii	4.3	3.8
Strawberry Ice	4.8	4
Sylphides	4	4
Sun Chariot	4.5	4

SAN MATEO CHAPTER

San Mateo is located halfway down the peninsula from San Francisco. The peninsula has water on three sides with a range of mountains extending down the center, maximum elevation of 2,500 feet. Temperatures are very moderate seldom venturing below 32°F or above 95°F. Rain falls primarily between October and April, averaging 20 inches. Soil is for the most part clay.

ELEPIDOTES	Votes	Flower	Plant	Comments
R. aberconwayi	3		4	Best forms
Antoon van Welie	4		3	
R. arboreum	5		4	Best forms
R. auriculatum	4		4	
Bow Bells	4		5	
R. bureavii	3		5	
R. calophytum	4		5	Needs shade

Cotton Candy	4	4
Cynthia	4	4
R. decorum	4	5
R. elliottii	5	4
Leo	5	4
Loder's White	4	4
R. makinoi	3	5
Markeeta's Flame	5	4
R. metternichii	4	4
Noyo Chief	4	5
Ruby F. Bowman	4	4
White Swan	5	4
R. yakushimanum	5	5

LEPIDOTES

R. augustinii	4	3	
Bric-a-Brac	4	3	
R. burmanicum	4	4	
R. cinnabarinum	4	3	Best forms
R. davidsonianum	4	3	Best forms
R. edgeworthii	5	3	
Else Frye	4	4	
Forsterianum	4	4	
Fragrantissimum	4	2	
Lemon Mist	3	5	
R. lindleyi	5	2	
Mi Amor	5	2	
My Lady	4	4	
R. nuttalli	5	2	
R. oreotrephes	4	3	Best forms
Owen Pearce	4	4	
Pink Snowflakes	4	3	
Seta	4	3	
R. tephropeplum	4	3	
R. veitchianum	5	4	

EVERGREEN AZALEAS

Bride's Bouquet	5	4
Coral Bells	5	5
Fielder's White	4	4
Gay Paree	5	4
Gumpo	3	5
R. kiusianum album	4	4
R. nakaharai	3	5
Perle de Swynaerde	5	5
Starlight	5	5
Ward's Ruby	5	4

DECIDUOUS AZALEAS

Cecile	4	3
Gibraltar	5	3
Gold Crest	4	3
Lila	5	3
Mrs. Betty Oliver	5	3
R. occidentale	4	3
Princess Royal	4	3
R. schlippenbachii	4	4	Difficult in some areas
R. vaseyi	4	3	Difficult in some areas
Yellow Altair	4	3

DE ANZA CHAPTER

The De Anza Chapter has members in the San Jose and Santa Clara valley areas of California. Frost will occur occasionally with normal lows in the high 30's to mid 40's. Midwinter highs are 50 to 60°F. Average rainfall is 15 to 30 inches a year, mostly in the winter months.

ELEPIDOTES	Votes	Flower	Plant	Comments
Anah Kruschke	3	3	4	
Anna Rose Whitney	2	4	3.5	
Antoon van Welie	2	3.5	3.5	
Cotton Candy	3	4	3.7	
Halfdan Lem	2	5	4	
Helene Schiffner	2	4.5	4	
R. hyperythrum	2	3	4	
Jean Marie Montague	5	4.2	4.2	
Leo	2	4.5	4.5	
Marinus Koster	2	3.5	4	
P. ponticum	2	3	2.5	
Trude Webster	2	4.5	4	
R. yakushimanum	2	4	4.5	

LEPIDOTES			
R. augustinii	2	4	4
R. burmanicum	3	3.3	3.5
Cilpinense	2	4	4
R. concatenans	2	2.5	3.3
R. davidsonianum	2	4.5	3
R. formosum	3	3	3.8
Fragrantissimum	3	3.3	3
R. johnstoneanum	2	3.5	3.3
R. keiskei	2	3.5	3.5
R. keleticum	2	3.8	3.8

R. lutescens	2	4	3.5
R. racemosum	2	4	3
R. yunnanense	2	4	3

EVERGREEN AZALEAS

Fielder's White	2	3.5	3
Nuccio's Happy Days	2	3.5	3

MONTEREY BAY CHAPTER

Members of the Monterey Bay Chapter live mostly in Santa Cruz County, 75 to 100 miles south of San Francisco. Elevations range from sea level to approximately 2,000 feet inland. Temperatures range from a normal maximum of 90°F near the coast to 105°F in the mountains and from a normal minimum of 35°F near the coast to 20°F in the higher areas. Rainfall can be as low as 20 inches per year in some coastal locations and up to 80 inches per year at places in the mountains. Most of the rain occurs between December and April. Soil types range from nearly pure sand to adobe.

ELEPIDOTES

	Votes	Flower	Plant	Comments
Alice	4	3.3	3.3	May, pink
Anah Kruschke	4	3.8	3.8	Lavender blue
Blue Peter	4	4	2.8	
Jean Marie Montague	9	4.2	4.1	
Mrs. Betty Robertson	3	3.7	3.7	May, yellow
Mrs. G. W. Leak	6	3.5	3.3	Late April, blotched
Noyo Chief	5	3.4	4.2	Beautiful foliage
Pink Pearl	5	3.8	2.8	
R. ponticum	4	3	3.2	Mid-June, purplish
Purple Splendour	3	4.3	3.6	Rich purple
Sappho	3	5	2	
Scintillation	3	3.6	4.3	Good May pink
Trude Webster	5	4.6	4.2	Good May pink
White Swan	3	4.6	3	

LEPIDOTES

R. augustinii	6	4	3.3	Willowy, bluish
R. burmanicum	4	3.8	3.6	April, yellow
Cilpinense	3	3.6	3.6	March, blush pink
R. davidsonianum	3	4.3	3.3	Good pink
R. impeditum	3	4.3	4	Dwarf, purple
R. racemosum	3	3.6	3	
Ramapo	3	3.6	3.3	Dwarf, bright violet pink, frosty new growth

EVERGREEN AZALEAS

Hexe	3	4	4	Crimson red
Ward's Ruby	5	4.6	4	Red red, earlier

DECIDUOUS AZALEAS

Gibraltar	6	4	3.6	Brightest orange
Homebush	6	4.5	3.3	Rose pink trusses
Hotspur Yellow	3	3.6	3	
Life	3	4	3.3	
R. occidentale	4	3.8	3.5	Native azalea, wonderful fragrance
Oxydol	3	4	3.3	

SOUTHERN CALIFORNIA CHAPTER

The Chapter encompasses territory from San Diego to Santa Barbara along the coast and eastward into the mountains to an elevation of 5,000 feet. Soils are heavy clay along the coast and decomposed granite in the mountains. Rainfall varies greatly but averages 12 to 15 inches near Los Angeles. Summers are dry and hot. Tolerance to alkaline water is desirable.

ELEPIDOTES   Votes Flower Plant Comments
A. Bedford
Anah Kruschke
Blue Ensign
Goldsworth Crimson
Gomer Waterer
Helene Schiffner
Mrs. Charles Pearson
Mrs. E. C. Stirling
Noyo Brave
Pink Pearl
Sappho
Vulcan

LEPIDOTES
R. cubitii var. Ashcombe
Else Frye
Emasculum
Forsterianum
Jamesii
My Lady
Pink Forsterianum
Rose Scott

MALAYSIANS
R. brookeanum var. *gracile*
(R. christianae x *macgregoriae)*
Dr. Sleumer
Kurt Adler *(lochae* x *phaeopeplum)*
R. laetum
R. lochae
Narnia *(aurigeranum* x *zoelleri)*
Ne Plus Ultra *(javanicum* x *(brookeanum* x *longiflorum))*
(Pink Delight x *jasminiflorum)*
Princess Alexandra *((jasminiflorum* x *javanicum)* x *jasminiflorum)*
Red Prince
Taylori (Princess Alexandra x *brookeanum* var. *gracile)*
Valentine *(gracilentum* x *lochae)*

EVERGREEN AZALEAS

Benigasa	the following Nuccio Hybrids
Content	Allegro
Duc de Rohan	California
Gumpo	Carnival Candy
Gumpo variegated	Carnival Clown
Gunbi	Carnival Dancer
Gunrei	Carnival Fanfare
Hexe	Carnival Firecracker
Phoenicia	Carnival Jackpot
Pink Gumpo	Carnival Magic
Pink Lace	Carnival Music
Pride of Dorking	Carnival Queen
Red Poppy	Carnival Rocket
Red Wings	Carnival Time
Revery	Friendship
Rosebud	Garden Party
Ruffled Giant	Happy Days
Sherwood Pink	Melody Lane
Sherwood Red	Pink Bubbles
Shiho	Pink Snow
Snowbank	Purple Glitters
White April	Red Glitters
	Rose Glitters

NOTES

NOTES